OLIVER TRICKETT

DOYEN OF AUSTRALIA'S CAVE SURVEYORS

1847-1934

Gregory J. Middleton

SYDNEY SPELEOLOGICAL SOCIETY
OCCASIONAL PAPER No. 10

PUBLISHED BY THE
SYDNEY SPELEOLOGICAL SOCIETY

in association with the
JENOLAN CAVES HISTORICAL AND PRESERVATION SOCIETY

1991

Oliver Trickett – Doyen of Australia's Cave Surveyors

Gregory J. Middleton

Sydney Speleological Society Occasional Paper No. 10

First published 1991

Sydney Speleological Society
P.O. Box 198, Broadway
N.S.W. AUSTRALIA 2007

in association with

Jenolan Caves Historical and Preservation Society
Post Office, Jenolan Caves
N.S.W, AUSTRALIA 2790

Editor of Society Publications — Ross Ellis

National Library of Australia card number and
ISBN 0 9599608 6 4

Cover: A studio photo of Oliver Trickett, L.S., M.S., with theodolite, taken in the late 1890s by the renowned photographer of Jenolan and other caves, Charles Kerry, then of 810 George Street, Sydney.   [See also Figure 88, page 105]

DEDICATION

To the late
Oliver Glanfield
who understood the pleasures and benefits
of cave documentation
and
Anthony Bradley (1882-1971)
a colleague and admirer
of Oliver Trickett
-
both of whom helped to kindle
my interest in spelean history.

NEW SOUTH WALES
Immigration and Tourist Bureau
Challis House
Sydney
11th May 1915

… I record the appreciation of this Department of the invaluable services rendered to it by Mr Trickett, whose long association with, and active control of the development of the limestone caves of New South Wales has done so much, not only to open up these wonder caverns, but to obtain for them pride of place amongst the tourist attractions of the world. …

Percy Hunter, Superintendent

CONTENTS

FIGURES

FIGURES (Cont.)

FOREWORD

It is a great pleasure and privilege to be asked to write this foreword. My interest, and that of my colleagues, in the person and activities of Oliver Trickett, was aroused in the late 1940s, when the Sydney University Speleological Society was in the process of formation.

It was inevitable that, in our search for information about limestone deposits and caves which we wished to visit, the name of Oliver Trickett came up again and again.

Despite some years in the Geological Survey of New South Wales, I was unable to gain much more information about Trickett, but I became aware of the variety of work he had done as draftsman in the Survey, and grew to admire the skills he had used, and the results of his dedication.

Greg Middleton has located descendants of Trickett, and thus has been able to fill in details of much of his early life. He has also carefully researched Trickett's general survey work, and his more important cave surveys. Unfortunately Trickett's detailed notebooks remain lost, buried no doubt in some dusty government archive, so some questions remain unanswered, and some cave surveys have never surfaced.

As Greg Middleton himself says, he found no answer as to why Trickett took to caving. Trickett's mining survey experience certainly prepared him for the work, but he brought to caving a dedication that went far beyond the mere duty it might have been. It seems to have been that serendipitous event—the right man in the right place.

Cavers throughout Australia will welcome the story of Trickett's life. This is a landmark publication which will be read with pleasure and profit.

DAVID BRANAGAN
Research Affiliate
Department of Geology and Geophysics
Edgeworth David Building
University of Sydney

ACKNOWLEDGEMENTS

A number of people have assisted me in various ways to piece together the life and work of Oliver Trickett. To all of the following I acknowledge my particular indebtedness:—

First and foremost, Mrs N.B. Herrick, a granddaughter of Oliver's and two of his daughters, the late Miss Gwen Trickett and the late Mrs M. Selmes, who kindly made available to me Oliver's personal scrapbook and other personal papers. Without their invaluable contributions this biography would have had to rely almost entirely on published works.

Mr Andrew Valja, Cartographer with the Geological Survey of N.S.W., who had himself gathered together quite a deal of information on Trickett, one of his more illustrious predecessors, but never published it. He kindly made the results of his work, including the location of previously unpublished photographs and a map, together with information on Trickett's register of mining companies (in the Public Library of New South Wales) available to me without hesitation. He also kindly carried out further research on matters which arose during the preparation of this biography and commented on early drafts. I gratefully acknowledge his considerable assistance.

Mr A. C. Bashford, Librarian in the Department of Mineral Resources, Sydney, who tried, with regrettably no success, to track down unpublished Trickett correspondence and reports. The Archives Office of N.S.W. described them all, simply, as "missing". [Subsequent investigations have lead me to doubt whether all the documents have actually been lost—some may simply have been filed elsewhere. However time has not permitted me to investigate the NSW Archives further.]

Ross Ellis, Editor of S.S.S. publications, who despite the passage of many years, has unfalteringly continued to provide encouragement and assistance with this and other projects, provided access to his voluminous speleological library and arranged the publication of this volume.

Likewise, Ben Nurse, long-time President of S.S.S. and sometime President of the Jenolan Caves Historical and Preservation Society, who has consistently encouraged the recording of spelean history and this project in particular.

For numerous items of information, photographs, encouragement and constructive criticism I am also indebted to Elery Hamilton-Smith.

For producing the large format colour transparencies of the four colour plates and the large map of Jenolan, my sincere thanks to John Voss.

Greg Middleton
Sandy Bay, Tas.

INTRODUCTION

Like, I suspect, many other cavers in New South Wales in the 1960s and 70s, I found an early source of information and inspiration in the cave reports and surveys of Oliver Trickett. It mattered not that they were 60 or 70 years old; they were clear reports, accompanied by high standard maps; they were official documents and therefore likely to be accurate, and they were fairly readily available. Copies of the *Annual Report of the Department of Mines* (in which much of Trickett's work relating to caves originally appeared) were held by the major libraries and photocopiers were becoming commonplace. Furthermore, whenever one looked at the few secondary sources that were available, references to Trickett abounded. Carne & Jones' *The Limestone Deposits of New South Wales* (1919), the caver's bible of the time, was peppered with his maps and the monumental compilation by Ronald Anderson (1956) in SSS's *Communications* No. 2 (Cave Areas of New South Wales) also has numerous references to his reports.

Trickett's (posthumous) impact on the development of speleology in New South Wales is doubtless very significant, but has unfortunately not been documented. The experiences of Quentin Burke, bushwalker and speleologist in the years 1954-59, are probably typical of many:

> *Trickett was one of the first to take any interest in caves. He approached the job of mapping the caverns with zest. At the time the state of this art was almost non-existent. Anyway, once we found out his interest, we set about tracing every document in the NSW Public Library, Mitchell Library and Sydney University Library that he put his name to.*
>
> *We would have these photostatted, then go out and trace down the entrance to caverns he had located and explore them ourselves. The majority of these were in the Jenolan Caves area; some were at Colong, and others at Yarrangobilly.*
>
> *We were constantly amazed at the energy of this middle-aged surveyor, likening his interest in caves to our own. But we were enthusiastic youths, and more flexible in cave-exploring than he.*
>
> *We found and explored an extension of one cave system (I believe it was Colong) and named it after him. I have learned that it has since been desecrated, but at the time it was the site of the only known oolites in that part of the world. ... ...*
>
> *We all have our childhood heroes, and he was one of mine.*

(From a letter to the author by Quentin Burke, 9 January 1972)

As Burke says, Trickett, by the time he became officially involved with caves, was 'middle-aged'; in fact he was 49 when he took charge of the limestone caves of NSW, in 1896.

In 1970 I set out to discover more about this man and to try to bring together his work in an easily accessible volume. Although having an interest in history, I had no formal training in that field so I did the obvious things: I copied every map and report of Trickett's I could find, I asked the Mines Department about other records and I wrote to every Trickett in the Sydney phonebook. While the Mines Department (apart from the later personal contribution of Andrew Valja) was unable to be of much help, my letters were rewarded with a response from Oliver Trickett's youngest daughter, Mrs Margary Selmes, who had been told of my letter by Miss Gwen Trickett, Oliver's third eldest daughter, both of whom have since passed away. Subsequently, through a ranger's interest in the Abercrombie guidebook, I also contacted a granddaughter of Oliver, Mrs Gwen Herrick. These ladies kindly lent me Oliver's personal scrapbook (which is referred to as 'the Scrapbook' in what follows) and a number of other papers which, along with his published works, form the basis of this biography.

These sources have been supplemented by documents from the personal libraries of Ross Ellis, Ben Nurse and Elery Hamilton-Smith, along with papers and photographs from the collections of the Geological Survey of New South Wales and the NSW State Archives.

It should be stressed that this is an unashamedly biased biography. My original and principle purpose was to collect Trickett's cave and cave area (limestone deposit) maps together for ease of reference. In doing this I have come across much other information, about Trickett, the places he worked and the people he was associated with. I have tried to include all the information I could which related directly to Trickett but have not pursued many interesting related issues and stories which have been raised. It is necessary in a work such as this to impose limits and I hope the reader will accept those I have set.

It remains for others to investigate the many other strands of Australia's spelean history. I will be content if I have assembled an adequate record of Trickett's work and helped ensure he retains his rightful place of preeminence in the history of the documentation, promotion and protection of Australia's cave heritage.

ORIGINS AND EARLY LIFE

Oliver Trickett was born in Yorkshire on the 29th May 1847 when the chimes rang all over England in commeration [sic] of the restoration of King Charles the Second[1] an old custom which has probably passed into the oblivum [sic] of forgotten events.

His father a minister of a church in Suffolk, voice failing, brought his family to Australia and settled in Victoria at East Melbourne over 70 years ago in a house at the corner of Fitzroy Gardens where a daughter still resides (Margin note: *"See Melbourne Herald 5.3.32"*).

The Scotch mother, an accomplished musician and pianist, for many years became musical instructor to the boys of the Scotch College where young Oliver received his education and subsequently entered the Victorian Mines Department.

So begins Trickett's autobiographical note, written sometime between March 1932 and his death in March 1934. Unhappily this is brief, sketchy and incomplete (the second page is missing and the sentence at the bottom of the third page is unfinished) but it appears to be almost the only source of details of his birth and early life. [The note, among Trickett's papers, is written in the third person and may have been prepared for a friend or at the request of another person.]

Among the Trickett papers (Scrapbook, p. 150) there is also an old newspaper cutting (perhaps from the Manchester *Daily Despatch)* about Bridlington's new sea wall. This is annotated in Trickett's handwriting "Bridlington Yorkshire England 1927 Birthplace O. Trickett 1847, 29th May".

Another newspaper cutting (Scrapbook, p. 140), an obituary for Oliver's mother, Mrs Henrietta Trickett, who died in 1907, names Oliver's father as the Rev. Edward Trickett, one time pastor of the Baptist Church at Bradlington [sic?], in Yorkshire. The article does not say when or why they came to Australia, only that "they decided upon coming to Australia" and that in Melbourne the Reverend "undertook preaching engagements and other Christian work so long as his strength permitted, and until by death he was called away to higher service."

The *Melbourne Herald* article of 5 March 1932, cited above (Scrapbook, opp. p. 125), is entitled "70 years in one house– Miss Trickett looks back". This states that Miss Ellen Trickett and her parents had rented the house on the corner of Albert and Lansdowne Streets, East Melbourne, for more than 70 years[2]. It also relates that her brother, Oliver, was named after Oliver Cromwell, "for whom his father had a deep admiration" and that he "was the man who charted the beautiful Jenolan Caves. He is also the author of the official

guide book to the caves and is said to be the greatest authority in Australia on this branch of natural beauty. One of the caves is named after him."[3]

In an annotation to a photo of the family home in his scrapbook (p. 140), Trickett wrote that in 1931 his sister had been living in the same house in East Melbourne for 71 years. This appears to be more precise than the 1932 newspaper article and, assuming that the family went virtually straight to this house on arrival in Australia, puts the date of that event at 1860. Oliver would then have been 13 years old.

As noted above, he was educated at Scots College and then joined the Victorian Mines Department. In June 1864 he passed the Victorian Civil Service entrance examination in English (orthography, grammar and composition), Arithmetic (vulgar and decimal fractions), Euclid, Algebra and History (certificate at rear of Scrapbook).

Figure 1. Oliver Trickett in 1868 - age 21
[Photo: Hill & Co., Melbourne]

---

1   Perhaps, although *Pears Cyclopaedia* (66th Edn. 1957) gives the date of the Restoration as 8 May (1660); it also states Charles II's birthday was 29 May (1630).
2   The house, built of bluestone and granite, unfortunately no longer exists (Hamilton-Smith pers. comm. 1986)
3   There is no cave at Jenolan named after him, but see 'Geographical Names', p. 126.

LICENSED SURVEYOR IN VICTORIA

On 12 October 1868 Trickett officially became a licensed surveyor in the Colony of Victoria. His certificate (bound into the rear of the Scrapbook) is shown in slightly reduced form in Figure 2.

Trickett must have continued studying surveying for in 1870 he passed another exam which entitled him to become a Mining Surveyor in Victoria. (Presumably this is the origin of the letters 'M.S.', which he subsequently appended to his name for professional purposes.) The elaborate certificate awarded by the Department of Mines is reproduced in reduced form in Figure 3.

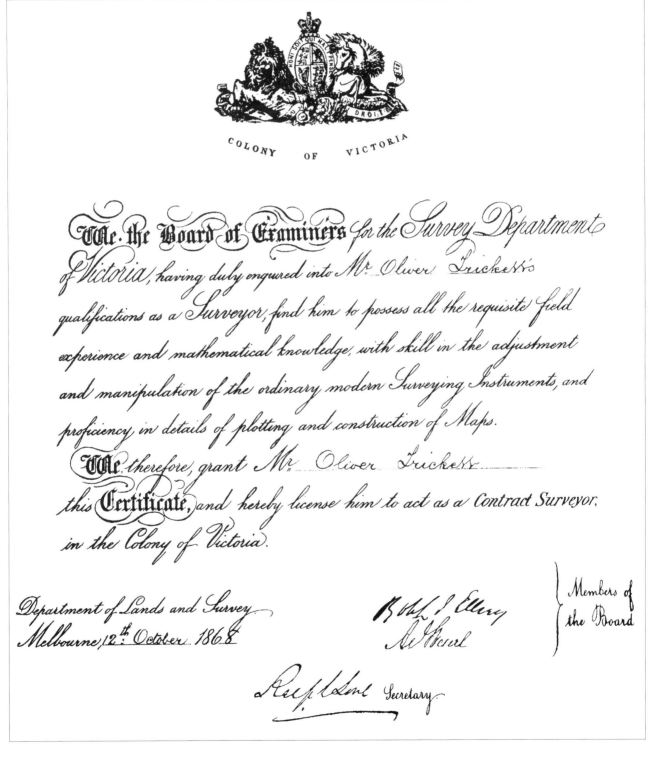

Figure 2. Trickett's certificate as a Contract Surveyor, Victoria 1868
[Reduced from the original in the scrapbook]

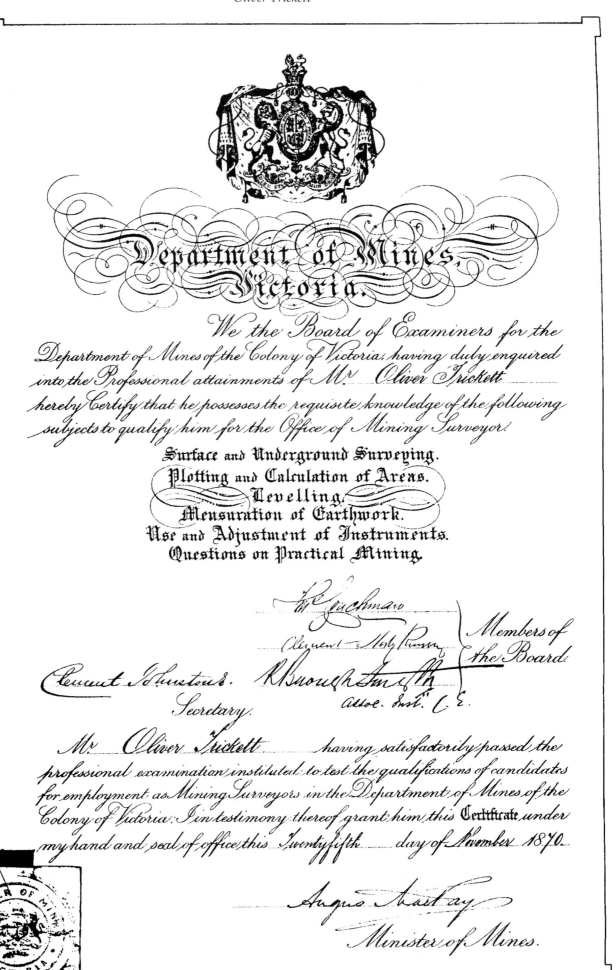

Figure 3. Victorian Mining Surveyor's certificate 25 November 1870 [reduced]

Of Trickett's work in Victoria there is very little recorded in his papers. One of his functions, however, was secretary to the Board of Examiners for Mining Surveyors. An undated printed notice, 'Examination of Candidates', (at rear of Scrapbook) invites candidates to present themselves for examination in:

1. *Surface and underground surveying*
2. *Plotting and calculation of areas*
3. *Levelling*
4. *Mensuration of earthwork*
5. *Use and adjustment of instruments*
6. *Questions in practical mining (including hydraulics)*

   By order of the Board of Examiners,

   OLIVER TRICKETT

Trickett was, apparently, considerably more than a paper shuffler for the Board, as his own annotation makes clear. At the bottom of the notice the following appears in his own hand:

> *O.T. Prepared all questions - Examined the answers. All the Board did was to approve results and examine candidates for instruments and personal records and experience.*

His superiors had nothing but praise for him, judging from the glowing reference the Chief Mining Surveyor and Acting Secretary for Mines gave him on his departure:

> *Melbourne, 28th July 1876*
>
> Sir,
>
> *As you are now on the eve of your departure for New South Wales after a very lengthened period of service in the Office of Mines, I deem it right to bear the most favourable testimony as regards the good conduct, care and general efficiency displayed by you while engaged as draughtsman, computer, Secretary to the Board of Examiners for Mining Surveyors, etc., under my supervision.*
>
> *I have little doubt if you continue to display the same good qualities that you will meet with success in your future career, and you may be assured that it will afford me much pleasure to hear of your advancement in life.*
>
> I am, Sir
> Your obedient serv[t.]
> [signed] Thos. Couchman
> Chief Mining Surveyor and
> Acting Secretary for Mines
>
> Oliver Trickett Esq. etc. etc.
> Mining Department, Melbourne.

So, after some twelve years with the Victorian Mines Department, at the age of 29, Trickett decided to move to NSW. There is no hint in his papers as to his reasons for going north.

PROWESS AS OARSMAN

Oliver Trickett became an oarsman of some note in Victoria (though he should not be confused with Edward "Ned" Trickett, who won international competitions as a sculler at about the same time and may have been related). As Oliver recorded in his autobiographical note:

> *While there* [at the Mines Dept., Melbourne] *he took an active part in rowing contests which commenced at the Melbourne Regatta in 1868 when he stroked the winning crew of the Civil Service Rowing Club. This was the first regatta in which that Club took part. Members of the crew included the late Sir Edward Carlisle* [sic, Carlile] *and the late J.W. Colville[4] who subsequently became a member of the League of Nations.*
>
> *An enthusiastic Club supporter of the crew has risen to fame as Justice Sir Frank Gavan Duffy.[4]*
>
> *Among other successes Mr. O. Trickett had the unique experience of being a member of the winning crew of the first eight oared races in Australia – namely the Footscray Challenge Plate rowed on the Lower Yarra 1875 and the Barwon Challenge Plate 1876. Rowed in the first regatta held on the Barwon River Geelong. Both races won by the C.S.R.C. now merged in the Melbourne Club.*

The 1868 Melbourne Regatta was only the second time the CSRC had competed and its crew won the Maiden Four, "which was the great race in those days" (page torn from an unidentified book, p. 3 of Scrapbook). The crew was J.W. Colville (bow), B.C. Jones (2), E. Carlile (3) and O. Trickett (stroke).

The *Victorian Oarsman & Rowing Register* (Lang 1919) records that at the 1871 Melbourne Regatta Trickett won the Challenge Pair with A. Carmichael[5], rowing for the St. George Club. Oliver's weight was recorded as 10 st. 10 lbs. (68 kg). The (Melbourne) *Daily Telegraph* of 17 April 1871 (Scrapbook, p. 2) described the race:

> *This was a tolerably easy victory for the winners, who made up all their advantage in the latter portion of the race, as to the turn the pairs were no great distance from each other. Some little excitement was caused at the finish by the Melbourne boat [there were only two boats in the race] turning over when just opposite the reserve, and the occupants were precipitated into the water. This accident was occasioned by bow jamming his oar. Assistance was speedily rendered, and the unlucky pair brought safe to shore none the worse for their ducking. The race was performed in 8 min. 23 sec.*

4   Trickett remained friends with these, and other, prominent citizens and took some pride in these associations, as demonstrated by letters and notes among his papers—see 'Friends and Associates'.

5   Association with Carmichael was to lead to the naming of a creek after Trickett in what became the Northern Territory—see 'Commemoration in Geographical Names', p. 126.

A cutting from another paper says:

> The start was fair for both sides, but the St George pair cut out the running by rowing their hardest from the start. This rather disconcerted their opponents, who began to steer wild. At the baths Messrs Willan and Vickers were three or four lengths behind. Mr Carmichael is deserving of great praise for the quick powerful stroke he pulled from the start to past Brander's. Mr Trickett's excellent steering is equally deserving of notice, especially at the bath corner; they won by three or four lengths. Time 8 min. 35 sec. Messrs Willan and Vickers, in trying to turn their boat at the winning post, managed to capsize it, and of course received a thorough soaking. A couple of boats put off to their rescue, and soon put them right again.

According to the *Victorian Oarsman*, Trickett again won the Challenge Pair with Carmichael in 1872 and in 1874 and '76 he was in the crews which won the Grand Challenge Senior Fours at the Melbourne Regatta.

But the eight-oar race of 1875 seems to be the one of which Oliver was personally most proud. The Melbourne Regatta in March of that year saw three crews race for the Footscray Cup, against newspaper reports of which Trickett wrote (p. 4 of Scrapbook) "First eight oared race in Australia. A challenge cup open to all".

A newspaper item of the day recorded:

> This was the great event of the regatta, and public interest was excited to the very highest pitch as the several crews took their places in their boats and paddled down stream to the starting-place … All the men seemed to be perfectly at home in their boats and the splendid rowing which marked the race proved the wisdom of the committee in introducing an eight oared race on the programme. …

Despite a protest from the Warehousemen crew, the Civil Service crew won "the grandest contest ever seen on the Saltwater River", "amidst deafening cheers". The crew is shown in Figure 4.

In later years Trickett had photographic cards made up (which were sent to family and friends), featuring himself in 1875 and 1922, and in 1868 and 1928 (see Figure 5). They also featured photos of seven cups and some had a small photo of the eight-oar boat used in 1875. All had captions which prominently mentioned the 1875 race.

The *Victorian Rowing Register* for 1878 records that a CSRC crew, including Trickett, also won the Champion Four in the Moama Regatta on the Murray in 1875.

The second Australian eight oar race was held on the Barwon River at Geelong in April 1876 and again the Civil Service Rowing Club crew, including Oliver Trickett, was victorious (cuttings, pp. 6 & 8, Scrapbook).

Trickett left for Sydney in August of 1876 and seems to have taken no further interest in rowing. He was, however, made an Honorary Member of the Civil Service Rowing Club (on the nomination of the President, Sir Edward Carlile), on 25 August 1917 (typed notice in Scrapbook, p. 10).

WINNERS OF FIRST EIGHT-OAR RACE ROWED IN AUSTRALIA, MARCH, 1875.

J. Forrester (7)   C.H. Wheatland (4)   A.F. Ross (Coach)
O. Trickett (2)   D. Mackintosh (6)   H.C. Crofs (5)   B. Goldsmith (3)   A.D. Michie (1)   P. I. Carter (Str.)

Figure 4.   The crew which won Australia's first 8-oar race, 1875

O. TRICKETT, L.S., M.S. late of Geol. Branch, Dept. of Mines, Sydney. Produced Surveys, Maps, Models and Guide Books of Limestone Caves. Map of Blue Mountains Models of City of Sydney and Broken Hill Lode. Member of winning crews, Footscray Plate 1875, Barwon Plate, **First 8 Oar races in Australia** & other challenge cups, 1868-76

Figure 5. One of Trickett's cards featuring himself in 1868 and 1928, with cups won for rowing. These cards were sent to friends and relatives—this one to his daughter, Margary.

SHIPWRECKED!

To get from Melbourne to Sydney, Trickett chose to travel by the Torres Strait mail steamer *Queensland*, a ship of 1437 tons which was described in a contemporary newspaper as "one of the grandest vessels that have ever visited these waters". According to the [Melbourne] *Argus* of 3 August 1876, the ship

> took her departure from the Sandridge railway pier yesterday for Sydney. ... The Queensland took away several saloon passengers, amongst them being Mr O. Trickett, of rowing repute on the Yarra. A number of Mr Trickett's brother oarsmen accompanied him to the steamer to wish him good-bye and success in his new sphere of duty. (cutting, Scrapbook, p. 11).

Disaster was near at hand, however, as *The Australasian* of 5 August recorded:

> The light at Wilson's Promontory was sighted at 2 am and the steamer was abreast of it at 4 am. ... The morning [of 3 August] was fine and clear, but there was a misty light to the eastward as is often the case just before dawn. The steamer was going at full speed through the water, and, being light, she was making good way. The water was smooth, and there was a light wind from the eastward. ... Soon after 5 o'clock the lookout man forward reported to the quartermaster that there was a ship's light about two points on the starboard bow. This was at once reported to Mr Paterson, the chief officer, who then saw the bright light, and also the green, or starboard light, of an approaching steamer. As her red—or port light—could not be seen, Mr Paterson of course concluded that the two vessels would go clear of one another, and therefore did not alter the Queensland's course. A few minutes after this he noticed that the other steamer had suddenly altered her course, as her red light became visible. Thinking that she was trying to go across his bows, he jumped to the telegraph on the bridge to give the engineer orders to stop the engines, but before he could signal to the engineroom the collision had occurred, the Barrabool striking the Queensland fairly amidships on her starboard side. The crash was terrific, and for a few minutes it was thought that both vessels would go to the bottom. The shock of the collision awakened everyone on board. Captain Craig seized a pair of trousers and at once rushed on deck. On looking over the side he saw an immense rent about 14 ft long reaching down to the water's edge, or as he expressed it, "big enough to drive a wagon and a pair of horses through". ...

The report gives dramatic accounts of people getting out of their cabins but eventually—

> The crew [and, presumably, the passengers] having been placed in the boats, Capt. Craig ordered Mr Paterson to take his place in one of the boats, then ran round the decks to see that no one else was left on board. As he reached the stern he felt the ship sinking under him, and he at once slid down a rope over her stern into one of the boats. The boat's crew had barely time to back her clear of the ship's stern when she gave a heavy lurch to port, and then sank, stern first. As the water reached her midship section, the force of the compressed air in her hold was so great that her decks were burst open with a report like that of a heavy cannon. ...

> The officers of the ship saved nothing but what they stood up in, and the captain did not even secure a pair of boots. The purser, Mr Glen, however, made sure of the ship's papers, and also his cash-box. Mr O. Trickett, who was one of the passengers, is the loser of £140 in cash by the wreck.[6] When he was awakened by the collision, he took the box containing the money on deck and placed it in one of the port boats, expecting it was going to be lowered. In the confusion he forgot all about the money and got into another boat, and the cash went to the bottom with the ship.

The *Barrabool*, although losing a large part of its bow (see Figure 6), remained afloat and picked up the *Queensland*'s passengers and crew (except the second steward, James Thompson, who was lost) and conveyed them back to port.

PHOTOGRAPHED BY
209 BOURKE ST. EAST.

Figure 6. The S.S. *Barrabool* in dry dock in Melbourne after the collision with the S.S. *Queensland*.
[Photo by A.W. Burman, 1876 - from the Scrapbook]

---

6 And, adds Trickett in a rueful marginal note, "also instruments for surveying and personal property" (scrapbook, p. 16).

On the passage to Melbourne the passengers of the *Queensland* presented Capt. Craig with the following address:

> *The undersigned saloon passengers by the s.s. Queensland cannot part without expressing our sincere sympathy with you in the unhappy circumstances in which the loss of that magnificent vessel places you, and our admiration of the coolness, seamanship, and courage displayed by you from the moment of the collision in doing all that was left possible to be done, viz., in saving the lives of your passengers and crew.*
>
> *In the trying circumstances it says much for the discipline of your ship that there was an entire absence of confusion or 'rushing', officers and men, 'death staring them in the face', quickly and efficiently working in the teeth of the greatest difficulties to launch the boats, and so successfully, that nine-tenths of your hands were got safely into the ship's boats even before the prompt and generous assistance of Captain Pain could reach us.*
>
> JOHN JAMISON
> D. M. LITTLE
> O. TRICKETT
> E. ASHTON
> F. L. MAYES

3rd August 1876

To Captain R. Craig

The 'Steam Navigation Board', following a detailed enquiry, found that fault lay with Mr Charles Ainsworth, the second officer of the S.S. *Barrabool*, who had "improperly ported his helm, thus causing the collision" (unidentified newspaper cutting amongst papers).

As to whether Mr Trickett was covered by insurance, or was otherwise compensated for his very considerable losses, the scrapbook is silent. In any case, it was a most inauspicious start in "his new sphere of duty".

INITIAL WORK IN NEW SOUTH WALES 1876-1888

There seems to be some doubt about just when Trickett started work in New South Wales. Although he clearly travelled to Sydney in August 1876, this was apparently not the first time.

According to an official-looking document (which may be an extract from an employment register), apparently completed in 1892, bound at the rear of the Scrapbook, Trickett started with the NSW Department of Lands as a draftsman on 10 August 1876 (which would indicate that he wasted little time getting over the experience of being shipwrecked off Wilsons Promontory on the 3rd!).

Somewhat confusingly, however, the form also shows " - June 1876" in the "Date of first appointment to Civil Service" column and "21 Oct 76" in the "Date of first appointment to this [Lands?] Department" column. It also states [service] "Continuous for 12 years" to "1 Jany 1888" and "Salaried Surveyor year 1880". "16 June 1892" is another entry in the "Date of first appointment to this Department" column. Below the form proper is written "Gazetted a Mining Surveyor 20th February 1880." Further below that is written (apparently by Trickett, as though to help explain the ambiguities above):

> *During my employment in the Lands [Department] I was employed as a draftsman for a few months on temporary salary from June 1876. Then up to 1889 as a Licensed Surveyor of which time one year 1880 was on salary.*

Certainly, on 27 June 1876 he had been licensed by the New South Wales Government

> *for the survey of the Waste Lands of the Crown, either for the purpose of the adjustment of the boundaries of runs, or for the survey and measurement of Lands conditionally purchased or applied for at auction sale, or in the survey of claims for mineral leases, or in the survey of roads, under written instructions from me.*
>
> [Signed] *R. Adams   Surveyor-General*

(Certificate bound in rear of Scrapbook.)

Subsequently Trickett appended the letters 'L.S.' (Licensed Surveyor) to his name, in consequence of obtaining this qualification.

The *Public Service List* (known also as the 'Blue Book'), which was issued annually (except for 1895 and 1896), contains a detailed record of Trickett's employment from 1876 to 1919. Table 1 shows information from this source to 1889. Trickett ceased to be involved with the Lands Department in 1888.

Table 1
References to O. Trickett in the *Public Service List* of N.S.W. 1876-89

YEAR	page	DEPARTMENT	OFFICE	FEES
1876	77	Lands	Licensed Surveyor	£71.12.10
1877	85	Lands	Licensed Surveyor	£752.10.2
1878	'p. 3'*	Lands	Licensed Surveyor	£1522.6.5
			[Note: 'Specially licensed under provisions of the Real Property Act']	
1879	83	Lands	Licensed Surveyor	£1458.19.0
1880	91	Lands	Licensed Surveyor	£616.19.7
"	133	Mines	Mining Surveyor, District of Moama**	
1881	91	Lands	Licensed Surveyor	£1148.9.9
"	136	Mines	Mining Surveyor, District of Moama	
1882	102	Lands	Licensed Surveyor	£1818.1.5
"	157	Mines	Mining Surveyor, District of Warialda***	
1883	105	Lands	Licensed Surveyor	£2365.13.10
"	175	Mines	Mining Surveyor, District of Warialda	
1884	108	Lands	Licensed Surveyor	£681.13.1
"	185	Mines	Mining Surveyor, District of Moree	
1885	115	Lands	Licensed Surveyor	£839.15.9
"	188	Mines	Mining Surveyor, District of Warialda	
1886	111	Lands	Licensed Surveyor	£1381.7.4
"	176	Mines	Mining Surveyor, District of Warialda	
1887	125	Lands	Licensed Surveyor	£1037.2.10
"	182	Mines	Mining Surveyor, District of Moree	
1888	190	Lands	Licensed Surveyor	£240.13.0
"	164	Mines	Sydney	
1889	170	Mines	Sydney	
"	194	Lands	Indicates Licensed Surveyors 'paid by fees', but O. Trickett no longer listed under Lands Department.	

* Somebody blundered this year; Trickett is not listed in the index, but is shown on the third page of a number of pages inserted after page 84.

** No date or salary are shown but indicated as appointed by Governor and Executive Council.

*** A footnote says: 'Licensed Surveyor - see Survey [Lands?] Dept.'

It is evident that during this period some form of dual engagement arrangement applied, though no salaries are indicated in the 'Blue Books' (even for the year 1880, when Trickett's note, above, indicates he was on salary).

The payment of fees (and they appear to be extremely high ones) seems to indicate a form of contract engagement, under which he was only paid for work actually done. In 1883 the sum of £2,365 must have been an extraordinary sum, particularly compared to the salary of £260 p.a. which he received as a draftsman with the Mines Department from 1897.

Some of these facts are confirmed, and others added by a copy of a page from the Mines Department's Employment Record Book provided to the author by Mr Derek Elmes, a former employee of the department. The page is approximately reproduced in Table 2.

Trickett's papers contain a few letters and other papers relating to this period; there is one personal snippet which may have been recorded for a friend, or some form of publication, or even his memoirs. Figure 7 shows the contents of a scrap of paper pasted to page 15 of the Scrapbook.

Table 2

Extract from Employment Record Book of NSW Dept. of Mines

Name				Position	Branch	Annual Salary £ s. d.	Remarks
Date of Birth — *Trickett Oliver* / *May 29th 1847*							

[Date]				Position	Branch	Annual Salary £ s. d.	Remarks
1880	Mar	25		Surveyor, Grafton West	Temp	300	Equip £230
1881	Jan.	1		Licensed Surveyor		Fees	
1887	Dec.	7 ?		do		"	
1892	June	16		Draftsman, Mines	Temp	£5 per week	
1895	Dec.	23		do	Perm	do	
1896	July	1		do	"	260	
1899	July	1		do	"	275	
1901	Jan.	1		Draftsman & Surveyor	"	325	
1906	Jan.	1	Regrading	do	"	360	
1910	July	1	10.7090	do	"	380	
1911	"	1	Gaz. 13. 24.1.12	do	"	400	
				Retired			
			Last day of Service 22.3.1920	ps. 19.7637 145			

Some survey experiences

An odd coincidence Kurri Kurri, Moulamein, March 1878

Country flooded   Rode into a tank sunk in middle of track

Got out with the aid of horses tail — lost stirrup

At the same instant Jones, Supdt. of Police drove buggy and four into tank on opposite side.

Had some difficulty in rescuing buggy and horses.

The sudden surprise

Snakes plentiful - chiefly black

Sometimes at close quarters with tiger snakes

Figure 7. A sketch, presumed to be by Trickett, illustrating an event during his survey work in southern New South Wales.

[Handwritten text has been transcribed. Moulamein is located between Deniliquin and Balranald in the far south of central NSW, not far from the Victorian border.]

There is also a photo which, from its age, very likely relates to this period - Figure 8. It is captioned, by hand, *Survey Camp on the road.* It shows three horse-drawn carts. *O. Trickett* is the only named person but there are three men to his left, labelled only *Axemen & Chainmen,* there is a *Cook* standing to the right and another man drives the front cart. Perhaps this picture explains the apparently high fees Trickett received. It appears that from these fees he had to finance this retinue: pay wages and living expenses, hire horses and carts, and provide his own equipment.

On 16 April 1878 Trickett received a letter from the Surveyor-General, written in a beautiful hand, conveying his "certificate of appointment as a Surveyor under the Real Property Act". It is signed, in the then customary style, "I am, Sir, Your obedient Servant, R. Adams, Surveyor-General". The certificate itself is not among the papers.

The next piece of correspondence is a copy (probably made by Trickett) of an official letter from William Orr, who was probably the District Surveyor, Deniliquin:

Figure 8. "Survey Camp on the Road"—
O. Trickett with axemen, chainmen, Cook and another, probably somewhere in central NSW, in the 1880s.
[from an original photograph among the Trickett papers]

On 1 January 1878 the Government Astronomer, Robert Ellery, wrote to Trickett from the Observatory, Sydney:

My dear Mr. Trickett,

I got both your letters and when in Sydney spoke to Mr. Adams [the Surveyor-General] *about you - he seemed to consider you "all right" and spoke in good terms of you. He evidently deals with surveyors on their merits and soon finds out good work so I have no doubt you will be among the "Elect".*

Wishing a happy and prosperous new year,

I remain, etc.

[signed] *Rob*. *Ellery*

There is no indication of why Trickett had written to the Government Astronomer but they appear to have been friends. Ellery was, like Trickett, a former Victorian - note his signature on Trickett's 1868 Victorian surveyors' certificate (Figure 2).

District Survey Office Deniliquin
Report 15th Oct. 1878

To—The Surveyor-General

Mr Trickett has invariably given me the greatest satisfaction in all my dealings with him and in my opinion he is worthy of all confidence as he performs his work faithfully.

I look upon an examination of isolated surveys as a fair test of a surveyor when the portion is almost surrounded by old work and in all such measurements of Mr Trickett's that I have inspected I found him correct.

[signed] *Wm. Orr*

The next document, dated only six weeks later, is in equally glowing terms and yet is from the other end of the State—

> Ministerial
> 6465
> 5Dec79
> Lands Department

Inverell

30th Nov. 1879

No. 79/70

Sir,

Mr Licensed Surveyor O. Trickett having personally requested me to report to you on his fieldwork, I have the honor [sic] to inform you that I examined some of Mr Trickett's fieldwork in the County of Cadell and beg to forward you the following report.

(a) The instrumental work was very good, no error exceeding one minute.

(b) The chaining was also very good, all of it being within three links in the mile.

The marking was good and up to the regulation standard.

In my opinion Mr (L.S.) Trickett is eligible for a district; not only from his qualifications as a surveyor but he also possesses those characteristics which will enable him to fill the position with credit to himself and also to the Department.

> *I have the honor to be, Sir,*
> *Your obedient Servant*
> [signed] *F. G. Finley (Actg. D.S.)*

This is annotated in the margin:

The Surveyor-General

Judging Mr Trickett from an office point of view I can state that he has given the very greatest satisfaction.

I am at one with Mr Finley in the opinion expressed by him in the concluding paragraph of his letter, so far as an examination of Mr Trickett's plans and reports enables me to be so.

> (it.) *F.W. Watt*
> *12 Dec 79*

and:

Forwarded for the information of Mr Lic. Sur. Trickett.

> (it.) *P.F.A.*
> *S.G. 22 Dec 79*

On 26 February 1880 the Under Secretary for Mines, Harrie Wood, wrote to Trickett at Moama advising him of his appointment by the Governor as a Mining Surveyor; gazetted 24 February 1880 (Scrapbook, rear).

A fellow surveyor wrote to him in the following terms:

Deniliquin 3 October 1881

Dear Trickett,

I received your long and interesting letter of the 21st September this morning. You have the happy nack [sic] of cramming a great deal of information onto a small space whereas I am obliged to cram very little news into a large space as we are still going on in the same way without anything fresh of any importance happening.

I have had to inspect the whole of the improvements on the Perricoota Reserves again in order to report if the valuations made by you are current or if they have depreciated in value but I agreed in toto with yours and expressed an opinion that if altered in any way the valuation should be increased by at least 25 per cent as a tank for instance full of water was of much greater value to an intending selector than the actual cut of the excavation.

I found Hopkins in the usual state of do-or-die-attitudes tearing along for his existence one would think. I am sure he will go mad in a year or two, especially when the land racket is over. Saw McGowan who was starting for Queensland with sheep on a 9 month tour to Moselle Downs. The Holroyds were at Perricoota and "Old Swiney" as Hopkins calls him doing the la-di-da with the ladies.

I saw the Cemetery Hill Womburta[?] Village and must confess it is not quite as high as shown on your map. I wrote to Danny and Edwards thanking them for the evident interest shown by them in the matter urging them to select a site to be buried in. Poor Hopkins would gladly act the gravedigger instead of Hamlet for once if he could only bury a few of the Dannys, McConnells and others of that kidney.

Forest Ranger Wilshire has protested against your survey of the Forest Res. at Moree but that does not matter much. I will go out there, inspect the country and slate him somehow or another for it.

We have had much sickness in the town since you left. Our youngest - 15 months - nearly succumbed to the prevailing sickness inflammation of the lungs; several children died. The second boy says he would like to go to heaven only he is frightened of the thunder.

I suppose you know that Bill was appointed to the Cooma district about a week or so after you left here. I have only two surveyors left, one (Lardner) won't work and the other (McCullock) can't work correctly.

You seem to have paid a very fair price for your horses and [?] of £13 but you will soon make it up at farm[?] work. Know what grass 6 feet high means as it was that height all over the plains here in 1870. We had to use short iron waddies for knocking it down nothing else answered. We tried ..., sharp knives, reaping hooks, etc., etc. I fear you will have some difficulty in getting pegs in the country you describe. Don't forget the gaspipe system of marking (I suppose you received a circular) it will answer in the Cartibar[?] country.

I have just finished my monthly progress journal in a new kind of form lately instituted for the sole purpose of driving poor hard worked Salaried Surveyors to commit suicide. Why should we only toil while you lucky licensed fellows are getting all the honey or sugar without the horrible necessity of reporting how little you do for your money.

Speaking of money reminds me that I have not heard[?] of any more investments at 10 per cent but will let you know if I do.

I hope you will send me a line now and again describing your work, your successes, your misfortunes and your hopes.

Mrs Orr joins me in kindest regards and believe me ever

Dear Trickett,
Yours faithfully,
[signed] William Orr

P.S. Thank you for your portrait, I enclose one of mine taken about five years ago.

And (Acting District Surveyor) Finley wrote in personal terms in 1883:

Inverell
10 Oct. 1883

Dear Trickett,

I owe you a line or two in reply to your last two kind wishes which were duly received. I was pleased to have your photo as also Crowleys altho at a first glance I thought it was intended for Arabi Pasha and his Diplomatic advisors. While I think the picture fairly good of both of you I also thank you for 'Meteor'. Horsey as usual, what an original cuss Mr. Orr seems - the idea of photographing disputed improvements is certainly novel.

Your remarks about the Moree Land Office is news to me. I have had some correspondence with the Surveyor-General about an office site and I will be in Moree to mark it out during the end of this month probably about the 22nd or 23rd. To tell you the truth I am a little hurt about the Surveyor-General's course of procedure in the matters of the Moree Office and I am going to make a stand. Of course, anything I now say to you is strictly confidential and I would not express my feelings to anyone on this matter - Lang has been writing privately to the Surveyor-General about getting to Moree and he (Lang) wrote to me the other day "regretting that any misunderstanding had arisen between us". In reply I also 'regretted' but I clearly let him understand that the Gwyder District was in my charge as a District Surveyor and that any proposed

changes or applications for employment therein should from the standpoint of official etiquette come through me - and I am going to see this thing through, if, as you tell me, Salling has been engaging an officer. I do not want Lang at Moree but if no better and more experienced officer can be had (and I told this to S.G.) I am prepared to work with him for a time. He has been gazetted a first class officer!! Mr. Lang is a gentleman who to my thinking has not "gone through the mill" enough for me and the idea of placing him in charge (as he calls it) of a district with such men as yourself, Russell and Salling in it is not to my mind a good one to say nothing else. I can hardly believe the Surveyor-General would go by me in this Moree Office business and take the matter out of my hands. I did not want to live in Moree certainly but I am jealous somewhat of the interests of the officers working under my supervision and I do not want things interfered with. However, I hope I will see you at Moree whither I start in about a week. You will probably be at the Races there, I am not (?) anxious to see them.

Things are going pretty well here. I see you had 75/100 of rain. We had only 59/100. Our grass is coming on and I hope things will be looking well at Moree when I go down. Corn! has it come to that? I certainly thought you could manage to get along without feeding. We have had a frost or two here lately and it was very cold here last night.

I am Mr Trickett
Yours sincerely
F. G. Finley

PS none of Cowper's tracings to hand yet. He has gone to Sydney [to] prepare plans and I am daily expecting them.

There is a further letter from Finley in 1885:

Moree
23 March 1885

My Dear Trickett,

I expect Mr McMaster to relieve me today and I cannot sever my connection with the district -on a professional point of view - without giving you a farewell line.

I trust in the first place that your association with McMaster will be as pleasant as they have been with me. I have always had great satisfaction from your work in every form and I may say that I looked upon you as the most reliable officer I had working under my supervision.

I also venture to hope that you have been satisfied with me. I have always done my best to promote your every wish and if I have ever done anything that has not been pleasant to you it was simply done from a point of duty and not from any wish to harass or trouble you.

I think you will have a years remunerative work at all events and if you ever think you would like a change and follow me, why write to me and I will see what is to be done.

With these few words I will now say Good Bye to you.

And believe me
Yours sincerely
F. G. Finley

[It is of interest to note that the same F.G. Finley, L.S., while based in Bathurst, had surveyed the location of Jenolan Caves as early as 1869 and "suggested that if a reserve were made the caves should be as nearly as possible in the centre of it" (Havard 1934, p. 17).]

An insight into conditions in the north of NSW in 1884 is provided by an item which appeared in a column in *The Australasian*, 3 May 1884, under the heading "Talk on 'Change":

To towns men the effect of drought is unfamiliar and even in some parts of the country it is (happily) unknown. The following graphically portrays, while it does not exaggerate:— "On leaving Narrabri I found myself surrounded by the familiar signs of drought. The coach took me through 90 miles of dust, which sometimes was as deep as the nave of the wheels, while ever and anon there was the smell of dead beasts to offend one's nostrils. The horses for the most part were too weak to do more than walk. On arrival at ———, the first station in my district, I found the proprietors making preparations to abandon the homestead, for its only

water was nearly dried up. That night, through want of water, I was obliged to remain in the thick coating of dust I had acquired during the coach journey. Next day I drove to ———, where I arrived half an hour before the only son of the family died of typhoid fever. ... A day afterwards I rode by a waterhole in which the dead and dying cattle were so thickly crowded as to touch each other. To see the living cattle bogged, without any hope of relief, except death, is a shock, until one by use becomes hardened. ... The losses in stock continue to be very disheartening. Forty thousand sheep on the next station have had no water for a fortnight, while all the cattle are dead. Preserved meats are passing through to many stations, while others are wholly abandoned, having lost all living animals." We who sit at home at ease can scarcely realise the sufferings and the losses caused by the awful drought of 1884. ...

- ÆGLES

The piece is annotated: "From letter by O. Trickett" and "1884 Drought, NSW. Self and men had to walk 7 miles to work - Temp 112°. Experienced Queensland Border by O.T."

As shown in Table 1, Trickett worked in the Moree and adjacent Warialda districts of northern central NSW from 1882 to 1887. During that time he took some sort of interest in a property by the name of *Midkin*, near Moree. A photograph survives among his papers showing Trickett and friends engaged in a game of tennis in front of the house (Figure 9).

Figure 9. Oliver Trickett and friends playing tennis at *Midkin*, near Moree — sometime between 1882 and 1887.
[from an original photograph among the Trickett papers]

A note among the papers indicates that A.W. Robertson, Chairman of "Goldsborough & Co." (elsewhere, probably more correctly referred to as "Goldsborough Mort & Co.", major stock and station agents) had some hand in dealings with "Midkin". While it has been suggested that Trickett owned "Midkin", a testimonial sheet that he produced about 1888 (Figure 11) states that A.W. Robertson was "Lessee Perricoota Station, Midkin Station, &c."

Also in 1888, evidently to provide a testimonial (reference), Robertson wrote:

> *Sydney April 23rd 1888*
>
> O. Trickett Esq.
> Sydney
>
> My Dear Trickett,
>
> In reply to your note I have much pleasure in saying that I have known you for many years and it has rarely been my good fortune to fall in with a man who combines as much energy with perseverance and at the same time such an honorable and trustworthy fellow as yourself. If you at any time desire me as a reference please use my name and at all times [I] shall be pleased to here [sic] of your success in life.
>
> > I am, my dear Trickett
> > Yours sincerely
> > A. W. Robertson

PRIVATE ENTERPRISE 1888-1892

Although there is no indication of the reasons for it among the Trickett papers, it is clear that there was a major change in direction of Oliver's life during 1888. For the last time he drew fees from the Lands Department and the Mines Department recorded his location as Sydney (Table 1).

It is evident that he became involved in mining ventures and dealing in equities at this time. Among the papers is a cutting from the *Australian Star* 3 June 1888:

A Midnight Scene at Lewis Ponds
—
HOW CLAIMS ARE JUMPED
(BY OUR SPECIAL REPORTER)

The history of mining affords many instances of strange scenes in contesting claims, but perhaps none of such a weird and extraordinary character as that which was to be witnessed at the bleak ridge of Mount Ragan, Upper Lewis Ponds, at midnight of Wednesday last. In the Government Gazette of May 7, there appeared a notification to the effect that four 40 acre conditional purchases, which were described, had been forfeited, and would be open for taking up in 30 days time. Mt Ragan is one of the roughest and steepest ridges in the mountainous country which encircles the Ponds, and though it has only previously been worked for copper, there are splendid surface outcrops of gossan, including silver and gold. ... Applications had been put in for these forfeited areas a few weeks ago by persons under the impression that they had never been taken up, and it was known on Wednesday that there was going to be

A RUSH FOR THE GROUND.

About 150 persons went out, including a number of people from Sydney, specially; and all the horses and vehicles available in the Orange livery stables were chartered. Numbers were on the ground from 3 in the afternoon, all well provided with tomahawks, lanterns, blankets, rugs, overcoats, and such like. Each watched the other jealously, but no move could be made in the way of taking possession until 12 pm. As darkness came on, campfires were lit, and men flitted about with lanterns in the gloom like a pack of body-snatchers of old. ...

AT ONE SPOT 14 MEN STOOD,

each determined to have the datum posts in first, and muttered threats were made as to what would happen [to] those who resisted them. ... As the midnight hour drew near watches and chronometers were consulted and a stern resolution was set on every face. Captains of gangs of men placed their subordinates in position, when suddenly the report of a rifle was heard—it was the pre-arranged signal to one of the parties that

TWELVE O'CLOCK HAD AT LAST ARRIVED and everyone realising the meaning thereof, commenced the exciting work of pegging out. There was no Government stroke about this business, but spades were stuck in the ground with a devilish earnestness, and the work proceeded as though sappers were forming defences in the face of an enemy. As each party finished they raced to their horses and vehicles on the return to Orange, and a rough journey they had in the darkness. On reaching the Registrar's office they waited outside the barred gate, until 9 o'clock, the hour of opening, and then money was planked down on the counter in frantic haste with some disputation as to who was first. The Registrar had prepared himself for this, and coolly remarked that where there were two or more applications for the same lease, the question of first should be decided by ballot. This was not satisfactory to some, but it was authoritative and had to be obeyed. Mr Oliver Trickett secured two of his drawings, a fact that was hailed with delight, because he had been the victim of

A MEAN AND DASTARDLY ACT.

In order to prevent his getting back to Orange in time, someone had removed his horses from the enclosure in which they had been tethered, and he had to walk to Orange, a distance of 18 miles. Thus the last was the first in the end. Another party had waited at Mt Ragan from noon to midnight, but when the critical time arrived for him to be up and doing, he was wrapped in peaceful slumber under the broad canopy of heaven, and no one chose to disturb him until not an inch had been left to peg out.

Though it is not clear whether it was on the above-mentioned ground or elsewhere, Trickett became involved with the "New Lewis Ponds" mine and on 14 February 1889 had a letter published in the Daily Telegraph, defending the quality of the ore in the mine, on the basis of a report by a Mr Du Bois. He concluded:

No doubt the mine has been a disappointment to those who expected the shares to run up to a capital of something like half a million [pounds] sterling, but I think Mr Du Bois' report goes a long way to encourage investors to hold the shares at an advance on present prices.

The extracts I have quoted are very favourable, and yet Mr Du Bois winds up his report by saying 'he is satisfied he has presented the worst side of the case'—Yours, &c.,

O.T.

By this time Trickett was not just dabbling in mining shares, he had set himself up as a sharebroker and "property, land and mining agent", with an office in Pitt Street, Sydney, and a GPO box - see Figures 10 and 11. With a Mr R.W. Harvey he published, in 1889, the "Handy Register of Mining Companies—containing a list of the principal coal, copper, gold, rubies, silver and tin mines in the Australian Colonies" which sold

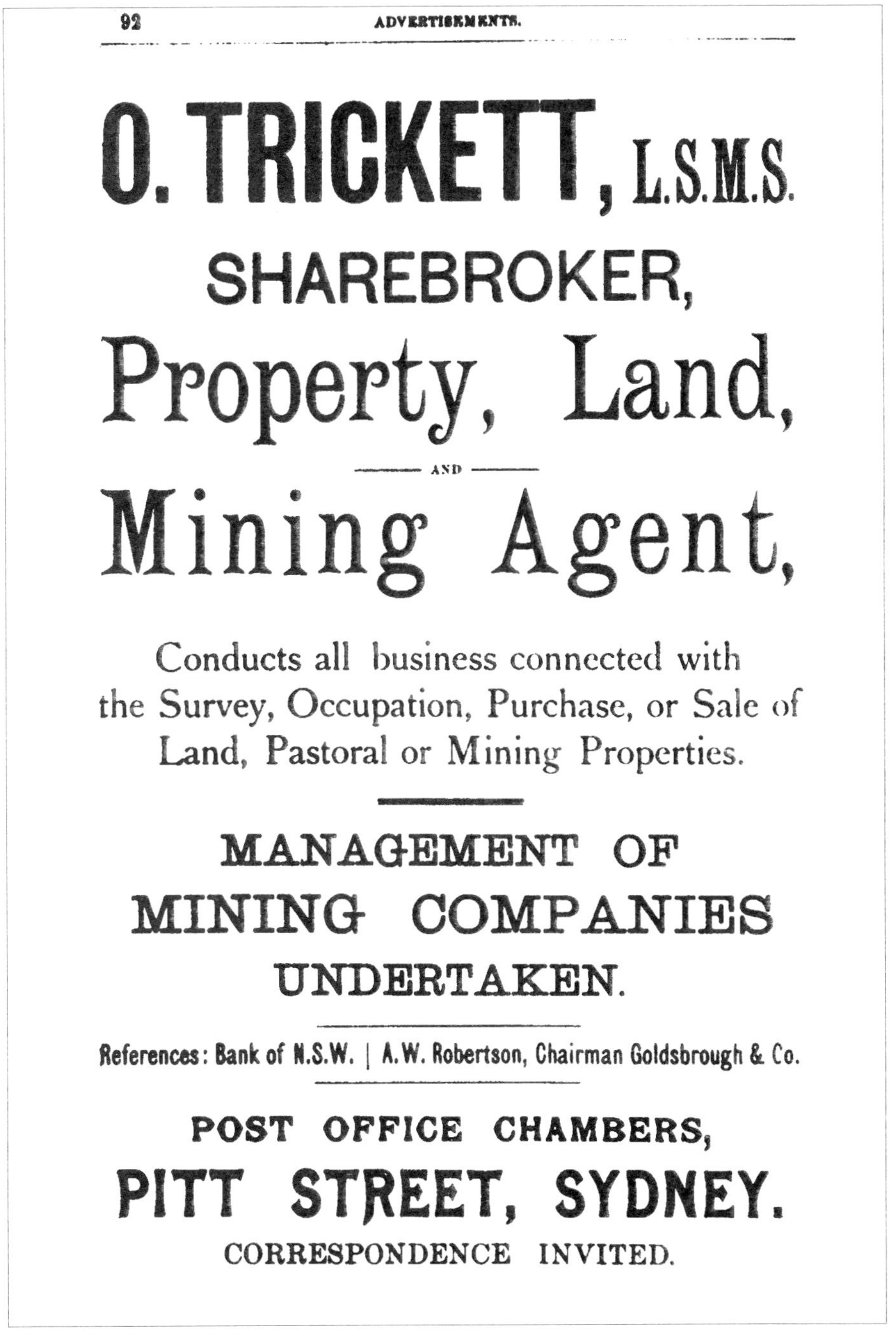

Figure 10. Advertisement for Oliver Trickett, sharebroker, published in his and R.W. Harvey's *Handy Register of Mining Companies*, 1889

for the princely sum of 10 shillings (Harvey & Trickett 1889). A great deal of work went into the compilation of this volume. As Trickett & Harvey record in their preface:

> *It will be readily understood that the particulars contained in the REGISTER were not obtained without much trouble and expense. The compilation was commenced six months ago ... An experienced draftsman was engaged, and a staff of collectors were appointed in the adjacent colonies and at Broken Hill. ...* Sydney Nov., 1888

(Harvey & Trickett 1889)

They intended to publish further editions for 1889 and 1890, but there is no evidence that these ever appeared.

Published with the book were maps of major mineral fields: Broken Hill, Croydon, Hillgrove, Mount Costigan and Lewis Ponds. Unfortunately these are missing from the copy held by the State Library of NSW but the Cartographic Branch of the Mines Department holds at least one (information from Andrew Valja), that showing the Hillgrove gold mines. When published the map bore the imprint: "Published by O. Trickett, Sharebroker, Post Office Chambers, Sydney" but this has been obliterated on the Mines Department's copy.

Trickett also produced a printed sheet, reproducing extracts from his best references and testimonials, doubtless for the purpose of reassuring clients as to his experience, reliability and connections. The sheet is reproduced as Figure 11.

An individual with whom Trickett did business during this period was one T.S. Huntley. On 20 July 1889 Huntley wrote Trickett a promissory note to the value of £676, presumably on account of a loan from Trickett. The amount was due on 23 January 1890, but was evidently not paid. Trickett has written across it in a thick pen: "Dishonored - money lost" - Figure 12.

Despite the fact that this would appear, on the face of it, to have been an unpleasant (and costly!) experience for Trickett, he continued to do business with Huntley (perhaps the money was paid later). A newspaper cutting in the Scrapbook (p. 19), dated 30 September 1890, records a rather unsavoury incident at a coal mine in the Hunter Valley, involving Mr Huntley:

THE DISTURBANCES AT GRETA

Non-unionists Brutally Assaulted

Inadequate Police Protection

The most disgraceful, and certainly the most serious, event that has darkened the present great labour crisis occurred at Greta early yesterday morning, when a party of non-unionist labourers, engaged to load small coal at the pits, were severely maltreated. ... All sorts of rumours were current as to the result of the brutal outrage, and it was generally believed that one of the unionists had been wounded by a revolver bullet; but, fortunately, this turns out to be utterly without foundation, the shots which were fired being let go

IN THE AIR.

There were several large heaps of small coal lying at the Greta pit, the aggregate quantity being between 10,000 and 12,000 tons. Mr T.S. Huntley, a gentleman well-known in the colony, purchased the coal from the company, and, after vainly endeavouring to secure the services of the union men to fill it into trucks, he was forced to engage non-union men to do the work. He applied to the police for protection some days ago, and was informed that an adequate force would be told off to guard his men. No one, however, anticipated the scenes which unfortunately followed. ... On Sunday evening Mr Huntley got his men together and left Newcastle shortly before 11 o'clock. The non-unionists, all Newcastle men, numbered 18, and two constables were sent with them. ... The news that the strangers were coming had apparently reached the ears of the Greta men, some 70 or 80 of whom were assembled in and around the station. It was luckily a bright moonlit night, and beyond hooting and yelling, the crowd contented themselves with jostling the newcomers until they had cleared the railway premises. [To reach their accommodation the men] had to walk along the main railway line for about 300 yards and then take the company's private railroad for an equal distance. Where this branch line connects there is a small cutting, the banks being some 8 feet high on either side of the rails. The procession was led by Mr Huntley and Mr Carter, the manager of the mine, the labourers coming next, and the police bringing up the rear. As the party reached the branch line a stone struck one of the non-unionists on the arm, and this was evidently the signal for the unparalleled scenes which followed. A large number of the yelling unionists got on the embankments on either side of the party, and

BLUE METAL,

which was plentiful in the vicinity, commenced to rain on the party. ... Mr Carter observed a man pick up a stone, and stopped to remonstrate with him, and endeavour to quieten the crowd. His efforts, however, were futile, and he got separated from the party. Mr Huntley was struck with several stones, and just managed to ward off one with his portmanteau, and so undoubtedly saved his head. The stoning then increased, and Mr Huntley's arm fell disabled by his side, three missiles having struck him between the elbow and the shoulder. The newly-arrived labourers fared much worse, and, on two of them being knocked down, a coloured man, who is well known in Newcastle, produced a revolver, which could be plainly seen in the moonlight. He cried out that he would use it if they struck him again, and, as he got out the words, a stone crashed on his left jaw.

TWO REVOLVER SHOTS

then rang out loud and clear above the din, the man having, according to his statement, fired in the air.

Passed the following Examinations :—Civil Service, Victoria ; Contract Surveyors, Victoria ; Mining Surveyors, Victoria ; Licensed Surveyors, N.S.W.

Extracts from Testimonials and Official Reports.

From the Chief Mining Surveyor and Acting-Secretary for Mines, Victoria, July 28, 1876.

As you are now on the eve of your departure for New South Wales, after a very lengthened period of service in the Office of Mines, I deem it right to bear the most favorable testimony as regards the good conduct, care, and general efficiency displayed by you while engaged as Draughtsman, Computer, Secretary to the Board of Examiners for Mining Surveyors, &c.

By Mr. Dist. Sur. FINLEY, Nov. 30, '79

The work was very good. . . . In my opinion Mr. TRICKETT is eligible for a district, not only from his qualifications as a Surveyor, but he also possesses these characteristics which will enable him to fill the position with credit to himself and also to the Department.

Mr. F. W. WATTS' minute on above, Dec. 12, 1879.

Judging Mr. TRICKETT from an office point of view, I can state that he has given the very greatest satisfaction. I am at one with Mr. Finley in the opinion expressed by him in the concluding paragraph.

Mr. Dist. Sur. DONALDSON, March 8, 1881.

(Feature Survey on temporary salary.) I examined nearly five miles, and found the angles correct, and the chainage good.

Mr. Dist. Sur. FIN-LEY, March 23, 1885.

I have always had great satisfaction from your work in every form, and look upon you as a most reliable officer.

Mr. Dist. Sur. McMASTER, March 16, 1889.

I have much pleasure in communicating the result of an examination of your work, as it proves your work to have been carried out in a very satisfactory manner.

Mr. Dist. Sur. ORR, Oct. 15, 1889.

Mr. TRICKETT has invariably given me the greatest satisfaction in all my dealings with him, and in my opinion he is worthy of all confidence, as he performs his work faithfully. In all measurements of Mr. TRICKETT's that I have inspected, I found him correct.

A. W. ROBERTSON, Esq., April 23, 1888, Lessee Perricoota Station, Midkin Station, &c., &c. *Chairman Goldsbourough Mort & Mort & Co*

I have much pleasure in saying that I have known you for many years, and it has rarely been my good fortune to fall in with a man who combines so much energy with perseverance, and, at the same time, so honorable and trustworthy. If you at any time desire me as a reference, please use my name, and at all times I shall be pleased to hear of your success in life.

Figure 11. Sheet produced by Trickett to inform his clients as to his experience and bona fides.

The non-unionists then broke and fled for their lives, dropping their swags and taking different routes, each pursued by a crowd of angry men who were now infuriated by the report of the firearms. Mr Huntley, however, stood between the rails, and one man, rushing at him, said "Run you ——". Quick as thought a revolver was presented, and the shining barrel probably scared the man, for he lost himself in the crowd. In a remarkably short space of time the railway was cleared, and here and there men could be seen running after fleeing figures, and shouting as they went. To trace the labourers in their wanderings over fences, through houses, along ditches and round trees, would fill a volume, so terrible was the experience of each of them.

The account continues in graphic detail of the injuries inflicted on the non-unionists and it seems amazing that no life was lost. The end result was that the men were so badly injured that they were not able to load the coal, but:

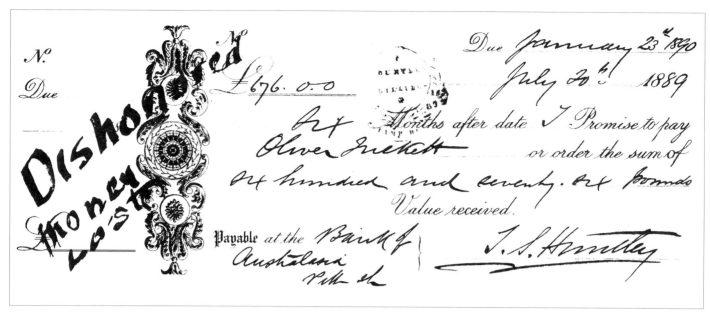

Figure 12. Promissory note issued by T.S. Huntley to Trickett in 1889 for £676; evidently it was not paid.
[From the Scrapbook - slightly reduced]

Mr Huntley, whose left arm is very much swollen and injured, is determined to carry out the work and, returning to Newcastle last evening, he made arrangements to secure more men, all of whom will be

FULLY ARMED.

Evidently this party was more successful and the coal was loaded, for Trickett wrote in the margin, showing no sign of concern for the men who he was employing at such peril, or for his partner:

Coal purchased by T.S. Huntley and O. Trickett at 7/6 - sold at 28/- Profit of £2,500. Would have cleared £8,000 in another 3 weeks.

Further business dealings involving T.S. Huntley are indicated by a share certificate in Trickett's name for 36 £1 shares in the Sydney and Port Hacking Coal Company Ltd, dated 12 June 1894 and signed by T.S. Huntley as Secretary & Manager of the company. A stamp across the certificate reads: "3 fully paid up Pref. shares in the Sydney Harbour Collieries Ltd (London Company), issued this day in respect of the within shares. Dated 11th day of June 1901. For the Liquidator of the Sydney Harbour Collieries Ltd." Perhaps this was one investment which didn't pay a profit.

While it is not conclusive evidence that he later avoided the stock market, there is no further evidence among his papers of Trickett's financial affairs.

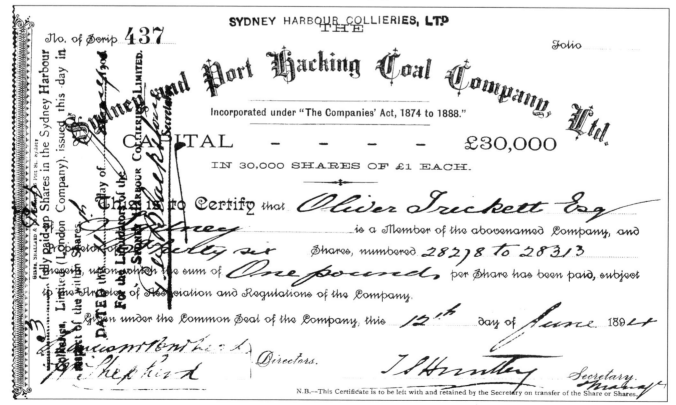

Figure 13. Trickett's 1894 certificate for thirty-six £1 shares in the Sydney and Port Hacking Coal Company Ltd.

MINES DEPARTMENT DRAFTSMAN AND SURVEYOR, 1892-1919

Between 1888 and 1892 Trickett continued to hold the post of Mining Surveyor in the Mines Department, based in Sydney (according to the *Public Service List*), despite the fact that he was clearly operating as a self-employed sharebroker and trader. No salary is shown so this may have been an appointment which authorised him to practice as a mining surveyor. Perhaps he made some bad investments, or business wasn't up to his expectations, or he found the private enterprise world not to his liking, but on 16 June 1892 he returned to working full-time in the Department of Mines as a draftsman. His initial appointment was temporary but he became 'permanent' on 23 December 1895 (see departmental record, Table 2).

The *Public Service List* for 1892, 1893 and 1894 shows Trickett as "Mining Surveyor". By 1897 (the List does not appear to have been published in 1895 and 1896) he was listed as "Draftsman, Charting Branch" and the date 16 June 1892 appeared in the "Date of appointment to present position" column. In 1898 he is shown as "Draftsman, Geological Survey Branch". By 1901 this entry had changed to "Draftsman and Surveyor", which remained the official title of his office until he retired in 1919.

Trickett's salary was £5 per week (£260 p.a.) in 1892, rising to £275 on 1 July 1900. It was increased to £325 in 1901 (an 18% increase on the previous year), £360 in 1907 and £400 in 1912, at which it remained until his retirement in 1919.

An early major project in his new post appears to have been the preparation of a *Geological Map of the Colony of New South Wales* (New Edition 1893).

> *During the year a new edition of the Geological Map of the Colony was published. Considerable care was exercised in obtaining the very best colours in the market, and in consequence of this, and the excellence of the draftsman's and lithographer's work, the map is generally considered to be in advance of anything of the kind yet issued by the Department. The boundaries of the different formations were drawn by Mr O. Trickett, L.S. ... The map has been awarded a medal at the Chicago Exhibition* (Pittman 1893).

The plan[7] bears the inscription under the legend: GEOLOGICALLY PLOTTED AND COMPILED BY O. TRICKETT. Also in 1893 Trickett drew a *Geological Sketch Map of the Barrier Ranges* and a *Geological Map of Broken Hill* from geological surveys by J.B. Jaquet, Geological Surveyor, which were published with his report (Jaquet 1894).

In 1895 Trickett was involved in the preparation of a *Geological Map shewing the principal stanniferous leads in the Tingha and Elsmore Districts*. His precise role is not clearly indicated on the map, which is annotated "Constructed from Parish Lithographs by O. Trickett" (Wilkinson & David 1895). Unusually, this map appears to have been issued without an accompanying report.

Trickett was heavily involved in the preparation of a Mineral Map of the Colony of New South Wales in 1895-96. A spin-off from this appears to have been a *Register of Mineral Localities*. How this came about is explained in the following memorandum which Trickett wrote to the Government Geologist, Mr E.F. Pittman (his immediate superior):

> Geological Branch
> Department of Mines
>
> 29th November 1895
>
> ### Re Mineral Map
>
> Sir,
>
> *In connection with the authority to prepare a Mineral Map of the Colony, I have the honor to submit the following remarks:-*
>
> *Two editions of a Mineral Map have been published, the second I think in 1884. In addition, a map was prepared in 1891 (vide Ann. Report for 1891 p. 212) indicating the positions of the following minerals:- Coal, Lime, Manganese, Wolfram, Chromite.*
>
> *Assuming these maps to be complete up to the date on which they were compiled or issued, I estimated that any additional information, the result of subsequent discoveries of minerals, could be compiled in something like two months.*
>
> *On examination I found however that the existing maps were not sufficiently accurate or complete, and although I could accept them as useful guides to a new compilation, it would be necessary to examine all available records in order to produce a map that could be recognised as a complete reference to localities of minerals as far as known. As the examination of these records did not appear to be covered by the authority for the compilation of the New Map I determined to commence the work at home. During my leisure I have made extracts from the Annual Reports of the Mining Department and from available maps. From these I have compiled three lists of recorded localities; see examples enclosed.*
>
> *It may possibly be considered that list No. 2 is worth preserving for reference - a book of some 500 leaves would be required with printed headings and for its greater usefulness two additional columns for "Authority" and "Report".*
>
> *But this list contains many errors which occur in the recorded descriptions. In very many instances the given distance of any mineral from a known locality is in excess of its actual distance in a direct line, while the direction is frequently inaccurate.*

---

7   A copy is held in the Mitchell Library map collection at reference Z M2 810 caq/1893/1. Scale: 1 inch to 16 miles.

For gold Parish Maps afford a means of correcting many of the descriptions; but for all minerals a ready means of correction is not supplied, as the Parish Maps do not define what mineral, other than gold, any leased land is supposed to contain.

On this work so far I have been occupied altogether nearly a week of official time and the greater part of my leisure (evenings, holidays, Saturday afternoons) for over six months.

Owing to the incomplete or inaccurate descriptions I have referred to above it will be necessary to examine and amend much of the data I have compiled.

It is extremely difficult to estimate the time this will take, possibly three months.

I beg respectfully to request you will be pleased to recommend that I be authorised to complete the work.

In addition to the work above referred to I beg to point out that information is constantly required of me which necessitates my working overtime and that I am seldom able to leave the office until after regulation hours.

I have the honor to be, Sir,

Your obedient Servant,

[signed] O. Trickett, Lic. Surv.

The work evidently proceeded, and on 25 April 1896, Trickett wrote to Pittman:

Geol. Survey

Mines 96/9440

25 Apl 96

Sir,

I have the honour to submit for your inspection the Register of Mineral Localities.

The Authority column still remains to be filled in from information to which I have access.

The Register will be found to be fairly accurate except in many of the described directions and distances of any known localities which I have only corrected at present from my own knowledge.

I beg now to apply for the use of Wardens Registrars and GF [Gold Fields] Commissioners Reports prior to 1876.

I have etc.   O. Trickett

The Govt. Geologist

On this Pittman noted:

This Register, which has been compiled by Mr Trickett entirely in his private time, will be of very great value not only in connection with the mineral map of the Colony which he is compiling under my supervision but also for purposes of future reference. There is no other compilation from which reliable information can be obtained as to the localities of the various mineral deposits in New South Wales and enquiries are frequently made in this Office which

shows the necessity [of] such a book of reference. If the reports of the Mining Registrars and Gold Fields Commissioners prior to the year 1876 can be supplied they will enable the information to be made much more reliable.

[signed] E. F. Pittman.

Pittman was clearly impressed by this register. In his contribution to the *Annual Report* for 1897 he wrote:

I would also like to specially allude to the important work performed by this officer in the preparation of an index to the known localities of the various mineral occurrences in the Colony. This index was commenced several years ago, and is continually being added to as new discoveries are recorded. It is of very great value for reference purposes, and will be largely used by the Geological Surveyors in preparing reports on our mineral resources. (Pittman 1897)

The register was used within the Department for many years and was eventually published in 1919 as *Bibliography of the Economic Minerals of NSW* (Trickett, 1919). Of this Trickett said in a letter dated 10 May 1920 to the Public Service Board (GS 20/005) (Trickett papers):

I spent the whole of my leisure for 9 months in the compilation of a Bibliograph of the Economic Minerals of NSW which has recently been published for the Mines Department at a cost of £500. As the manuscript has been constantly used by officers for the purpose of reference for 20 years, you can perhaps realize the very considerable sum in time which has been saved.

Few photos are known of Trickett in these years, however the historical collection of the Geological & Mining Museum in The Rocks, Sydney, includes some group photos which show him and his colleagues. Unfortunately they are not dated and not all those shown are named.

Figure 14 (Departmental No. 0052) shows a happy group at what must surely be the "geologists' picnic" of 1893 or 1894.

Figure 15 (Departmental No. 0238) is a somewhat more official-looking photo of the staff of the Geological Survey. It shows the Survey's first car (Branagan pers. comm.) and dates from around 1920.

Another photo (Departmental No. 1323 - not reproduced here) is more recent and shows Trickett among a number of officers of different departments. It was taken on the roof of the Lands Department building.

Figure 14.   Some officers of the NSW Mines Department, circa 1893-94. Left to right, back row:
W.S. Dun, L.F. Harper, R. Etheridge Jnr., (unknown); front row: G.A. Stonier, M. Morrison, O. Trickett.
[Photo courtesy Dept. of Mineral Resources, Geological & Mining Museum, Sydney]

Figure 15.   Staff of the NSW Geological Survey with the Survey's first car, about 1920.
Left to right: W.S. Dun, M. Morrison, (unknown), (unknown), (unknown), O. Trickett, L.F. Harper, (unknown).
[Photo courtesy Dept. of Mineral Resources, Geological & Mining Museum, Sydney]

RESPONSIBLE FOR LIMESTONE CAVES

The control of the [limestone] caves [of NSW] was transferred from the Lands Department to the Mines Department in 1879 (M.79/8,989) Between 1st January 1883 and July 1897 the sum of £23,131 had been expended on the care and improvement of the caves. Particulars of earlier expenditure are not readily available.

So wrote Trickett (1897) in the *Annual Report of the Department of Mines* (ARDM) for 1897.

Geological Surveyors and others (notably C.S. Wilkinson, W. Anderson and W.S. Leigh) furnished reports on various caves from at least the 1870s (Middleton 1988) and full-time guides and other staff were employed by the Department to run the established tourist caves at Jenolan, Wombeyan, Abercrombie and Yarrangobilly; and at various times at Bungonia, Wellington and Bendithera. In May 1888 Mr W.S. Leigh was appointed as the first (and only) Superintendent of Caves (Leigh 1888) and he held that position until 1896, when it was abolished (Pittman 1896). As Pittman put it:

The office of Superintendent of Caves having been abolished, the active supervision of the limestone caves has been undertaken by Mr Oliver Trickett, L.S., in addition to his ordinary duties as Geological Survey Draftsman. Mr Trickett has already furnished valuable reports on a number of the caves, giving details of past expenditure, and has prepared sketch plans which will be of great use to visitors, and which it is proposed to publish.

Pittman also recorded that year:

Mr W.D. Campbell, Licensed Surveyor, has been employed for some months in surveying the aboriginal carvings in the Hawkesbury sandstones of the coast district north and south of Sydney. These are being reproduced in plan form by Mr O. Trickett, and will shortly be published. It is believed that they will form an extremely interesting ethnological record, and the work has not been undertaken too soon, as many of the carvings in the suburban districts are becoming obliterated as population increases. (Pittman 1896)

These plans were subsequently published as *Aboriginal carvings of Port Jackson and Broken Bay* in the Memoirs of the Geological Survey (Campbell 1899). Trickett is credited with drawing the 12 plates, from field notes by W.D. Campbell, F.G.S., Licensed Surveyor. An example (Plate 8) is included as Figure 16.

A file of papers on these carvings still exists in the Archives Office of NSW (Special file #3: Aboriginal rock carvings around Sydney 1896-1922). This file shows that on 4 June 1896 S. Sinclair, the Secretary of the Australian Museum, wrote to the Under Secretary for Public Instruction, suggesting that the 'Wollombi Caves', containing outlines of Aboriginal hands, should

be reserved and protected. The matter was referred to the Department of Mines on 9 June and Pittman recommended that as the 'caves' were of considerable interest they should be reserved. On 30 June 1896 the matter was referred to the District Surveyor, Maitland (Department of Lands) for report. Surveyor H.W. Graeme reported on 29 April 1898 that most of the caves were on freehold land and recommended that the markings be cut out and preserved in the Australian Museum. On 9 May 1898 the District Surveyor, Maitland recommended that the Mines Department determine whether purchase was justified. On 19 May Pittman referred the matter to Oliver Trickett, who responded:

The caves appear to be close to a main road and to be used by swagmen. It would probably be impossible to protect them from injury. The resumption of the land on which they are situated may not therefore be deemed advisable.

E.F. Pittman concurred with Trickett's view and it appears that nothing further was done.

The reason for Trickett being chosen to look after the limestone caves of NSW does not seem to have been published and we may never know whether he sought the post or it was 'thrust upon him'[8]. There is also no evidence, either in the scrapbook or the published departmental reports, of any earlier involvement with caves but in any event he took to his new duties with enthusiasm and vigour.

That Trickett thoroughly enjoyed his involvement with the caves is clear beyond doubt from his published reports. Figure 17 shows him 'in action' using a massive rope, probably at Jenolan, assisted by Bailey, Edwards and Wiburd - the principal 1900s explorers.

Figure 17. Trickett descending a cave on a hawser.
[From an original lantern slide - Hamilton-Smith collection]

---

[8] It may well be that an 1896 memorandum, recorded in the *Index to the Register of Letters Received for 1896* (Archives Office of NSW) as #19709: "Re arrangements for the supervision of the Limestone Caves", could shed some light on this matter. It is shown as "put away" but unfortunately is no longer located under the number quoted and presumably became attached to subsequent correspondence.

MEM. GEOL. SURVEY. N.S.W., ETHNOL. NO. 1.

PLATE 8.

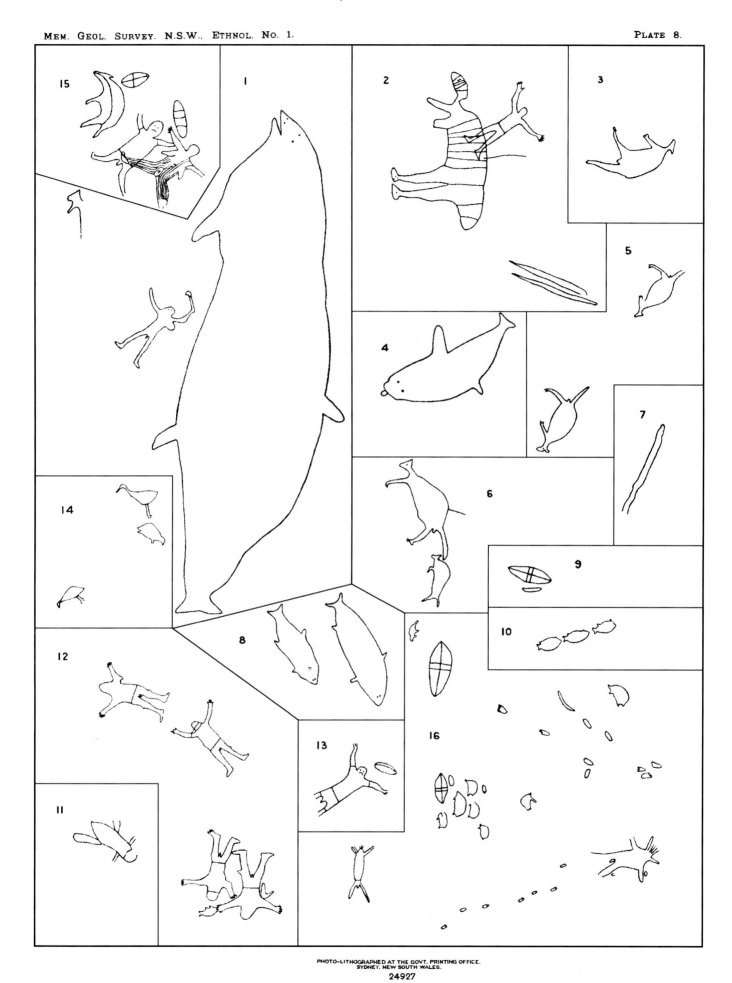

Figure 16. Aboriginal carvings on Hawkesbury sandstone; an example of Trickett's drawings, 1896
[from *Memoirs of the Geological Survey of NSW, Ethnology No.1,* 1896]

CAVE RESERVE REGULATIONS

Regulations affecting the operations of the various cave reserves were Trickett's responsibility. The following insight comes from original documents in the Archives Authority of NSW box number 19/2366, file 12795. In May 1897 F.J. Wilson wrote to the Under Secretary, Department of Mines:

> *Jenolan Caves*
> *24th May 1897*
>
> Sir,
>
> *I have the honor to apply that a clause be inserted in the Regulations, Prohibiting Shooting any Game on Cave Reserve. There is nothing in the regulations to prevent Shooting here. Some of the Visitors are as much interested with the wallabies and other Game, as the caves. The preservation of them would help to keep the place attractive.*
>
> *I have the honor to be, Sir*
> *Your most obedient Servant*
> *[signed] F. J. Wilson*
> *Caretaker*

On this Trickett wrote:

> *In the Yarrangobilly and Abercrombie printed regulations the following is included:—*
>
> *"The Shooting or trapping of any animal or bird within a radius of one mile of any cave on the reserve is not allowed"*
>
> *[signed] O. Trickett*

And the Government Geologist added:

> *It is recommended that a clause to the above effect be added to the Jenolan Caves Regulations and that [copies] on linen be provided.*
>
> *[signed] E.F. Pittman*
> *Government Geologist 29.5.97*

The Under Secretary for Mines and Agriculture agreed "This is very desirable" and the Minister (Sydney Smith) approved on 1.6.97. This was returned to Trickett and on 9.6.97 he wrote:

> *Geol. Branch*
> *9/6/97*
>
> *Memorandum for the Govt. Geologist*
>
> ### *Caves Regulations*
>
> *In connection with the directive to print notices against shooting or trapping birds or animals within the Caves reserves I beg to submit herewith general regulations for printing at the same time.*
>
> *These contain all regulations except those relating to charges for accommodation and for use of magnesium ribbon, and in the case of Jenolan Caves, the notice against Camping near the Reservoir.*
>
> *There is no power given to make regulations under the acts under which the Caves reserves are gazetted.[9]*
>
> *If the regulations herewith be approved, I beg to submit they be printed on calico in type not less in size than the obsolete notice (Jenolan) herewith. The more recent general notices are in small type and do not attract attention except when specially directed to them.*
>
> *O. Trickett*

The Government Geologist agreed and submitted to the Under Secretary who sought a proof. This was provided (14.6.97) and approved 12.7.97. Forty copies were prepared. The Minister wrote (21.7.97): "I do not think we should allow shooting on any part of the reserve". Whether the regulations were accordingly revised (to remove the limitation on shooting applying only within half a mile of a cave) is not known. The regulations, as drafted by Trickett, were as follows:

Regulations relating to the Management of the Caves

> *No person will be allowed to enter any of the caves unless accompanied by the Caretaker or an authorised guide.*
>
> *Visitors will be conducted through the caves by the Caretaker or guide for which service no charge is to be made, but the caretaker is authorised to charge for the use of magnesium ribbon and candles as per printed scale of charges.*
>
> *The Caretaker may exclude from the caves any person who is guilty of improper conduct.*
>
> *Any incivility or want of attention on the part of the Caretaker or a guide should be reported to the Under Secretary for Mines, Sydney.*
>
> *Any person found breaking, defacing by writing or marking or otherwise injuring the rocks,* **stalactites, stalagmites or other parts of the caves** *or their improvements, or the vegetation on the reserve for the caves will be* **prosecuted with the utmost rigour of the law.** *Visitors are requested to assist the Caretaker or guide as far as possible in the observance of this regulation.*
>
> *The shooting or trapping of any animal or bird within a radius of half a mile of any cave on the reserve is not allowed.*
>
> *The Caretaker is instructed to immediately report to the Under Secretary for Mines and Agriculture the name and address of any person infringing these regulations. Failure to comply with this instruction renders the Caretaker liable to dismissal.*
>
> *Visitors are requested to insert their names and addresses in the books provided for the purpose.*

A regulation "The sale of fermented and spirituous liquors is strictly prohibited" was included in the draft but against it is written "omit".

---

[9] The power to make regulations was included in the *Public Trusts Act 1897*.

MINES DEPARTMENT CAVE REPORTS

The *Annual Report of the Department of Mines* each year contains a report on the activities of the Geological Survey; included in this during the years 1896 to 1919 were reports by or about the work done by Oliver Trickett. The *ARDM* also provided the vehicle for publication of most of Trickett's cave and limestone deposit (cave area) maps.

1896 Report

Trickett's first report on the caves is modest enough; it reads, in full:

> *Geological Branch, Department of Mines and Agriculture,*
> *Sydney, 16 January 1897*
>
> *Sir,*
>
> *I have the honor to submit the following Progress Report on the Caves for the year 1896:—*
>
> *The following improvements have been authorised:—*
> *Opening up of the new cave, Jenolan.*
> *Building of a caretaker's cottage at Bungonia.*
> *Preparation of a Bathing-place at the Thermal Spring, Yarrangobilly Caves.*
> *Erection of ironwork to protect "The Alter" at the Wellington Caves.*
> *Sundry improvements at the Wombeyan and Abercrombie Caves of a minor character.*
> *Sketches of the surface features and improvements at the various caves are in course of preparation with a view to publication.*
>
> *Jenolan Caves*
>
> *A road through the Grand Arch has been completed. The road improvements include a handsome stone bridge over the creek. Visitors are now able to drive right up to the Caves House.*
>
> *In order to provide for the better accommodation of visitors, men are now employed excavating for the foundations of a new Caves House, for which designs have been prepared by the Government Architect.*
>
> *The electric lighting of the Lucas and Imperial Caves has been improved under the able supervision of Mr Fitzmaurice, of the Electric Telegraph Department.*
>
> *Mr Jeremiah Wilson was temporarily appointed as Explorer at the Jenolan Caves on 1st August, 1896.*
>
> *Number of visitors to the caves during the year 1896:*
>
> | | |
> |---|---|
> | *Abercrombie* | *962* |
> | *Bendithera Caves* | *84* |
> | *Bungonia Caves* | *313* |
> | *Jenolan Caves* | *1,816* |
> | *Wellington Caves* | *1,548* |
> | *Wombeyan Caves* | *330* |
> | *Yarrangobilly Caves* | *516* |
> | *Total* | *5,569* |

> *Some of these caves take more than one day to examine. If the above return were calculated on the basis of separate visits, the total would be very much larger; for instance, 841 visits were made to the Jenolan Caves during the month of December.*
>
> | | £ | s. | d. |
> |---|---|---|---|
> | *Magnesium ribbon issued to caretakers, 630 oz., cost* | *118* | *2* | *6* |
> | " *amount collected for use of* | *209* | *1* | *2* |
>
> *I have, &c,*
> *O. TRICKETT*
>
> *The Government Geologist* (Trickett 1896)

1897 Report

His second report (1897a), however, is much more extensive and includes 11 pages of plans (Figures 18 to 28) and a summary of previous reports and publications which may well be Australia's first cave bibliography. Part of this report was reprinted by the Department of Mines & Agriculture in 1898 as *Notes on the Limestone Caves of NSW with plans*. This included the 11 plans published in 1897 and two others that did not appear in the *ARDM* until 1900 (Figures 42 and 43). Because this report is of such interest the full text has been reproduced here as Appendix 1.

Pittman, in his report on the Geological Survey for that year, introducing Trickett's work, says:

> *Mr O. Trickett, L.S. has made a number of surveys and plans of the limestone caves which will prove of considerable use to visitors. It is proposed to publish these plans in the Annual Report, as the want of such information about these beautiful works of nature has long been felt by the public.*
>
> *In addition to conducting all the correspondence with the caretakers, and submitting recommendations with regard to proposed improvements at the Caves, Mr Trickett has performed all the geological charting in connection with this Branch.* (Pittman 1897)

Trickett itemised developments at each of the show cave areas Jenolan, Yarrangobilly, Bungonia, Bendithera [!], Wellington, Abercrombie and Wombeyan, and reported new discoveries at Jenolan, Abercrombie, Bungonia and Bendithera. In the Jenolan report there is reference to a new entrance to the Lucas Cave:

> *Construction of a new entrance to the Lucas Cave from the Grand Archway. Visitors will be enabled to reach the Lucas Cave without the necessity of climbing over the ridge in which this cave is situated.* (Trickett 1897a)

To his 1897 report Trickett appended his first set of published cave surveys. On this matter, he wrote:

Survey of Caves

I have realised that it would be a benefit to the caretakers at the various caves if they had a better idea of the direction of the underground channels and caverns as an aid to future exploration, and to enable the guides to answer questions which are frequently put by visitors.

I have commenced to define these channels, with the assistance of Mr Harper, Field Assistant, by making a compass survey of part of the Jenolan Caves, as indicated on plans herewith.

I would have preferred to make a theodolite survey, to avoid errors of magnetic variation arising from the presence of the protecting ironwork and netting, but I should have required more time than I had at my disposal, and extra assistance.

Reports on Caves

For the purpose of reference I have furnished general reports on each of the caves, which include such information as I thought might be of interest.

To illustrate these reports I made compass and pace surveys of the surface features and improvements at the different caves, which are shown on accompanying plans. (Trickett 1897a)

Trickett's reports on particular caves that year related to the Grove Cave, Abercrombie (September) (Trickett 1897b), Tuglow Caves (October), a "New Cave" at Jenolan [Aladdin, J19] and mutilation of the "Copper Mine" Cave at Yarrangobilly (both in December).

The Tuglow report (Trickett 1897c) is of particular interest because of the difficulties that must have been experienced in reaching the cave (although Trickett says nothing of this), the difficulties of descending this cave (he says he went down 500 feet) and the fact that he took a photo, with a camera lent by a Mr Rowe of Jenolan (the "photographer-in-residence"). Despite the vertical nature of this cave, he foresaw the possibility of future development (ordinary tourists in those days would suffer conditions only 'adventure' tourists would accept today). Notwithstanding his optimism, development has not occurred and is extremely unlikely.

The Aladdin report is interesting because it demonstrates, right from his first survey, the value of this work and the way he saw its importance for exploration. He records:

The caretaker [F.J. Wilson] was induced to search hereabouts from the information I had supplied him with respect to the position of the 'Lily of the Valley', fixed by my survey of the Imperial and Jubilee Caves. (Trickett 1897d)

His report on mutilation of Coppermine Cave [Y12] (Trickett 1897e) indicates Trickett's understanding of underground drainage, as he postulated a connection between Y12 and three sinks on the plateau near the main road, at least two of which (Y8 & Y45) have since been proven to drain to Y12. It also gives an insight into his feeling for caves and his foresight in terms of scenic protection and tourism:

Following the underground stream up from its exit for 500 feet, wading through icy cold water on the way in places, and then rising about 30 feet, the remains of what has been a magnificently ornamented cave is reached, about 300 feet long as far as explored.

Axes, crowbars, chisels and cartridges, have been used to demolish or remove the beautiful formations in this part of the cave.

Nothing appears to have been too large to destroy, for in one place the remains of a fine column over 6 inches in diameter, are lying on the floor. Fragments of semi-transparent "shawls" lie among the debris of broken stalactites, stalagmites and crystals of calcite. To secure the last-named, appears to have been the main object of the miscreants, who have destroyed as much as they could get access to, for the crystals have been carefully chiselled out. There can, however, have been no object other than destruction in breaking the "shawls", which come away in pieces, and have no beauty when removed.

The cave is still worth preserving, for the portion damaged probably represents a very small part of the attractive chambers which may be found in the future along the underground waterway.

It is important that the destruction of any of the caves at Yarrangobilly should be prevented, for it is not unreasonable to suppose that the impressive scenery, the number and extent of the caves, and the cool climate of this locality, will render it in future one of the most popular resorts of tourists in the Colony. (Trickett 1897e)

The appended plans are of Jenolan (entrance locations and limestone, caves in relation to surface features - Figure 18- and detailed plan and longitudinal section of the Right Imperial and Easter Cave [Devils Coachhouse] - Figure 19), Yarrangobilly (entrance locations and surface features, detail of the accommodation area and overall plan of limestone deposit - Figure 20), Wombeyan (reserve, entrances and surface features, accommodation house, extent of limestone - Figure 21 - and plan and sections of Wollondilly Cave - Figure 22), Wellington (reserve and cave entrances, surface improvements and plan and longitudinal section of Main [Cathedral] Cave—after Sir Thomas Mitchell, 1838 - Figure 23), Abercrombie (reserve, cave entrances and surface features, caretaker's cottage - Figure 24 - and plan and longitudinal section of Grove Cave - Figure 25), Bungonia (reserve, entrance locations and surface features and plan of Bungonia [Grill] Cave - Figure 26), Bendithera (reserve, cave entrances and surface features - Figure 27) and Tuglow (entrances and surface features - Figure 28).

When it is considered that all of this was done within two years, it represents a truly prodigious output. Most of the plans are original, though on the first Jenolan plan Trickett acknowledges "Use made of

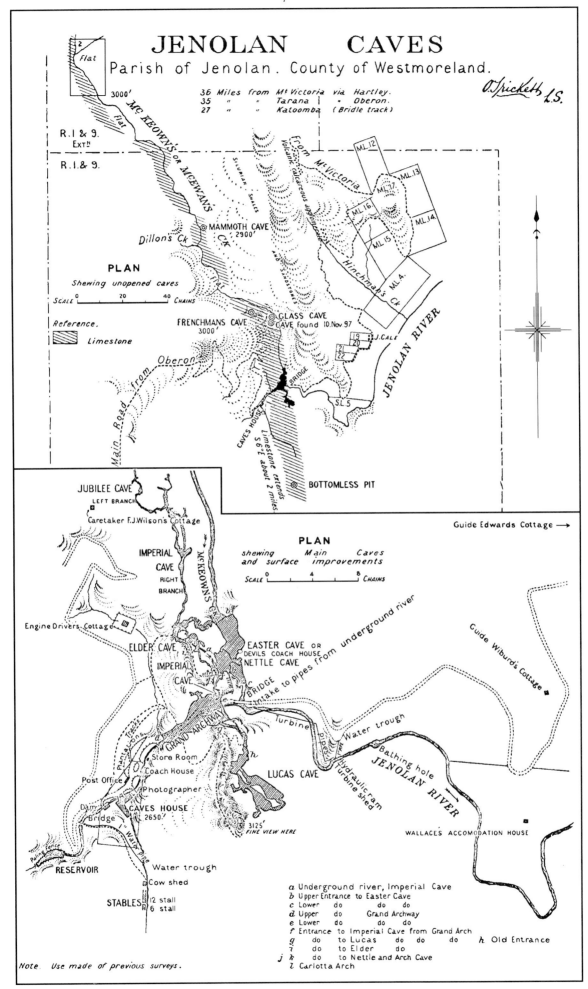

Figure 18. Jenolan Caves, Parish of Jenolan; Plans showing main caves and surface improvements (*ARDM* 1897 plan 1)

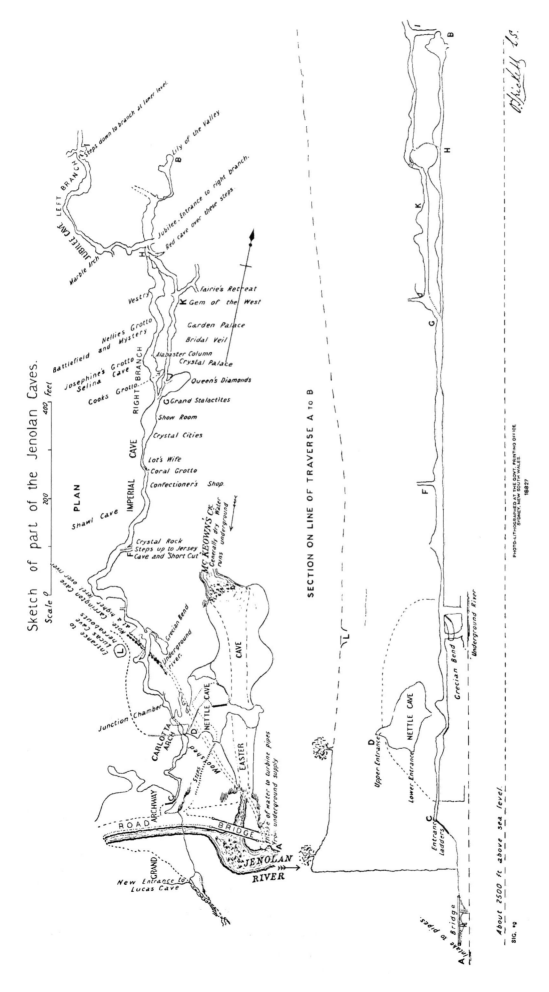

Figure 19. Sketch of part of the Jenolan Caves (*ARDM* 1897 plan 2)

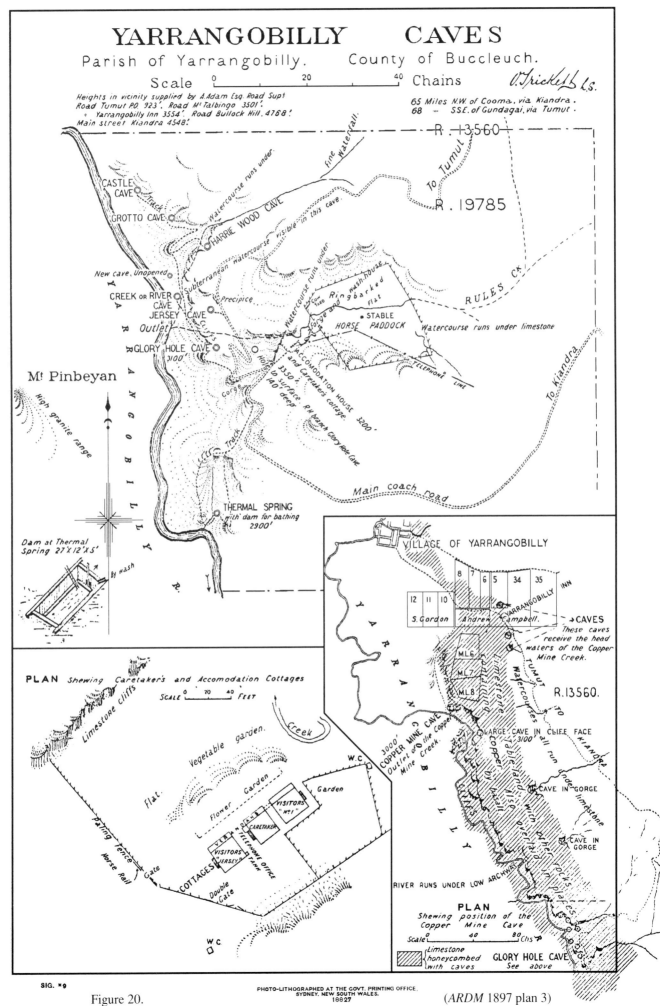

YARRANGOBILLY CAVES

Parish of Yarrangobilly.   County of Buccleuch.

Scale 0   20   40 Chains

O. Trickett l.s.

Heights in vicinity supplied by A.Adam Esq. Road Supt.
Road Tumut P.O. 923'.   Road Mt Talbingo 3501'.
" Yarrangobilly Inn 3554'.   Road Bullock Hill. 4768'.
Main street Kiandra 4548'.

65 Miles N.W. of Cooma, via Kiandra.
68 "   S.S.E. of Gundagai, via Tumut.

R. 13560

R. 19785

CASTLE CAVE
GROTTO CAVE
HARRIE WOOD CAVE
New cave, Unopened.
CREEK OR RIVER CAVE
JERSEY CAVE
Outlet
GLORY HOLE CAVE
3100'

Mt Pinbeyan

High granite range

Dam at Thermal Spring 27'X12'X5'
By wash

THERMAL SPRING with dam for bathing 2900'

fine Waterfall
Watercourse runs under
Watercourse visible in this cave.
Subterranean watercourse
Precipice
Watercourse runs under
Forge and Ringbarked Flat
Cow shed
wash house
STABLE
HORSE PADDOCK
Watercourse runs under limestone
RULES Ck.

To Tumut

ACCOMODATION HOUSE and Caretakers cottage 3200'
3350'. to surface R.H. branch Glory Hole Cave
Horse 140 deep
Gorge
Track
Main coach road

To Kiandra

TELEPHONE LINE

PLAN Shewing Caretaker's and Accomodation Cottages
SCALE 0   20   40   FEET

Limestone cliffs
Vegetable garden.
Creek
Flower Garden
Flat
VISITORS No 1
CARETAKER
VISITORS JERSEY
TELEPHONE OFFICE
Tank
Garden
W.C.
Paling Fence
Gate
Horse Rail
COTTAGES
Double Gate
W.C.

VILLAGE OF YARRANGOBILLY
8 7 6 5 34 35
12 11 10
S. Gordon   Andrew Campbell
YARRANGOBILLY INN
→ CAVES
These caves receive the head waters of the Copper Mine Creek.

ML.6
ML.7
ML.8

R. 13560.

3000'
COPPER MINE CAVE
Outlet of the Copper Mine Creek.
LARGE CAVE IN CLIFF FACE
3100'
CAVE IN GORGE
CAVE IN GORGE

Limestone Watercourses all run under Kiandra
Tableland also overlaid by basalt. Limestone honeycombed with other rocks plates.

RIVER RUNS UNDER LOW ARCHWAY.

PLAN
Shewing position of the Copper Mine Cave
Scale 0   40   80 Chs.

Limestone honeycombed with caves

GLORY HOLE CAVE
See above

SIG. ×9

PHOTO-LITHOGRAPHED AT THE GOVT. PRINTING OFFICE,
SYDNEY. NEW SOUTH WALES.
18827

Figure 20.

(ARDM 1897 plan 3)

Yarrangobilly Caves, Parish of Yarrangobilly; Plans showing position of Copper Mine Cave and cottages

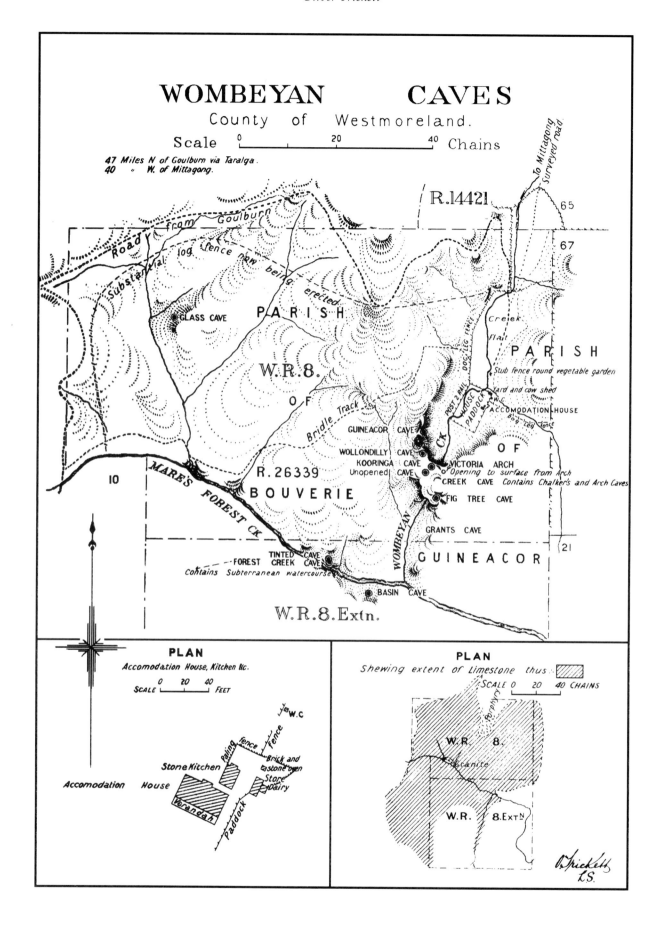

Figure 21. Wombeyan Caves, County of Westmoreland; Plan showing extent of limestone and Plan showing accommodation house (*ARDM* 1897 plan 4)

The Wollondilly Cave , Wombeyan Caves.

SCALE 0   50   100   150   200 FEET

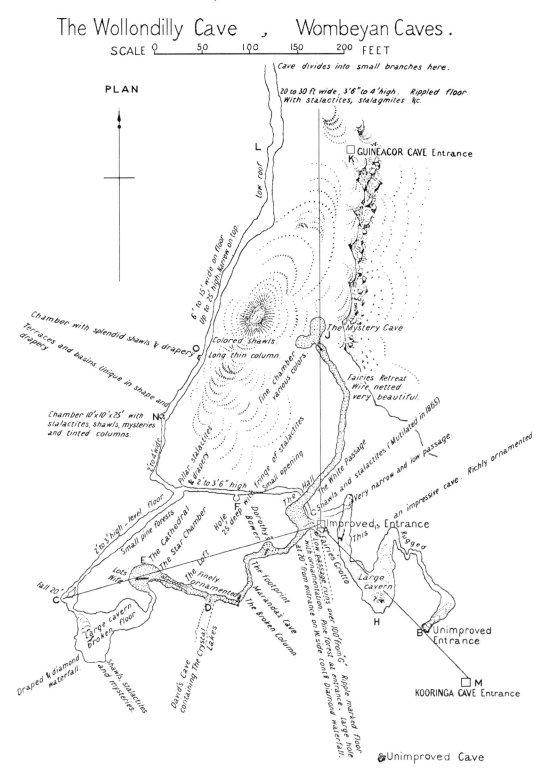

PLAN

Cave divides into small branches here.

20 to 30 ft wide, 3'6" to 4' high. Rippled floor.
With stalactites, stalagmites &c.

⬜GUINEACOR CAVE Entrance

The Mystery Cave

Chamber with splendid shawls & drapery
Terraces and basins. Unique in shape and
drapery

Colored 'shawls.
Long thin column.

fine chamber
various colors

Fairies Retreat
Wire netted
very beautiful.

Chamber 10'x10'x25' with
stalactites, shawls, mysteries
and tinted columns.

Shawls and stalactites (Mutilated in 1865)

Very narrow and low passage

an impressive cave. Richly ornamented

The White Passage

Pillar. stalactites
& drapery
2' to 3'6" high

Small opening

The Hall

⬜Improved Entrance
This

Fairies Grotto
Low passage ruins over 100 from G.
with ornamentation. Pine forest at entrance. large hole
at 20 from entrance on W. side cont.d Diamond waterfall.

2' to 3' high - level floor
Small pine forests

The Cathedral
The Star Chamber

The Loft

Dorothy's
Bower

The finely
ornamented

Large
cavern

Rugged

Fall 20'

Lots
Wife

The footprint Cave
Maranda's Cave
The Broken Column

C

Large cavern
broken floor

Draped & diamond
waterfall.

Shawls, stalactites
and mysteries.

David's Cave
containing The Crystal
Lakes

⬜B Unimproved
Entrance

⬜M
KOORINGA CAVE Entrance

🜁Unimproved Cave

SECTIONS of Cave, projected on to lines CA, AB, and AJ, giving the approximate level of the different branches.

SCALE 0   100   200 FEET

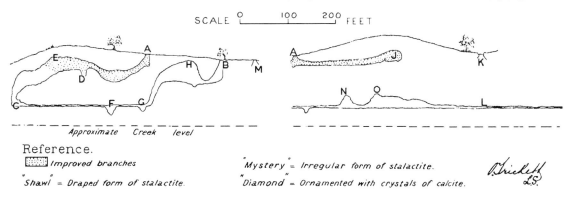

Approximate Creek level

Reference.

⬚ Improved branches

"Mystery" = Irregular form of stalactite.

"Shawl" = Draped form of stalactite.

"Diamond" = Ornamented with crystals of calcite.

Trickett
L.S.

Figure 22. The Wollondilly Cave, Wombeyan Caves (*ARDM* 1897 plan 5)

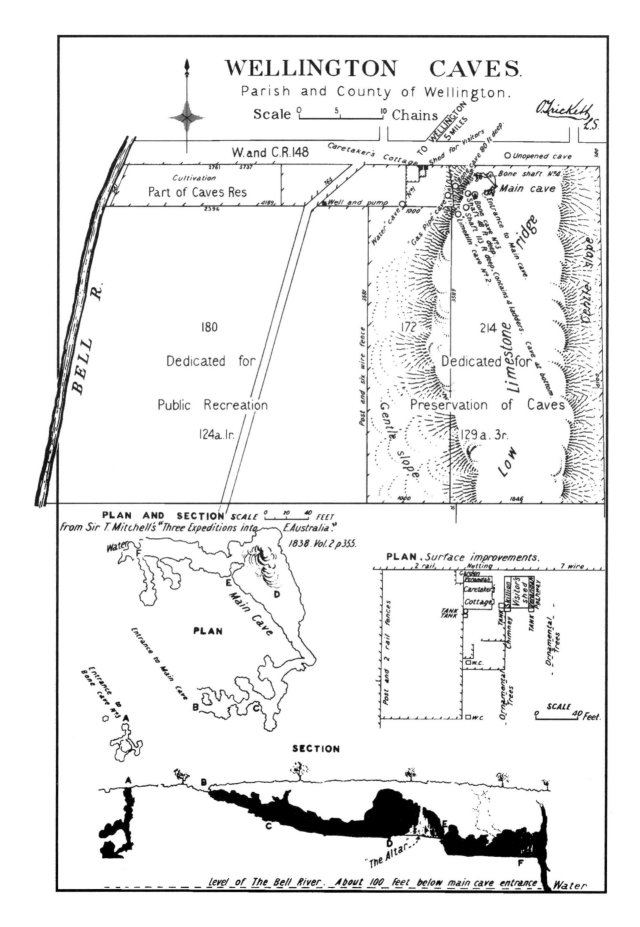

Figure 23. Wellington Caves, Parish and County of Wellington; Plan and section of Main Cave [after Mitchell] and Plan of surface improvements (*ARDM* 1897 plan 6)

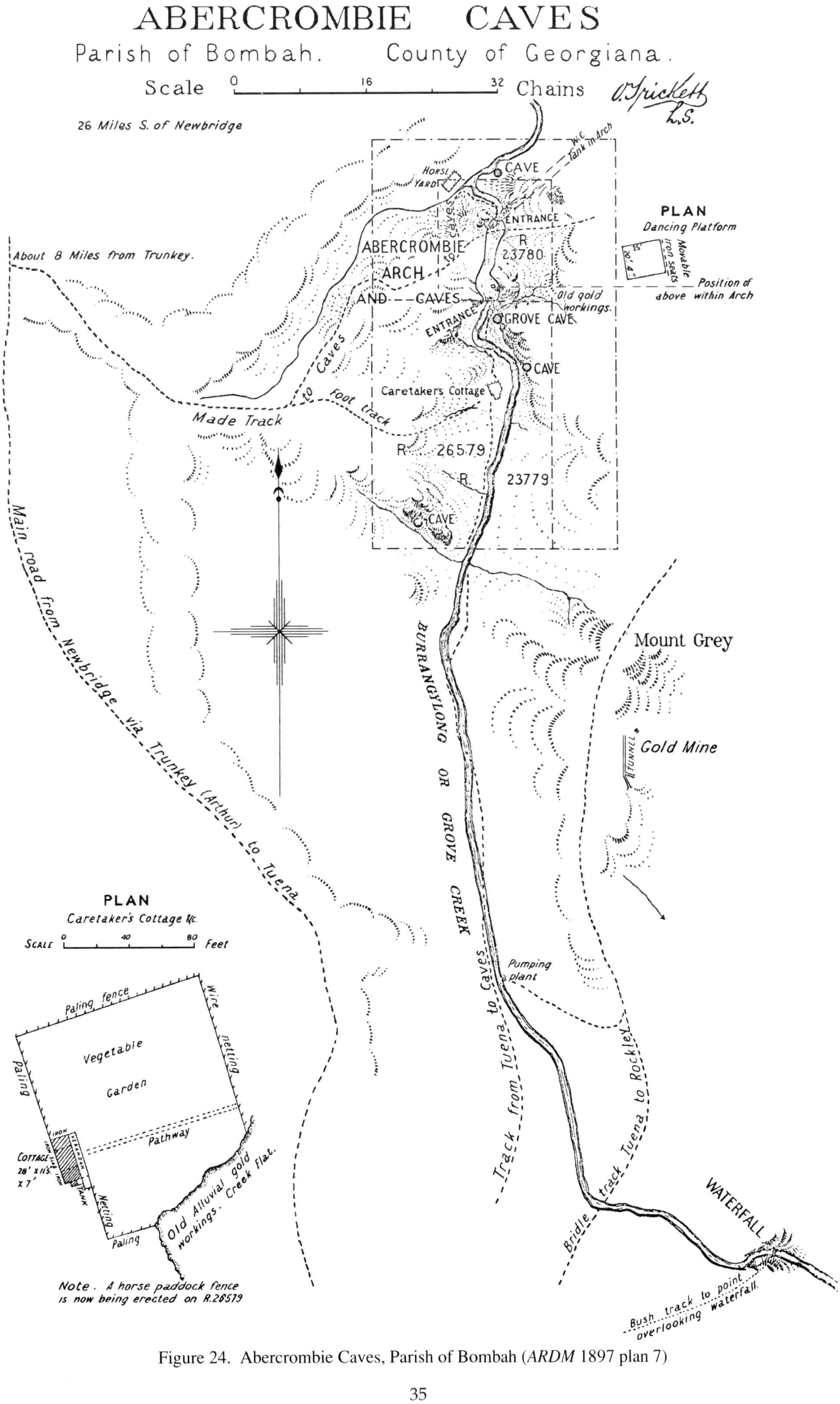

ABERCROMBIE CAVES

Parish of Bombah.   County of Georgiana.

Scale 0 — 16 — 32 Chains   *V.Prickett L.S.*

26 Miles S. of Newbridge

About 8 Miles from Trunkey.

W.C. Tank in Arch

HORSE YARD

CAVE

PLAN
Dancing Platform

ENTRANCE

ABERCROMBIE
ARCH

R 23780

Movable iron seats

Position of above within Arch

AND — CAVES

ENTRANCE

Old gold workings.

GROVE CAVE

CAVE

Made Track

to foot track

Caretaker's Cottage

R. 265.79

R. 23779

CAVE

Mount Grey

Main road from Newbridge via Trunkey (Arthur) to Tuena

BURRANGYLONG OR GROVE CREEK

Gold Mine
TUNNEL

Pumping plant

Track from Tuena to Caves

Bridle track Tuena to Rockley

WATERFALL

Bush track to point overlooking waterfall

PLAN
Caretaker's Cottage &c.

SCALE 0 — 40 — 80 Feet

Paling fence

Wire netting

Vegetable Garden

Paling

Pathway

IRON
COTTAGE
28' x 11½
x 7'

Netting

Paling

Old Alluvial gold workings. Creek Flat.

Note. A horse paddock fence is now being erected on R.26579

Figure 24. Abercrombie Caves, Parish of Bombah (*ARDM* 1897 plan 7)

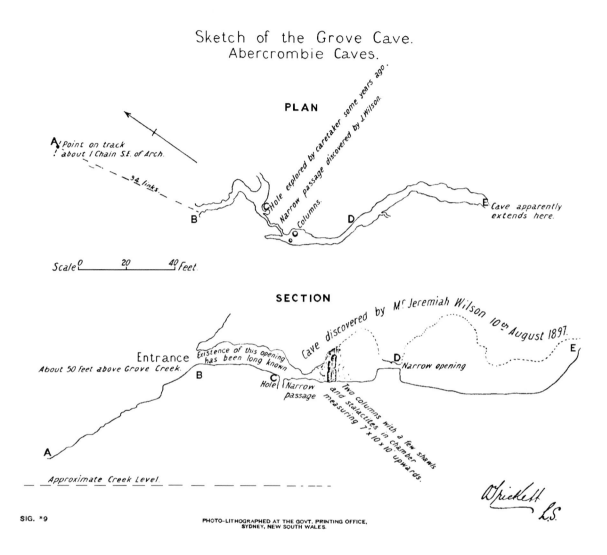

Figure 25. Sketch of the Grove Cave, Abercrombie Caves (*ARDM* 1897 plan 8)

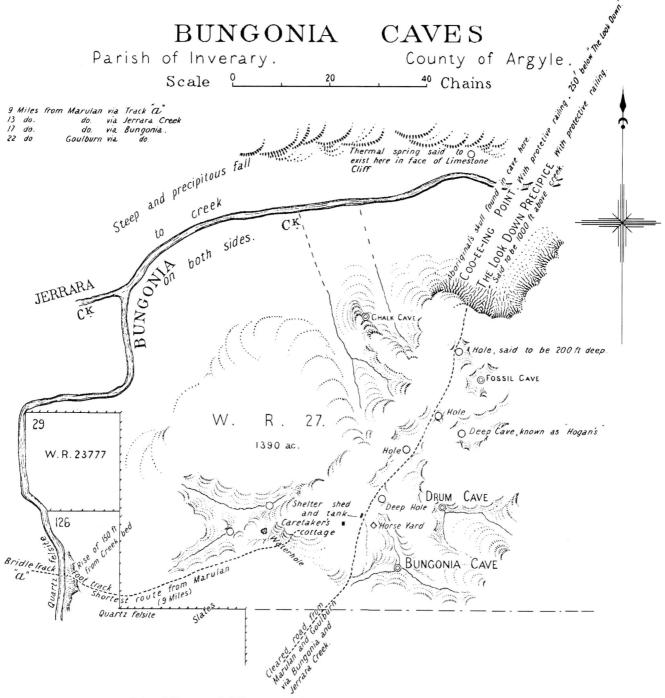

BUNGONIA CAVES

Parish of Inverary.   County of Argyle.

Scale 0 _____ 20 _____ 40 Chains

9 Miles from Marulan via Track "a"
13 do.   do. via Jerrara Creek
17 do.   do. via Bungonia.
22 do.   Goulburn via do.

Note. 640 acres of R.27 exempted from operation of wattle bark and other licenses by Gov.t Gazette 7.5.97.

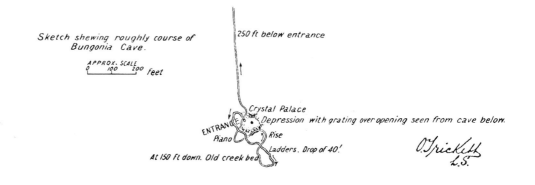

Sketch shewing roughly course of
Bungonia Cave.

APPROX. SCALE
0   100   200 feet

250 ft below entrance

Crystal Palace
Depression with grating over opening seen from cave below.
ENTRANCE
Piano   Rise
            Ladders. Drop of 40'
At 150 ft down. Old creek bed

SIG. *9

PHOTO-LITHOGRAPHED AT THE GOVT. PRINTING OFFICE.
SYDNEY, NEW SOUTH WALES.
18927

Figure 26. Bungonia Caves, Parish of Inverary, and
Sketch shewing roughly course of Bungonia Cave (*ARDM* 1897 plan 9)

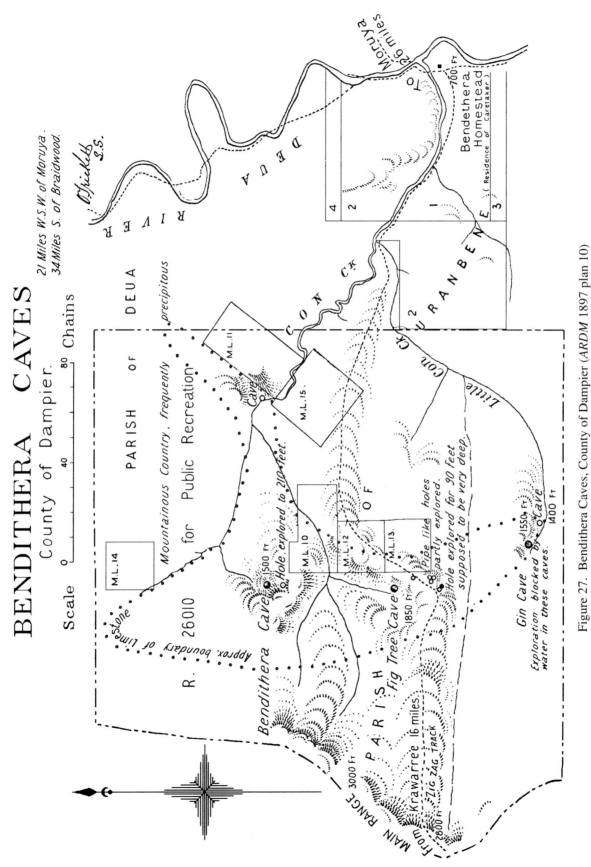

Figure 27. Bendithera Caves, County of Dampier (*ARDM* 1897 plan 10)

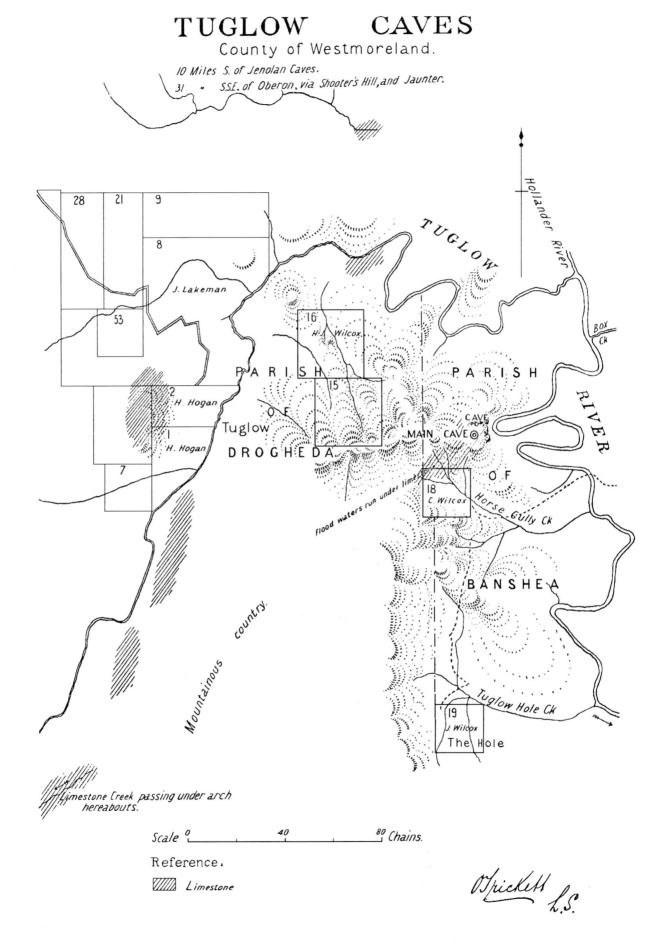

TUGLOW CAVES
County of Westmoreland.

10 Miles S. of Jenolan Caves.
31 " S.S.E. of Oberon, via Shooter's Hill, and Jaunter.

Figure 28. Tuglow Caves, County of Westmoreland (*ARDM* 1897 plan 11)

previous surveys". Unfortunately he does not say what these surveys were. The Department of Mines had only previously published one plan of a cave at Jenolan, a relatively crude plan of the Jubilee Cave accompanying a report by Leigh (1893) (an annotated copy of which is reproduced as Figure 29). It is most likely, however, that Trickett was referring to a survey plan published in Foster's 1890 book on Jenolan (Figure 30). In tiny type at the foot is written "Printed at the Department of Lands, Sydney 1889" and it seems reasonable to suppose that the cave surveys were carried out by Lands Department surveyors. That Figure 30 is the origin of the greater part of the cave plan shown in Figure 18 is indisputable.

The plan and section of the main cave at Wellington (Figure 23) were taken from Mitchell's 1838 *Three Expeditions into Eastern Australia* but this is a crude sketch compared to Trickett's work. (It is also the only example of another's cave survey reproduced by Trickett.) It remains difficult to understand how, in 1896-97, one man could visit so many far-flung cave areas (see Figure 31), carry out detailed surface and underground surveys, draw up the resulting plans and write the reports to go with them, as well as supervise the management of the many caves, and all "in addition to his ordinary duties as Geological Survey Draftsman" (Pittman 1896).

An instance where Trickett received help is shown by correspondence now in the State Archives. The map shown in Figure 29 was attached to Trickett's recommendation of 5 July 1897 relating to the limits of the 'Slattery' and 'Jubilee' Caves (Figure 32), which was approved by Government Geologist E.F. Pittman, Under Secretary D.C.W. Lachlan, and ultimately, the Minister, Sydney Smith. Trickett had sent this 1893 map to F.J. Wilson, Caretaker at Jenolan, requesting some information about this section of the Imperial system. Wilson's reply (Figure 33) was accompanied by his own sketch plan of the area (Figure 34) which he hoped Trickett "would be able to get some information from". This may be the only extant cave map by F.J. Wilson; it may not have been a great help to Trickett, being a very rough sketch and well below his standards (Middleton 1990).

1898 Report

In his 1898 report D.C.W. Lachlan, the Under Secretary for Mines and Agriculture, reported:

A guide-book to the Jenolan Caves, the manuscript and plans for which were prepared by Mr O. Trickett, Inspector of Caves, is now in the hands of the Government Printer for publication, and it is thought will be highly valued by visitors. (Lachlan 1898) [See Cave Guidebooks, p. 79]

This appears to be the first time that Trickett is referred to as "Inspector of Caves". It must have been a courtesy title, however, as he continued to be officially employed as "Draftsman and Surveyor" and he continued to be referred to as "O. Trickett, C.S., M.S., Vict., L.S., N.S.W."

Trickett's report for 1898 follows the same format as previous years: notes on improvements at tourist caves, numbers of visitors, new cave discoveries (Junction Cave at Wombeyan, chamber off Red Cave at Jenolan and an unidentified cave at Bungonia) (Trickett 1898a). This is followed by detailed reports: on Junction Cave (Trickett 1898b) (with plan - Figure 35) and on a small cave at Limekilns (Trickett 1898c) (with locality sketch - Figure 36).

1899 Report

Trickett's 1899 report follows the familiar pattern, recording improvements effected at the tourist caves, numbers of visitors to the various cave areas and detailed reports on his visits to Colong and Wyanbene Caves. Reaching these latter caves must have involved considerable effort, though Trickett makes no direct reference to this. In the case of Colong, however, he does say that "the country is marked by steep and rugged ranges and gorges with precipitous banks. It would be an exceptionally expensive undertaking to form easy tracks to the caves" (Trickett 1899b).

Trickett suggested the name "Colong" for the caves which were known to the locals as "Bindook" and it would appear that he was responsible for their protection in a caves reserve. Although there is no specific reference to this in his report, it seems unlikely that it is a mere coincidence that he reported on the caves in May 1899 and a Caves Reserve, No. 29,837, covering 1,400 acres was gazetted on 2 September of the same year (Middleton 1967). He attached a plan of the Lannigans, Billys and Church Creeks area (Figure 37). Trickett's report on Colong Caves and accompanying map were later reprinted in a report on the Yerranderie silver field (Harper 1930).

Trickett seems not to have been greatly impressed by Wyanbene Cave; he says:

Notwithstanding the mutilation which has taken place, the cave contains sufficient beauty to render it a source of pleasure to local residents, although it may not be sufficiently attractive to repay visitors from a distance for the trouble of travelling to it. (Trickett 1899c)

He also visited, and was impressed by, the Big Hole, which he described as a "striking feature"; like many others he wondered "what has become of the material that once filled it" (Trickett 1899c). He also prepared a plan showing Wyanbene, Cheitmore and Bendithera Caves and the Big Hole, but this was not published until 1900 (Figure 42).

He attached a plan of, and sections through, "The Abercrombie Caves", that is, the main archway and connecting passages - Figure 38 - "The Wombeyan Caves", that is, Victoria Arch, Creek Cave, Fig Tree Cave, Kooringa Cave and Wollondilly Cave (probably from Figure 21), together with "sketch sections" - Figure 39 - "The Yarrangobilly Caves", i.e. plans and sections of the Glory Hole Cave (North and South branches) - Figure 40 - and the Jersey and Castle Caves - Figure 41.

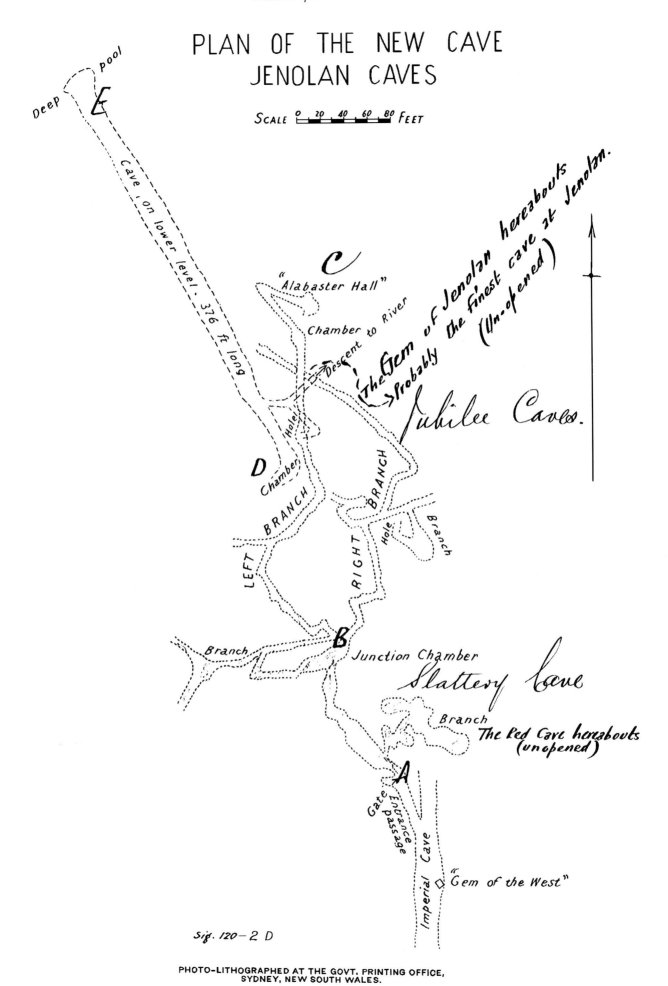

PLAN OF THE NEW CAVE
JENOLAN CAVES

SCALE 0 20 40 60 80 FEET

Deep pool

E

Cave on lower level 376 ft long

C

"Alabaster Hall"

Chamber to River

Descent to River

The Gem of Jenolan hereabouts
> Probably the finest cave at Jenolan.
(Un-opened)

Jubilee Caves.

Hole

D

Chamber

LEFT BRANCH

RIGHT BRANCH

Hole

Branch

Branch

B

Junction Chamber

Slattery Cave

Branch

The Red Cave hereabouts
(unopened)

Gate

Entrance passage

A

Imperial Cave

"Gem of the West"

Sig. 120 – 2 D

**PHOTO-LITHOGRAPHED AT THE GOVT. PRINTING OFFICE,
SYDNEY, NEW SOUTH WALES.**

Figure 29. 1893 plan of Jubilee Cave (an extension of the Imperial), with 1897 annotations by Trickett
[Original from *ARDM* 1893, p. 143. This copy reproduced with permission of the Archives Authority of NSW]

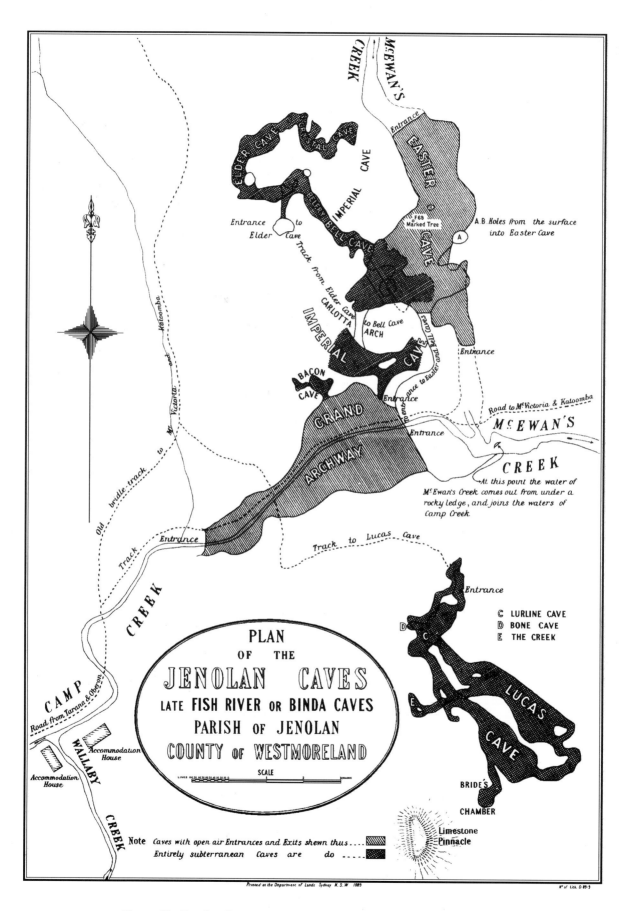

Figure 30. Jenolan Caves plan from Foster's *The Jenolan Caves* (1890) - basis for Trickett's Jenolan Caves plan of 1897 (Figure 18)

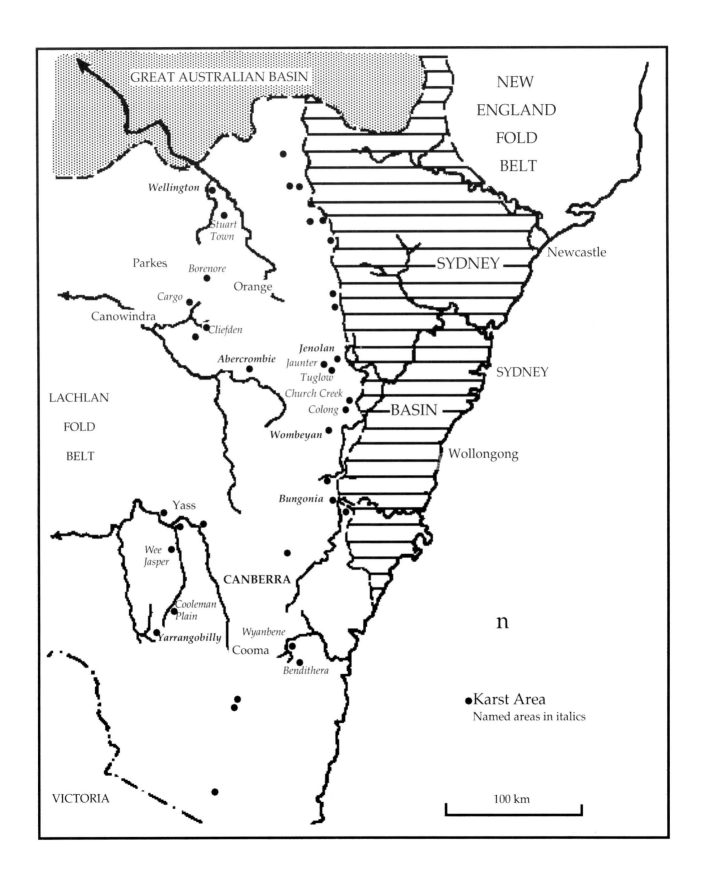

Figure 31. Location of major cave (karst) areas in the Lachlan Fold Belt of NSW,
including those visited and surveyed by Trickett between 1892 and 1919
[Based on a plan in Osborne and Branagan 1988]

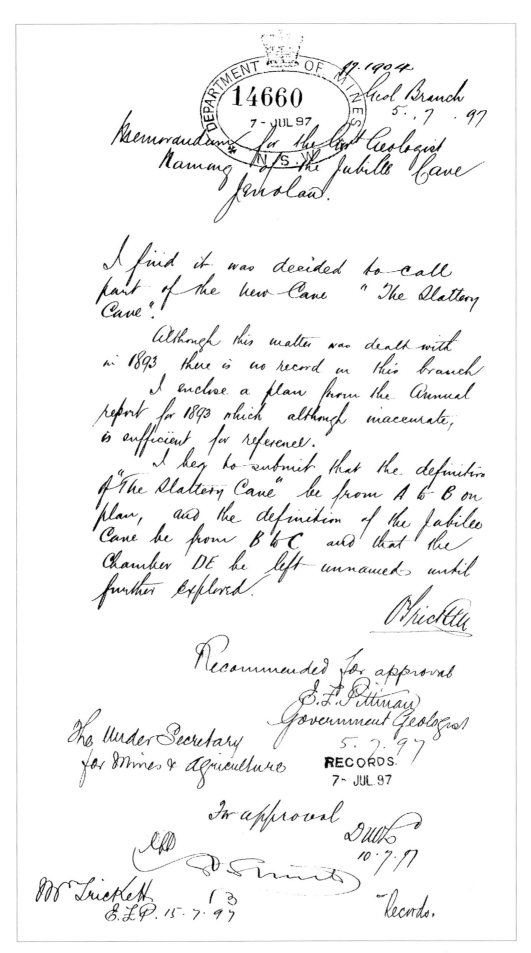

Figure 32. Trickett's letter of 5 July 1897 to the Government Geologist regarding the limits of the 'Slattery' and 'Jubilee' Caves [Reproduced with permission of the Archives Authority of NSW]

Jenolan Caves
2/7/97

Dear Mr Trickett:

I am enclosing plan which you sent to me. I have marked on it — where I think the "Gem of Jenolan" lies by that plan. I have sketched another plan of New Cave — which I hope you will be able to get some information from, — & you will see by Cave on "lower level" that it is the same, marked on your plan, as "Descent to River"; & I am of opinion, that the "Alabaster Hall" is immediately over it. The old entrance of "New Cave" as you will see by my plan was discovered past the "Gem of the West" — The passage, — which we now enter by — with gate on — starts from "Grand Stalactites", left Branch of Right Imperial — past "Alabaster Columns", & enters the Cave just below old entrance.

Trusting you will be able to understand my plan.

I am.
Yours faithfully
F. J. Wilson

Figure 33. F.J. Wilson's letter of 2 July 1897, conveying his sketch of part of the Jubilee Cave to Trickett
[Reproduced with permission of the Archives Authority of NSW]

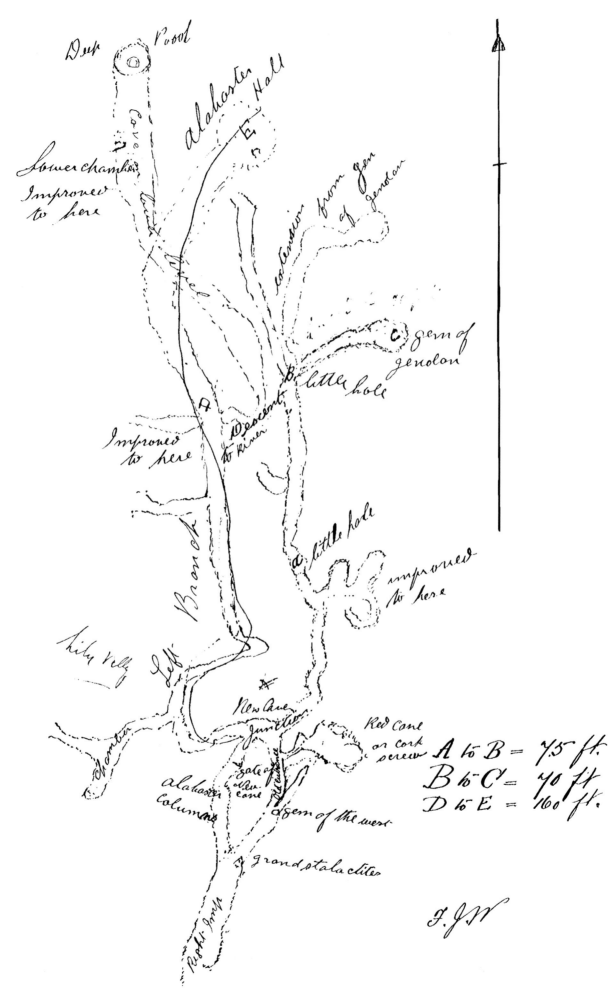

Figure 34. Wilson's 1897 sketch plan of extensions to the Jubilee Cave, as provided to Trickett
[Reproduced with permission of the Archives Authority of NSW]

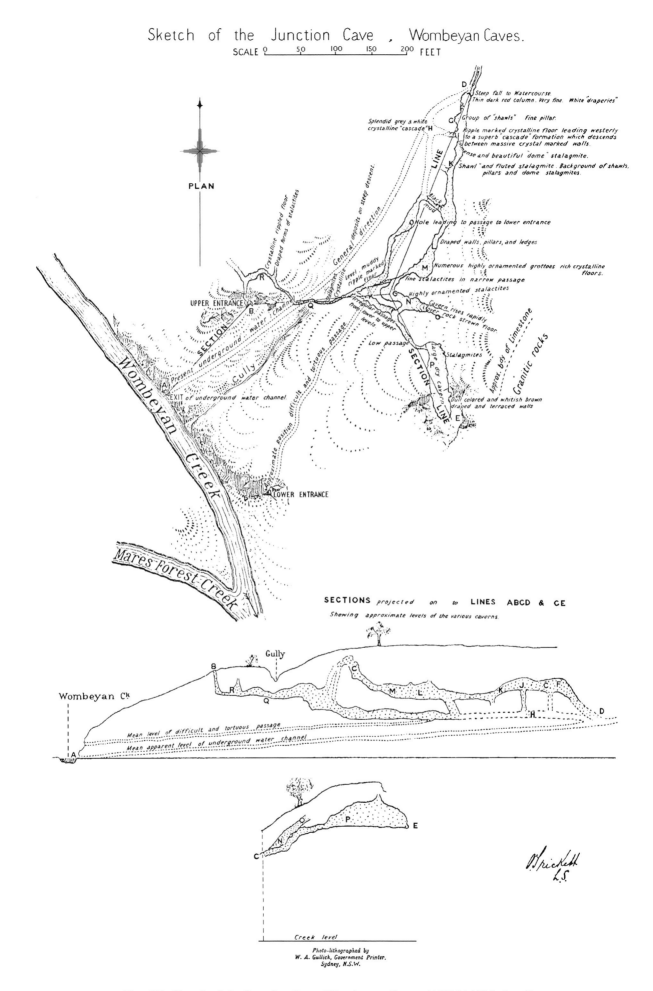

Sketch of the Junction Cave, Wombeyan Caves.

SCALE 0   50   100   150   200 FEET

Plan 35. Sketch of the Junction Cave, Wombeyan Caves (*ARDM* 1898 plan 1)

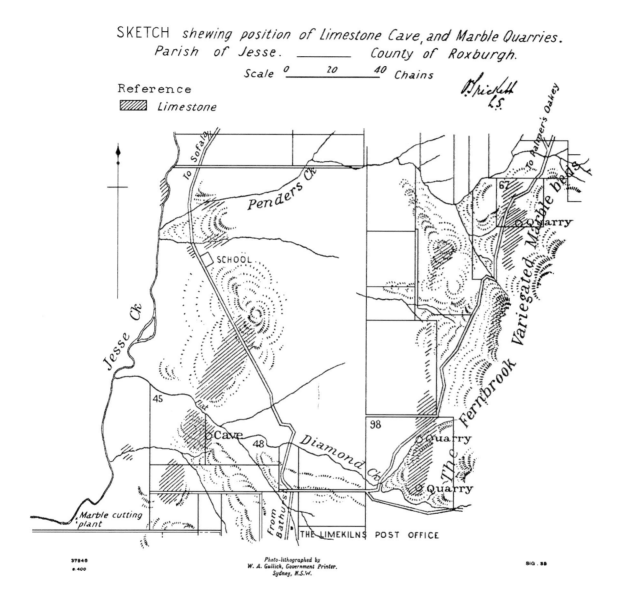

SKETCH *shewing position of Limestone Cave, and Marble Quarries.*
Parish of Jesse. _____ *County of Roxburgh.*

Scale 0   20   40 *Chains*

Reference
▨▨▨ *Limestone*

Figure 36. Sketch of position of cave near The Limekilns (*ARDM* 1898 plan 2)

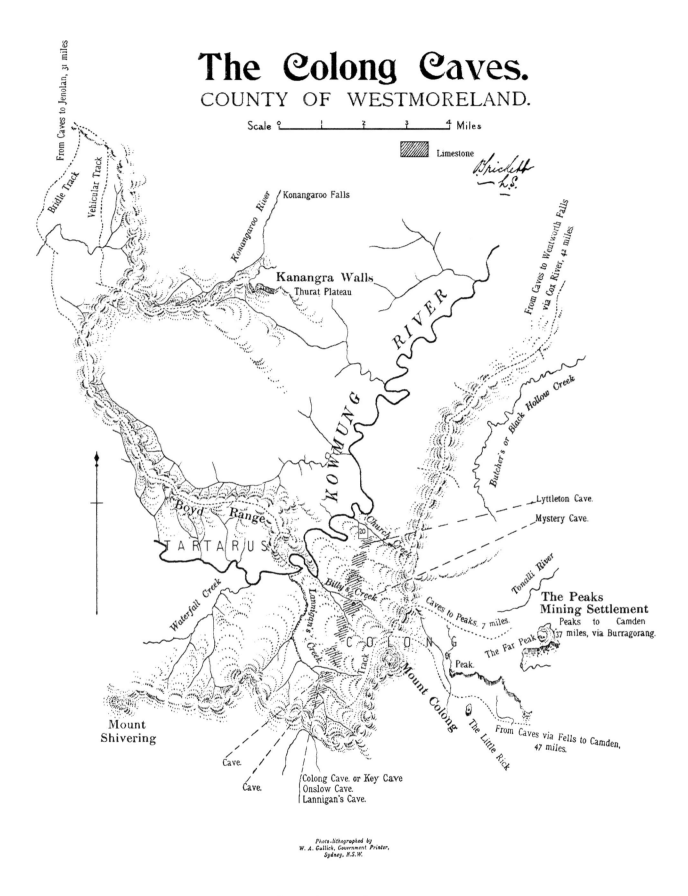

Figure 37. The Colong Caves, County of Westmoreland (*ARDM* 1899 plan 1)

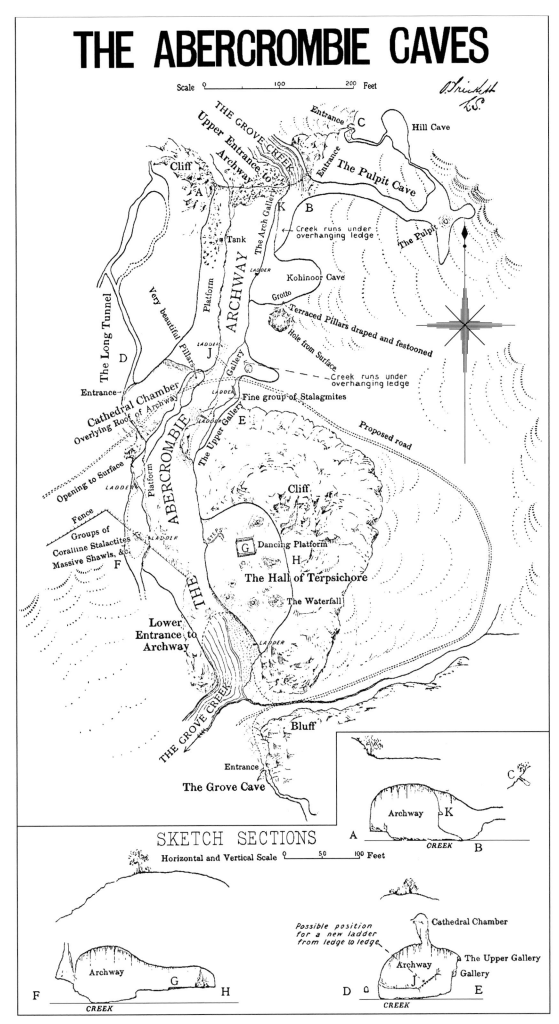

Figure 38. The Abercrombie Caves (*ARDM* 1899 plan 2)

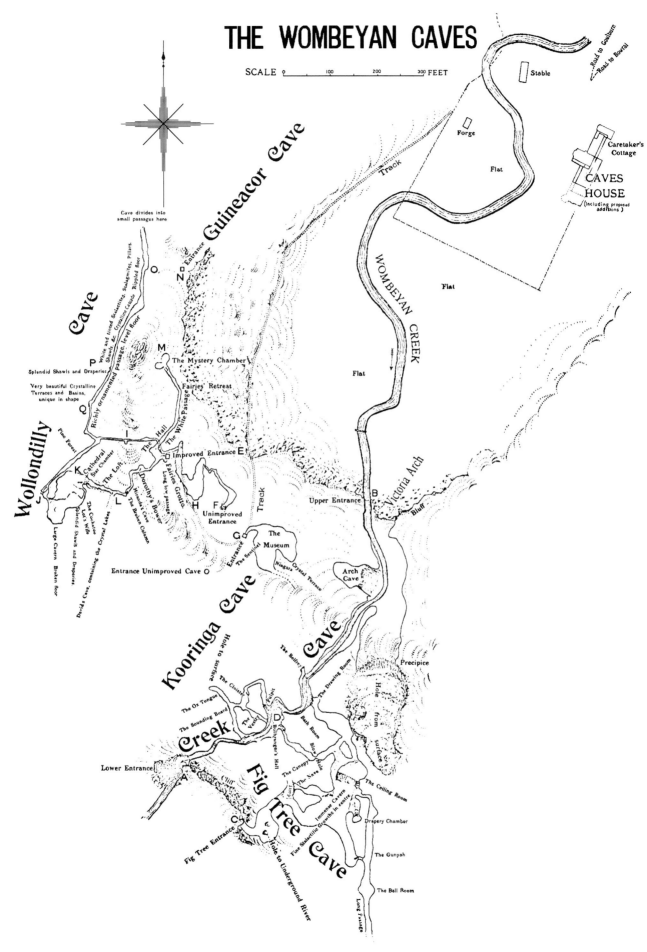

Figure 39. The Wombeyan Caves - upper portion of plan (*ARDM* 1899 plan 3)

- for continuation see next page

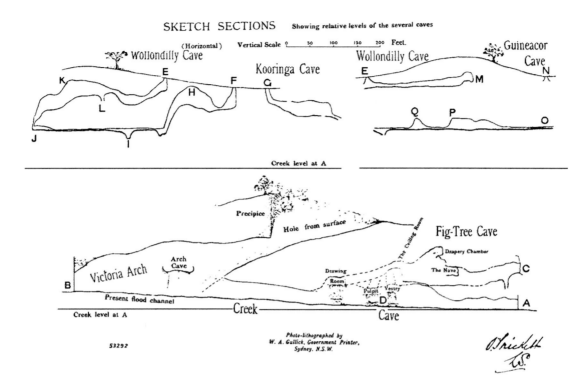

Figure 39 (cont.) The Wombeyan Caves - lower portion of plan (*ARDM* 1899 plan 3)

THE YARRANGOBILLY CAVES
The Glory Hole Cave.

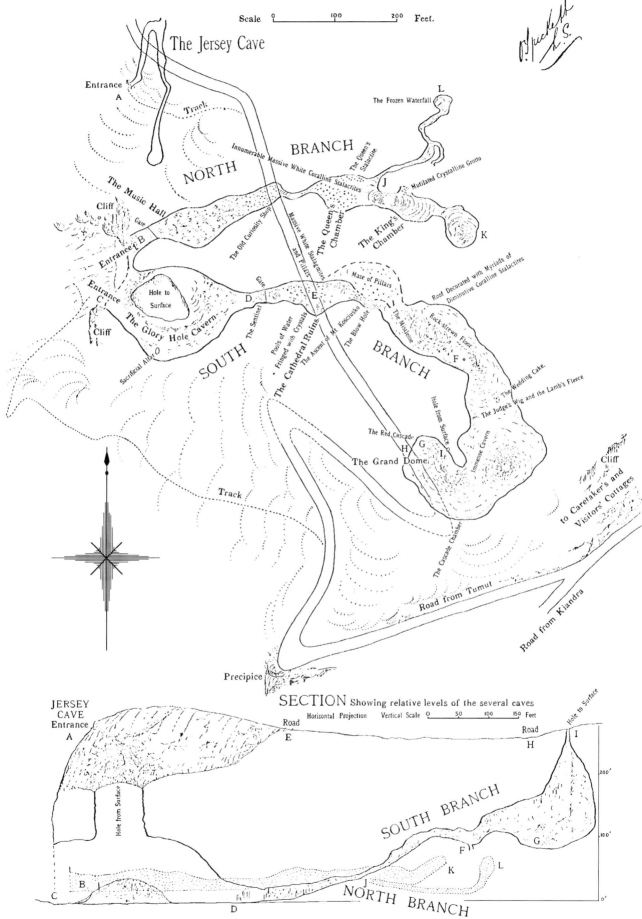

Figure 40. The Yarrangobilly Caves - The Glory Hole Cave (*ARDM* 1899 plan 4)
[Significantly reduced in size from the original]

THE YARRANGOBILLY CAVES.

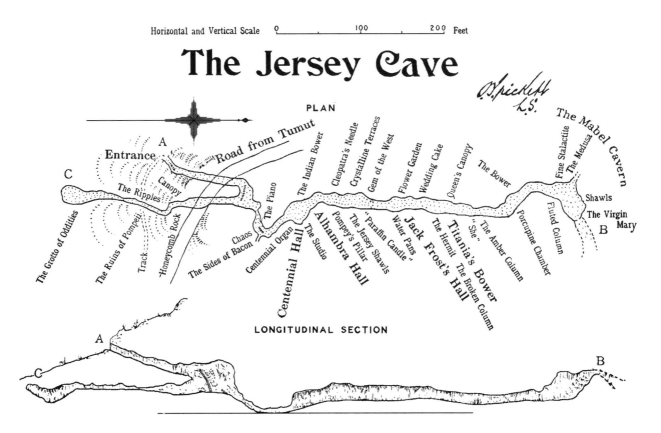

Horizontal and Vertical Scale   0   100   200 Feet

The Jersey Cave

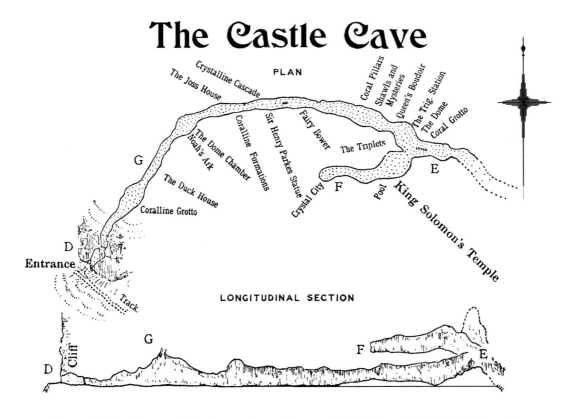

Figure 41. The Yarrangobilly Caves - Jersey Cave and Castle Cave (*ARDM* 1899 plan 5)

1900 Report

Pittman, in his 1900 report, paid tribute to Trickett's work:

Mr O. Trickett has very efficiently performed the work in connection with the limestone caves, both in recommending the carrying out of improvements, and in supervising the work of the caretakers and guides. He has also prepared all the diagrams, plans and sections illustrating my surveys and those of the other members of the Staff, and I take this opportunity of stating that Mr Trickett has accomplished a large amount of very useful work, with care and great expedition.

His guidebook to the Jenolan Caves has been very much appreciated by the public, and is in considerable demand amongst visitors. (Pittman 1900)

Trickett reported as usual on improvements carried out at the various cave reserves: Abercrombie, Bungonia, Bendithera (none), Jenolan, Wellington, Wombeyan and Yarrangobilly and listed numbers of visitors for each (Trickett 1900a). At Jenolan he notes:

In March a drill hole of 10 feet was made at the extremity of the cavern near the 'Crystal Fountain' in the Lucas Cave. It proved that a passage can be made which will enable visitors to travel direct to the 'Platform' and so avoid the tedious return by way of the steep vine [sic, 'wire'?] ladders (see plan herewith). [Figure 44, left]

In his more detailed report (Trickett 1900d) he made it clear that the closeness of these passages was revealed by his surveys:

My survey of the Lucas Cave showed that the two passages closely approached each other at AB on plan [actually A—see Figure 44]. That such is the case has now been definitely determined by the caretaker, Mr F.J. Wilson, who supervised the drilling of a hole from A to B [actually at A], distance 11 feet.

The knowledge thus gained is valuable, as it now appears to be practicable to form a passage from the 'Crystal Fountain' to the 'Platform', and so save visitors from the necessity of climbing the steep ladders at C [actually B], and of retracing their steps after inspecting the 'Fossil Cave', 'Crystal Fountain', &c.*

*Note—This passage is now in course of construction. (Trickett 1900d)

Other detailed reports in 1900 related to Bungonia (1900b) (illustrated by Figure 43), a new chamber off the Jubilee Cave at Jenolan (1900c) (see Figure 44, centre), a new branch of the Lucas [later named Mafeking Cave] (1900e) (see Figure 44, right) and Wellington Caves (1900f) (with a tiny sketch, Figure 45). Wyanbene was not reported on, but the plan referred to in the 1899 report was included (Figure 42).

At Bungonia he reported that exploration of 'Bungonia' Cave [now known as Grill Cave, B44] was stopped by foul air and that exploration of Drum Cave had proceeded to a depth of 350 feet (see Figure 43). Of this cave he said:

The Drum Cave is much superior to the one cave open to the public at Bungonia, although it cannot be said to be particularly fine. If it were opened it is questionable whether many visitors would be found who would care to travel down any series of steps which might be constructed on the perpendicular face of the 134 feet drop.

It is possible that there are no really beautiful caves at Bungonia, except at levels which may, owing to the immense thickness of the limestone, exist at a depth of as much as 1,000 feet. Foul air, probably the result of choking of the channels at their exit, by the talus from the cliffs above, has already been met with at less than half the above depth, and prevents complete exploration.

Attention will be given to the cliff faces in the hope of discovering additional caves. (Trickett 1900b).

The Wellington report related to a small cave which Trickett did not think worth opening to the public. He also included an historical résumé and volunteered the opinion "that attractive caves are not likely to be found here, as the limestone ridge has so small an elevation" (Trickett 1900f).

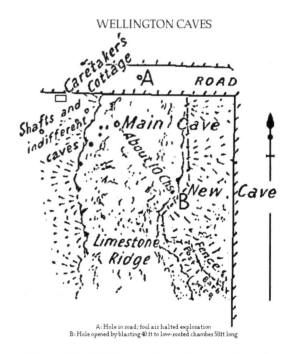

A: Hole in road; foul air halted exploration
B: Hole opened by blasting 40 ft to low-roofed chamber 50ft long

Figure 45. Wellington Caves sketch (enlarged)
(*ARDM* 1900 p. 200)

1901 Report

In 1901 Trickett's report was subsumed into that of the Government Geologist (Pittman 1901), a practice which, with some variations, was followed in subsequent years.

Trickett's surveying seems to have been confined to Wombeyan where he surveyed the Basin Cave and a newly explored branch of the Wollondilly (Figure 46, upper and lower portions).

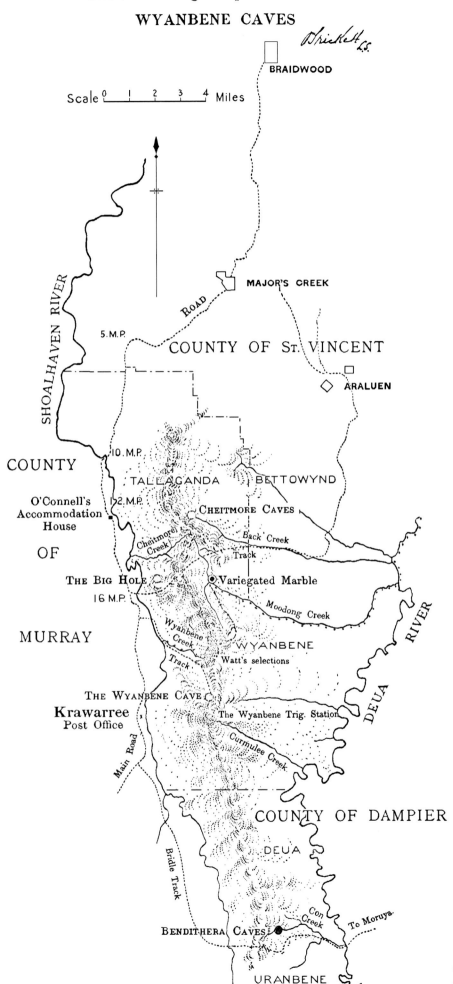

Sketch shewing the position of the
WYANBENE CAVES

BRAIDWOOD

Scale 0 1 2 3 4 Miles

MAJOR'S CREEK

5.M.P.

COUNTY OF St. VINCENT

ARALUEN

COUNTY

10.M.P.

TALLAGANDA   BETTOWYND

O'Connell's
Accommodation
House

12.M.P.

CHEITMORE CAVES

Cheitmore Creek

Back Creek

OF

Track

THE BIG HOLE   Variegated Marble

16 M.P.

Moodong Creek

MURRAY

Wyanbene Creek   WYANBENE

Track   Watt's selections

THE WYANBENE CAVE

Krawarree
Post Office   The Wyanbene Trig. Station

DEUA RIVER

Curmulee Creek

Main Road

COUNTY OF DAMPIER

DEUA

Bridle Track

Con Creek   To Moruya

BENDITHERA CAVES

URANBENE

SHOALHAVEN RIVER

ROAD

Figure 42. Sketch showing the
position of the Wyanbene Caves
[also Cheitmore, Bendithera and
the Big Hole] (*ARDM* 1900 plan 1)

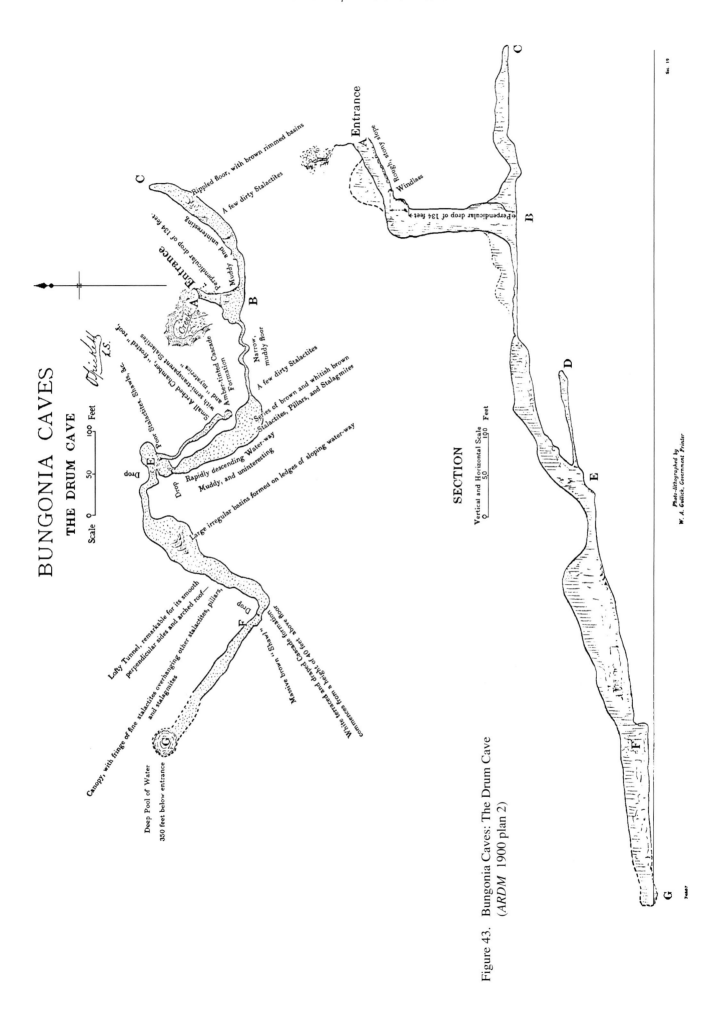

Figure 43. Bungonia Caves: The Drum Cave
(*ARDM* 1900 plan 2)

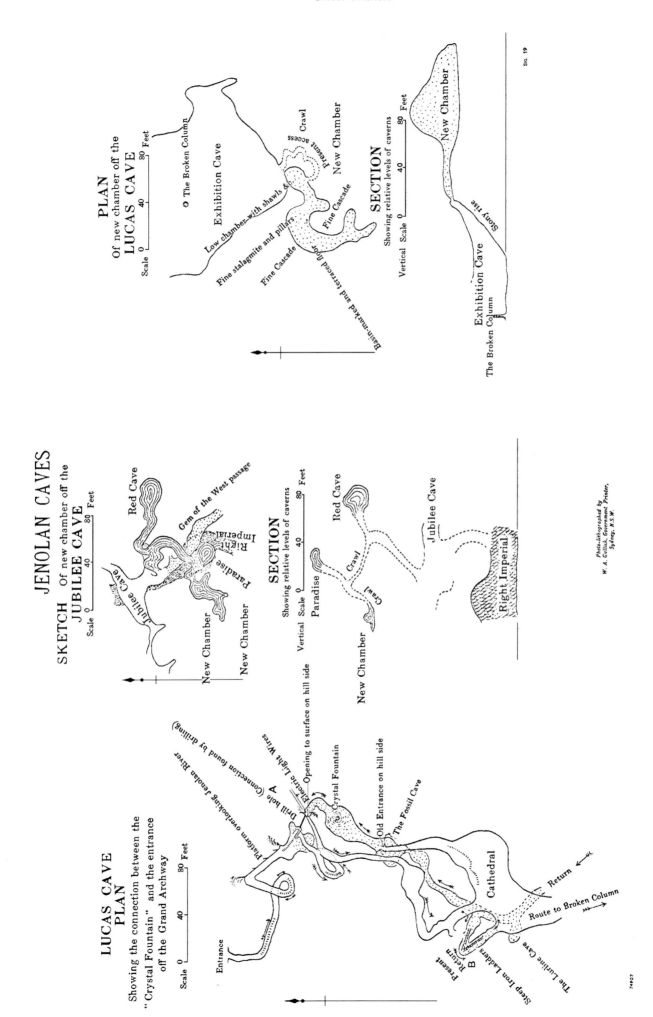

Figure 44. Jenolan Caves: Lucas Cave [showing new tunnel], new chamber off Jubilee Cave and new chamber off Lucas Cave [Mafeking] (*ARDM* 1900 plan 3)

WOMBEYAN CAVES

THE BASIN CAVE.

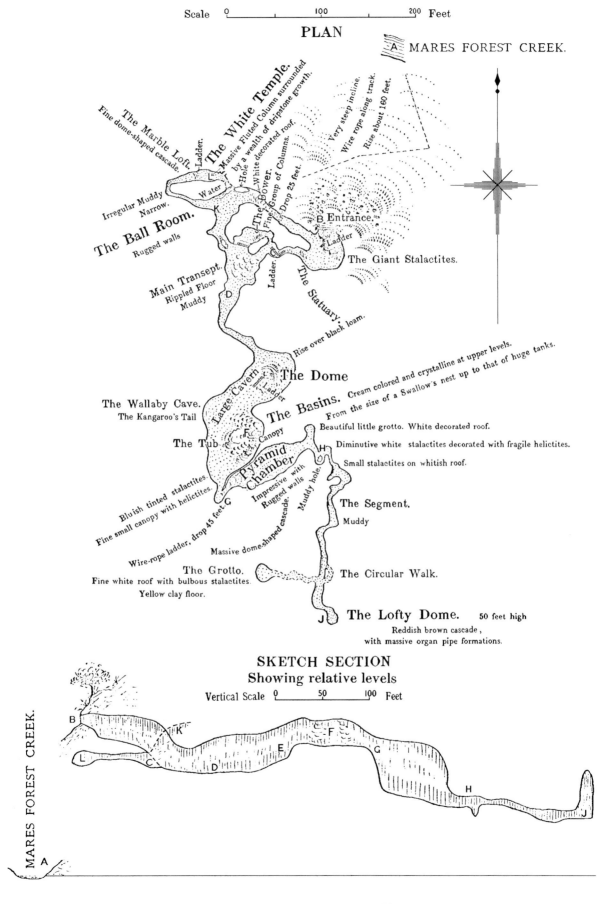

Figure 46. Wombeyan Caves: The Basin Cave (*ARDM* 1901 plan 1, upper portion)

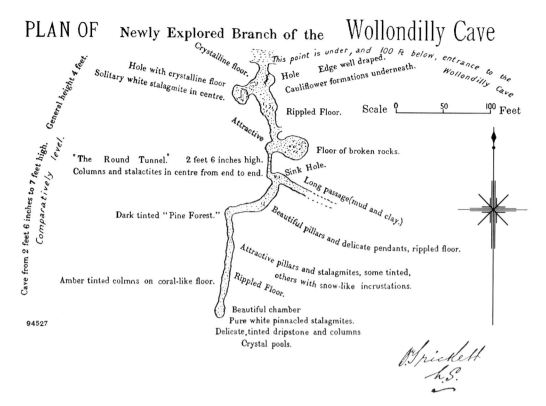

PLAN OF Newly Explored Branch of the Wollondilly Cave

Figure 46 (cont.) Wombeyan Caves: Plan of newly explored branch of the Wollondilly Cave (ARDM 1901 plan 1, lower portion)

1902 Report

Trickett's report on the limestone caves for 1902 records the usual developmental and maintenance works at the cave reserves. By way of a change, Pittman notes that Trickett reported on the sandstone caves or rock shelters at Wyong. Unfortunately this report appears not to have been published.

For the first time since 1897 the report does not include any cave surveys by Trickett.

1903 Report

In his report for this year, Trickett (1903a) records that after some years of small and declining interest, the services of a caretaker at Bendithera Caves were dispensed with. Normal works continued at Abercrombie, Bungonia, Jenolan, Wellington, Wombeyan and Yarrangobilly Caves. He notes with regret the departure of Mr F.J. Wilson, Caretaker at Jenolan, for Western Australia. Guide Wiburd was promoted to the position. Mr Kerry took over the lease of the photo kiosk and cottage[10].

The big event of the year, described in an appended report (Trickett 1903b), was the discovery by Wiburd, Edwards and Bailey of major extensions of the Lucas Cave [subsequently known as the River Cave and Skeleton Cave[11]]. Trickett declared this discovery "the most important event at Jenolan of recent years" and described the new passages and chambers in glowing terms:

highly decorated chambers, with some terraced stalagmites of singular beauty ... many grand caverns, one whose walls are covered with draperies, fluted columns, etc., for a height of 100 feet ... a superb mammoth, pear-shaped, amber tinted, stalagmite rests on a gracefully curved base, which terminates in a charming canopy ... superb 'shawls' 20 to 25 feet in length ... a succession of fairy-like grottoes, commencing with rich fringes, partly concealing groups of 'mysteries', and ending with a truly marvellous collection of these curiously twisted formations.

The coloured map of the Lucas Cave which Trickett included with this (1903) report shows the new (River and Skeleton) caves and also shows the Temple of Baal, not named but described as "Large Cavern / 80 feet high / exceptionally beautiful". This is strange because the official record (Trickett 1904) indicates the Temple of Baal was not discovered until 20 February 1904.

---

10 Trickett and Kerry became great friends; besides their common interest in caves, Kerry was a fanatical mineral collector and no doubt found Trickett's mineral map of NSW a great help. They were subsequently closely involved with photography and the production of post cards (see p. 103). Kerry's principal studio was in George Street, Sydney but he frequently visited Jenolan, and was often one of the first to follow the explorers. (I am indebted to Elery Hamilton-Smith for these notes.)

11 This cave is now known as the Cerberus Cave and, out of respect for Aboriginal wishes, the skeleton is not pointed out to visitors. For the same reason, Trickett's photograph of the skeleton is not reproduced here.

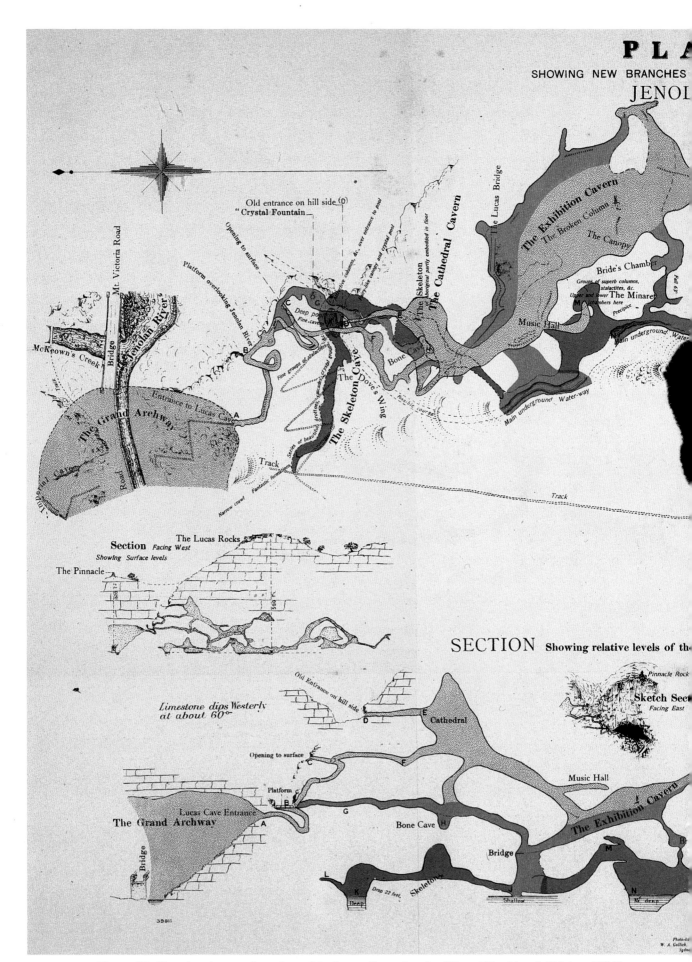

Figure 47. Plan showing new branches of the Lucas Cave, Jenolan [From Etheridge & Trickett 1904]
[This plan differs from that published in the *ARDM* for 1903 only in that the Orient Cave,
indicated by the letters U, V, W, X, Y, Z, has been added.]

Ralston (1990, p. 49) noticed this discrepancy and reported "When I queried this I was told that the Baal survey was presented before the map linens of [the] 1903 [Annual Report maps] were completed, so it was included." [12]

There was also a human skeleton, upon which a separate report was provided. The *Report on the discovery of a human skeleton in a branch of the Lucas Cave, at Jenolan* (Trickett & Etheridge 1903) gives a detailed account of the remains and their location, and discusses how the person, presumed from the evident age of the material to be Aboriginal, could have reached this place. Etheridge, who was Curator of the Australian Museum, no doubt contributed the technical description of the bones to the paper, together with comparisons with Aboriginal bones found in other caves; Trickett would have contributed the detailed information regarding the location, the difficulties the explorers had in reaching it and the relative positions of other chambers. The report was reprinted the next year in the *Records of the Geological Survey of NSW*, with only one minor change (Trickett & Etheridge 1904). Whereas the original report had stated "The bones visible on the cave floor are:" [followed by a list], the reprinted version stated "The bones visible on the cave floor appear to be:" [followed by the same list]. A case of retrospective scientific caution? The coloured map which accompanied the reprint (Figure 47) varied from that in the Annual Report in that the Orient Cave, discovered in the meantime, had been added.

A brief report records the discovery of the Bouverie Cave at Wombeyan (Trickett 1903). Trickett stated "the broken nature of the tortuous passages of access appears to render [the cave] too dangerous to open for inspection by the public". He appended a plan and section of the cave (Figure 48).

---

[12] Nevertheless, Ralston smells a rat here; he suggests (1990, p. 49) that the fact that the survey was completed so soon after the reporting of the discovery indicates that the cavern was already known. "Either Jenolan was peopled by supermen, or someone had been exploring in secret, and sitting on the results until Wiburd became Senior Guide, after the Wilsons had departed" (so that Wiburd would get the credit, not Wilson). There is, in fact, ample evidence that as far as cave surveying is concerned, Trickett was indeed a 'superman' (even though he was by then 56 years of age). Hamilton-Smith (pers. comm.) supports the conspiracy theory, citing inscriptions by Wiburd and Edwards in the cave prior to the 'official' discovery date and the prompt release by Kerry of photos of the new cave.

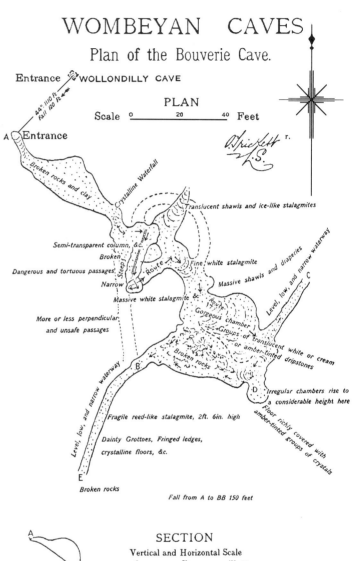

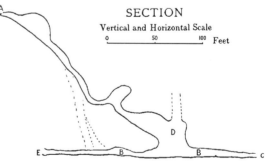

Figure 48. Wombeyan Caves: Plan of the Bouverie Cave
(*ARDM* 1903 plan 2)

1904 Report

As usual, Trickett (1904) reported on improvements at the various caves; no survey plans were included. He noted that the first edition of his Jenolan guidebook had sold out and a new one was in production, including the new extensions of the Lucas Cave (the River Cave). He also recorded the discovery of further extensions of the Lucas Cave:

> On 20th February, Caretaker Wiburd and Guide Edwards discovered 'The Temple of Baal', and on the 30th July, assisted by Guide Bailey, they found the Orient Cave. These are surpassingly beautiful and extensive branches of the Lucas Cave, leading from the 'River' series of caverns. In the course of exploration the guides have exhibited a perseverance and a courage in overcoming perilous obstacles which is highly to their credit. Temporary means of access to the new caves are being rapidly provided. This includes a punt, which has been placed on that part of the underground river named 'The Styx'. Permanent stairways will be added from time to time. (Trickett 1904)

Trickett obviously thought that the punt ride on the underground river was a high point of this cave tour and he photographed it (Figure 49) and included this in his later guidebooks[13].

At Yarrangobilly Trickett noted that "wire-netting in the various caves had been re-strained and added to". Also "The pathway which ran through the splendid 'Flower Garden' [in the Jersey Cave] has been re-modelled and has been constructed round the garden, and is an important improvement". This path had required the relocation of some spectacular pool crystal growths, such as that illustrated in the Yarrangobilly guidebook (Figure 50).

Figure 50. Spectacular pool crystal growth from the 'Flower Garden', Jersey Cave.

Figure 49. Tourist party on the punt on the River Styx, River Cave.
[From *Guide to the Jenolan Caves*, 3rd Edn., 1915, p. 45]

---

13 The party in the punt was apparently from a girl's academy in Bathurst (Hamilton-Smith, pers. comm.)

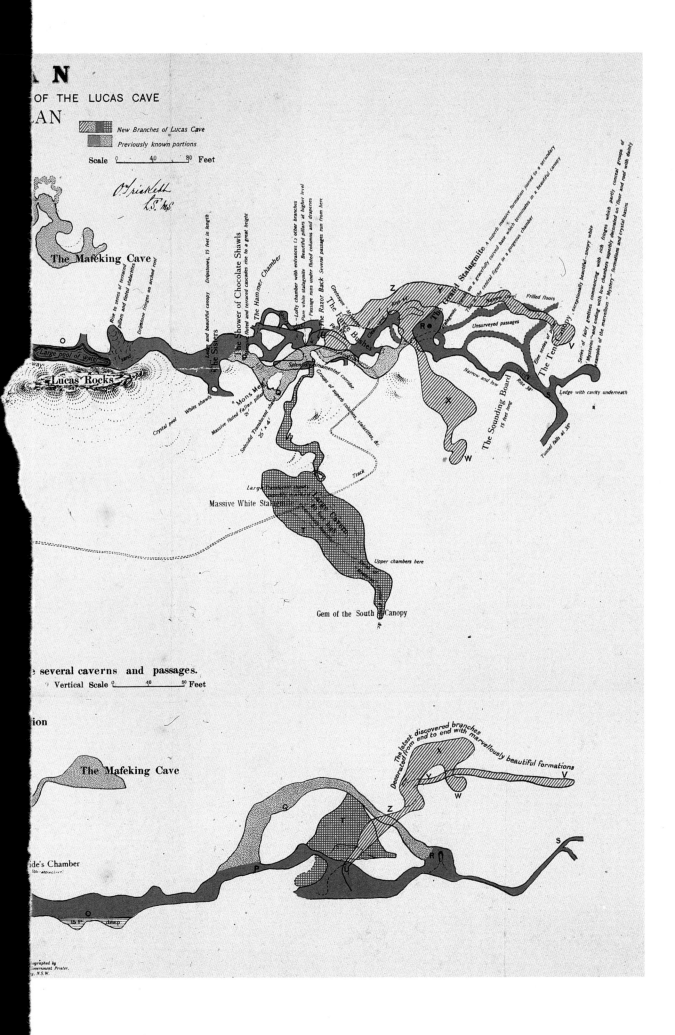

[From an original print, as included in *Guide to Yarrangobilly Caves*, 2nd Edn., 1917, p. 26]

1905 Report

In his report for 1905 Trickett (1905a) lamented that the year had been "an uneventful one in the history of the caves, as few new caverns were discovered". At Jenolan he reported the opening of the Skeleton [now Cerberus] Cave to the public, while at Yarrangobilly "a labourer was employed, after the tourist season was over, in cutting a new track to the Old Glory Hole Cave" (shown in Figure 87). This labourer was almost certainly Anthony Bradley (son of the 'Keeper', Harry Bradley), who built nearly all the paths at Yarrangobilly single-handed (Bradley 1972).

On the publicity side Trickett reported "An endeavour has been made to advertise the caves by the issue of 5,000 broadsheets and 5,000 leaflets, illustrated by views, which have been admirably produced by the Government Printer", and that the second edition of his Jenolan guidebook and his *Guide to the Yarrangobilly Caves* had been published. He also noted that his Wombeyan guidebook was "in the press". Again, no maps were included in the report.

1906 Report

It may be an indication of declining activity that in Trickett's report on Jenolan for 1906 only the River Cave was mentioned, and that on account of improvements to pathways "which reflect great credit on the workmen engaged on their construction". He also noted that a new billiard cloth and balls were supplied for Caves House [!], that the water services in Caves House were repaired and that a visitor was successfully prosecuted for breaking a stalactite (Trickett 1906a).

At Wombeyan, labourers were employed to open the Bullio Cave, of which he gave a brief description. He also recorded the publication of his Wombeyan guidebook but, perhaps surprisingly, he did not record the publication of three other guides, to Bungonia, Abercrombie and Wellington Caves. This may have been because they were published by the Government Tourist Bureau, whereas the Wombeyan guidebook was published by the Geological Survey.

New branches of the Glory Hole Cave were explored at Yarrangobilly; these were surveyed by Trickett and shown on a small plan which was included in the text (Figure 51).

1907 Report

The brief report of 1907 heralds the end of an era, in that control of the caves was transferred to the Intelligence Department (which presumably incorporated the Tourist Bureau) as of 1 July that year. Trickett continued to have a role, however, and he reported:— at Jenolan, on improvements in the River and Lucas Caves, opening up of the Temple of Baal and replacement of the River Cave punt by an iron one; at

Yarrangobilly, on the excellent work of labourer and guide, A.H.M. Bradley, on the new track to the Glory Hole Cave (see Figure 87); and at Wombeyan, on new temporary access to the Bullio Cave. He included a description of that cave and a survey of it as far as then explored (Figure 52).

1908 Report

There was no general report by Trickett in 1908; his work was reported by the Government Geologist (Pittman 1908), who said Trickett had reported on Cliefden Caves (see below) and suggested improvements at Jenolan, Wombeyan and Yarrangobilly— "with respect to the latter, on the proposed revocation of parts of the reserve". Pittman also reported on work done

under Mr Trickett's supervision:—better pathways and stairways in Wollondilly Caves [sic], Tinted Cavern, &c (Wombeyan Caves); at Jenolan the pathways, stairways and protective railings in the Nettle Cave were remodelled, those in the beautiful Temple of Baal were completed, and the cavern opened for inspection.

He also designed two iron stairways for the Yarrangobilly Caves. One of these will give access to additional features in the Jersey Cavern [sic]. The Aladdin Cave was opened for inspection. Steps and a platform were erected at the Nymph's Bath, and the tracks in the South Glory Hole were repaired throughout.

In addition to current work for the Geological Branch, Mr Trickett produced during his own time an exceedingly good topographical map of the Blue Mountains, which is being reproduced as a geological map and, to a larger scale, as a topographical map. It is confidently believed that this map will be much appreciated by tourists. [See Blue Mountains Maps, p. 100]

In his report on the Cliefden Caves, warm spring and fossil hill, Trickett (1908) referred to Belubula Caves on Licking Hole Creek which "are said to have been mutilated to such an extent as to destroy all their beauty". He then reported in detail on those on the north bank of the Belubula River which he found to

contain roomy chambers, and originally exhibited many interesting formations, whose beauty I found had long since been destroyed by visitors, except those in one small grotto.

Despite that, he went on to report "a beautiful creamy-white terrace formation", "a very fine group of stalagmites and stalactites", "a beautiful canopy" and "a richly-ornamented passage" — all from notes made by his "assistant", Mr Wiburd (Caretaker at Jenolan). Demonstrating that his understanding of caves went beyond the superficial, Trickett wrote:

The passages are unlike the generality of those in limestone caverns, inasmuch as the contour of their roofs, instead of showing the arched appearance of waterways, are rough and uneven, and are the result of fracture—that is, they have been formed by the detachment of rocks which have fallen.

REFERENCE

A. Very large cavern, 80 feet broad by 30 feet high, rising rapidly over broken rocks.

B. Group of stalactites similar to those in the King's Chamber.

C. Charming little basin filled with crystals. Between this and the point E are some very fine and massive chocolate-tinted terraces, surmounted by tinted stalactites and lime draperies. At E, amber-tinted waterfall formations rise up to a height of 30 feet.

D. Amber tinted floors, with crystal pools. In one superb basin, flakes of lime have been deposited, so thin that they give an appearance of softness reminding one of a bed of down. At the extreme end of the passage is a dainty little grotto of pillars and stalactites.

Figure 51. New Branches of the Glory Hole Cave (North Branch), Yarrangobilly (*ARDM* 1906 p. 173 - enlarged to 140% and 'Reference' text reset in Times)

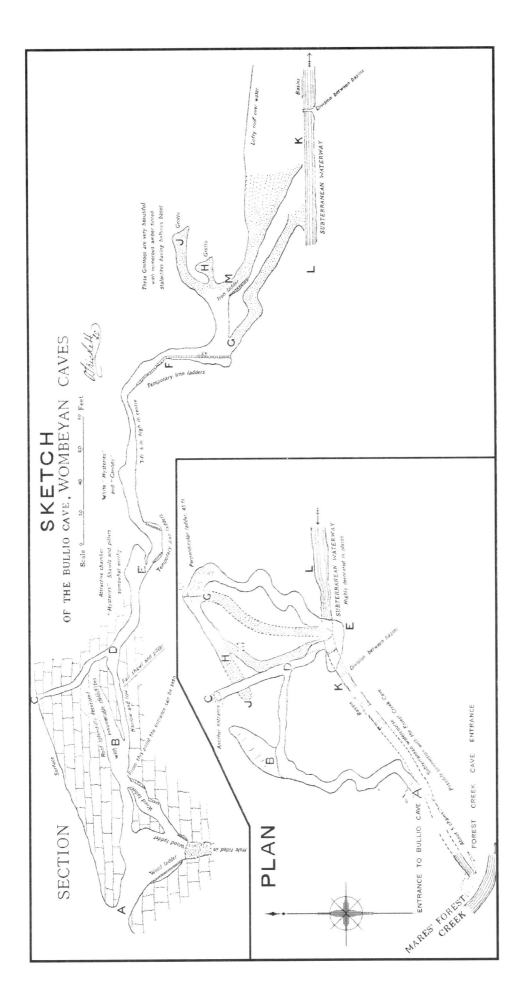

Figure 52. Sketch of the Bullio Cave, Wombeyan Caves (*ARDM* 1907)

He also noted and lamented the deterioration of the caves:

The floors are clayey; visitors' hands become dirty, and many of the formations have been soiled from this cause. In addition to this want of care, visitors have deliberately chiselled out the greater part of the crystal formations, which are of frequent occurrence. I have seen some of them which are larger and clearer than those usually found in other caves. It is a pity they have been removed. (Trickett 1908)

He felt the caves were worth preserving but urged that any action should be taken quickly in view of the continuing vandalism. He also reported on the nearby Fossil Hill, which is limestone containing an abundance of Silurian fossils, and a warm spring discharging 10,000 gallons of water per hour at a temperature of 84°F (28.9°C). The government of the day did not resume the caves and they remain in private ownership.

1909 Report

Again, in 1909, Pittman (1909) reported on the activities of "Mr O. Trickett, Draftsman" which included "in addition to his work in the Head Office", visits to Jenolan, Wombeyan and Yarrangobilly Caves where he suggested many improvements which were "for the most part", carried out. They included the opening of the Orient Cave at Jenolan and a beautiful chamber at the end of the Jersey Cave at Yarrangobilly, for both of which Trickett designed iron stairways. He also reported on the Gaden Cave at Wellington, though this does not appear to have been published. Pittman also mentioned that Trickett had constructed a model of the Broken Hill Lode for the Mining Museum [see Cave and Mine Models, p. 107].

1910 Report

In 1910 Trickett's report (included in Pittman's report) consisted of brief notes on Jenolan and Wombeyan but his major interest was obviously in Yarrangobilly, where he provided a plan of the main cave area (Figure 53 - this differs from Figure 61 only by the addition of the 'new road' - via Rules Creek) and reported the discovery of the Jillabenan Cave by Leo Hoad and his preparation of a plan of the Harrie Wood Cave (Figure 54). He also included plans of the Jillabenan (Figure 54) and the Glory Hole and Jersey Caves (Figure 55 - this differed from Figure 68 only by the addition of chambers to the end of the North Branch of the Glory Hole Cave). Trickett described the Jillabenan in effusive terms, saying "There is very little in the caves, which have been termed 'The Wonderland of New South Wales' to surpass the loveliness of this cavern" and then quoted a poem on the beauty of nature's colours.

1911 Report

Pittman reverted in this report to giving his own account of Trickett's work (Pittman 1911). At Jenolan he reported the construction of new paths and rails in the Orient Cave where new chambers were discovered by Wiburd. He included a sketch section by Trickett showing the positions of the Orient and Temple of Baal

caverns relative to the surface (Figure 56). Although Pittman failed to mention why this diagram was prepared it is evident that Trickett wanted to point out how easy it would be to dig a tunnel to give direct access to these important, but remote chambers. The tunnel was eventually cut in 1953-54 (Driscoll 1977). [Driscoll states that Trickett arranged for W.L. Cooke, a Public Works Department surveyor, to carry out a survey "to determine the exact position of the Orient and Baal systems in relation to a position on the hillside near the boiler house at Jenolan Caves". Unfortunately Driscoll does not cite the source of his information or reproduce Cooke's survey[14]. This survey was subsequently referred to by Trickett—see Trickett's Cave surveying techniques, p. 105, and also pp. 117-120.

Pittman (1911) also mentioned Trickett reporting improvements in the Harrie Wood Cave and the start of excavations to open the Jillabenan Cave at Yarrangobilly and progress with the opening of Junction Cave and opening of a new grotto in Wollondilly Cave, at Wombeyan.

1912 Report

Trickett's brief report of 1912 mentioned improvements in the main branch of the Orient Cave at Jenolan and a preliminary survey of the paths in this cave, initial opening of the Junction Cave at Wombeyan and progress on opening the Jillabenan Cave at Yarrangobilly "which included some very heavy rockcutting".

1913 Report

Trickett's 1913 report noted the opening of the main chambers of the Junction Cave at Wombeyan and improvements in the Orient Cave at Jenolan, but concentrated mainly on Yarrangobilly. He included a survey of the rockpile in the entrance to the Glory Hole Caves, which he felt "it may be desired to level at some future date"[15] (Figure 58), a plan of an easy grade track to the thermal spring (this was never built; the plan suggests, as an alternative, a rather fanciful suspension bridge across the gorge from the Glory Hole Cave track) (Figure 59), a re-survey of the Glory Hole and Jersey Caves[16] (Figure 60) and a general plan of the area (Figure 61 - which appears to be a re-draft of Figure 53).

1914 Report

Trickett's report for 1914 was the last to be published in his own words. It read, in full:

Report by O. Trickett, L.S., M.S.:— In addition to the preparation of detail[ed] geological and mining maps,

---

14 The section prepared by Cooke (Figure 57) was reproduced by Trickett as an inset to his 1925 plan of the Jenolan Caves, a copy of which is included in a pocket at the back of this book.

15 This was one of his less sensible and less practical ideas; the rockpile remains in place.

16 Note that the caption for this plan, which was bound at the back of the 1913 *Annual Report*, appeared, rather confusingly, below Figure 59 which was printed within the text of that report, on page 186.

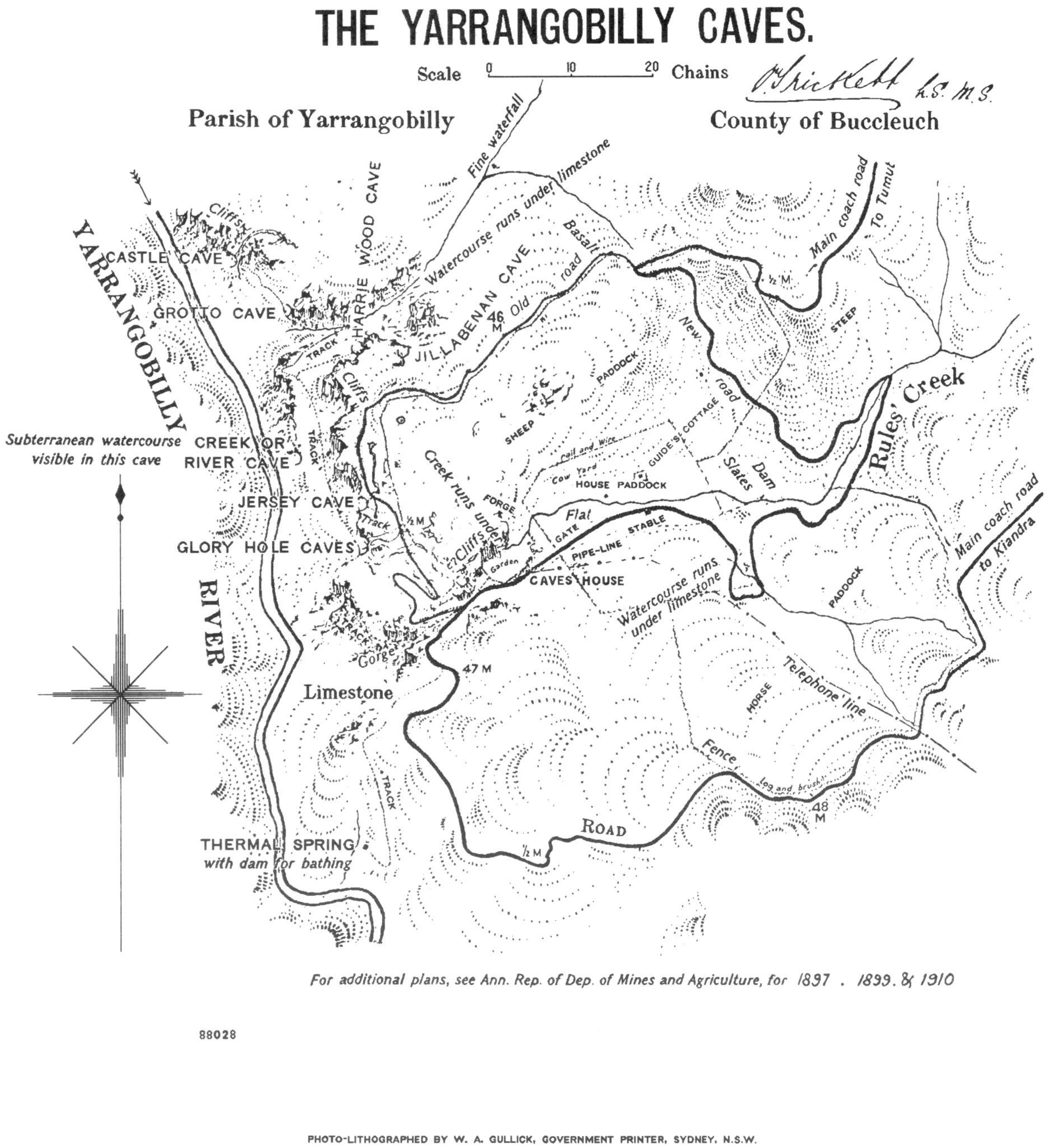

THE YARRANGOBILLY CAVES.

Scale 0 ___ 10 ___ 20 Chains

Parish of Yarrangobilly

County of Buccleuch

For additional plans, see Ann. Rep. of Dep. of Mines and Agriculture, for 1897 . 1899. & 1910

88028

PHOTO-LITHOGRAPHED BY W. A. GULLICK, GOVERNMENT PRINTER, SYDNEY, N.S.W.

Figure 53. The Yarrangobilly Caves (*ARDM* 1910 plan 1)

[See also Figure 61]

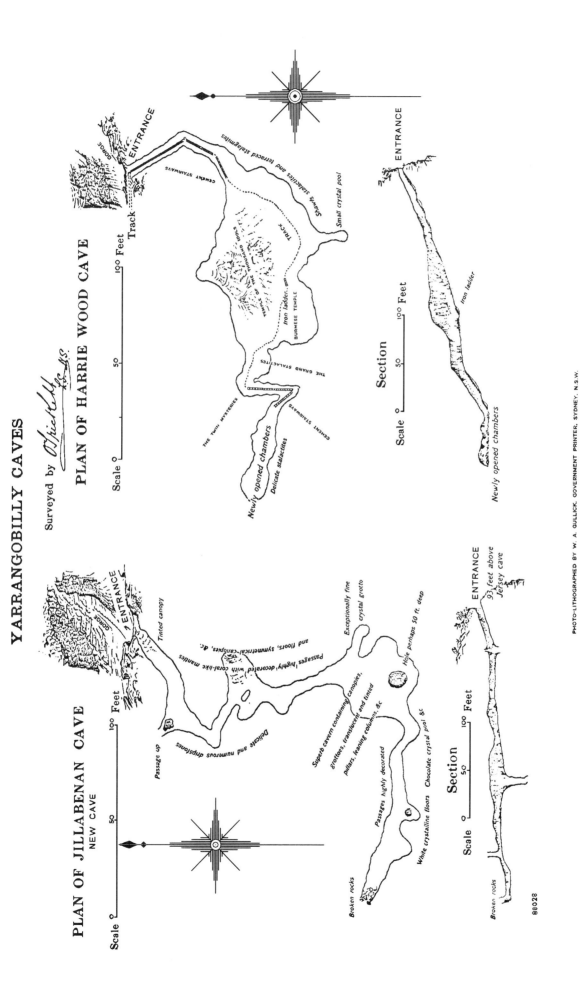

Figure 54. Yarrangobilly Caves: Jillabenan and Harry Wood Caves (*ARDM* 1910 plan 2)

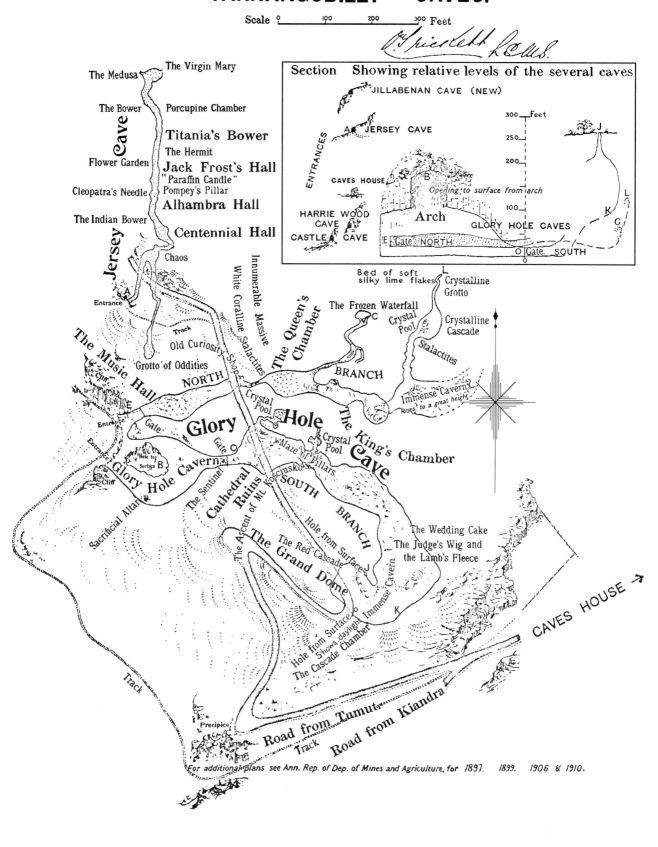

YARRANGOBILLY CAVES.

Figure 55. Yarrangobilly Caves: Glory Hole and Jersey Caves (*ARDM* 1910 plan 3)
[Modified version of Figure 68]

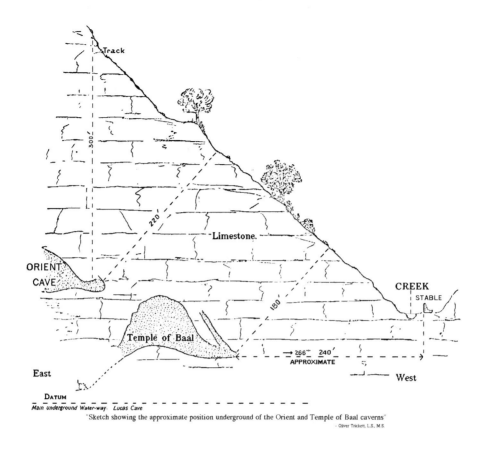

Figure 56. Section showing positions of Orient and Temple of Baal Caves relative to the surface
(*ARDM* 1911, p. 194)

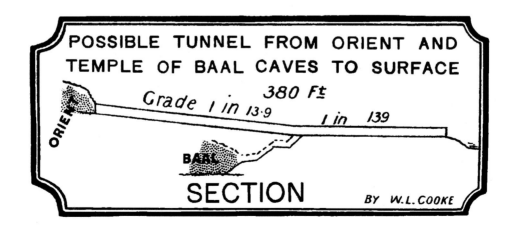

Figure 57. Section from survey by W.L. Cooke of "Possible Tunnel from Orient and Temple of Baal Caves to Surface"
[Reproduced from an inset in Trickett's large composite map of Jenolan published in 1925,
a reproduction of which is included at the back of this volume]

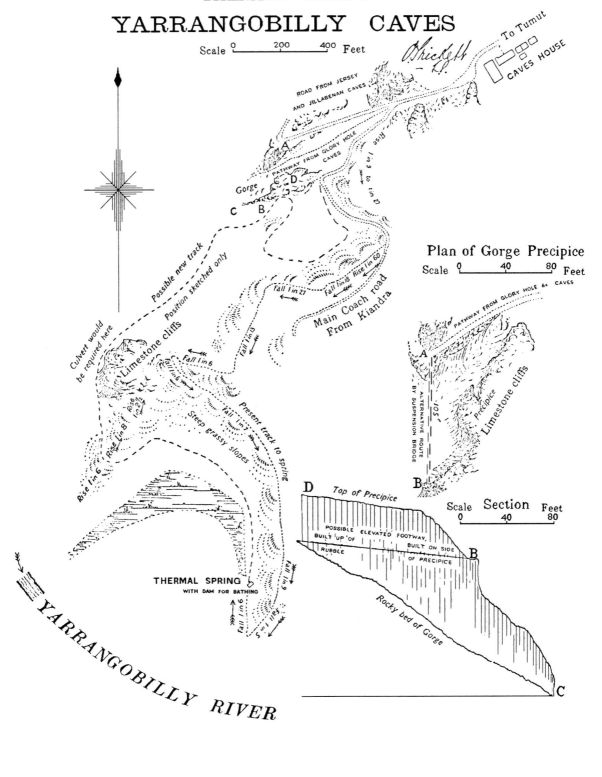

Figure 59. "Plan of possible easy grade track to the thermal spring, Yarrangobilly Caves"
(*ARDM* 1913 plan 2, p. 186)

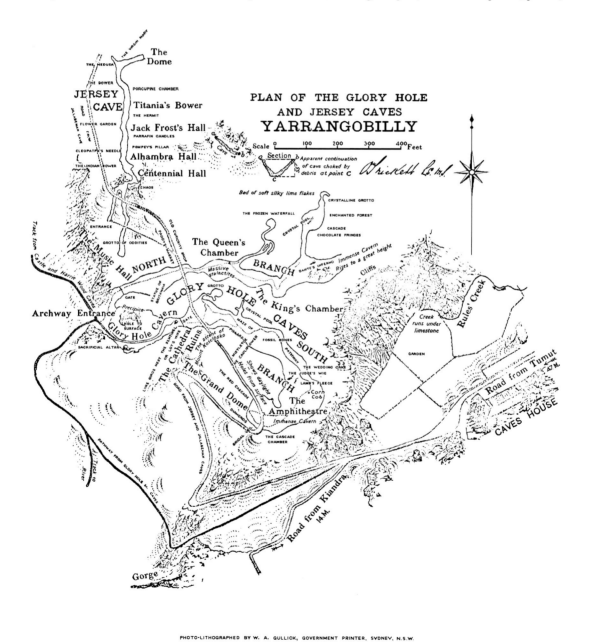

Mound of fallen rocks.   Glory Hole Cavern.
Yarrangobilly

Scale 0   40   80 Feet

This diagram indicates
fallen rock which it may
be desired to level at
some future date.

Northern wall of cavern

Track to North Branch

Track to South Branch

Sections

36'

c   *d*   *b*   *a*

177'   106'

Figure 58. "Mound of fallen rocks, Glory Hole Cavern, Yarrangobilly" (*ARDM* 1913 plan 1, p. 185)

PLAN OF THE GLORY HOLE
AND JERSEY CAVES
YARRANGOBILLY

Scale 0   100   200   300   400 Feet

PHOTO-LITHOGRAPHED BY W. A. GULLICK, GOVERNMENT PRINTER, SYDNEY, N.S.W.

Figure 60. "General Plan. Plan of the re-survey of the Glory Hole Caverns.
This plan also shows position of the new cave reported on 23rd December, 1913" (*ARDM* 1913 plan 3)

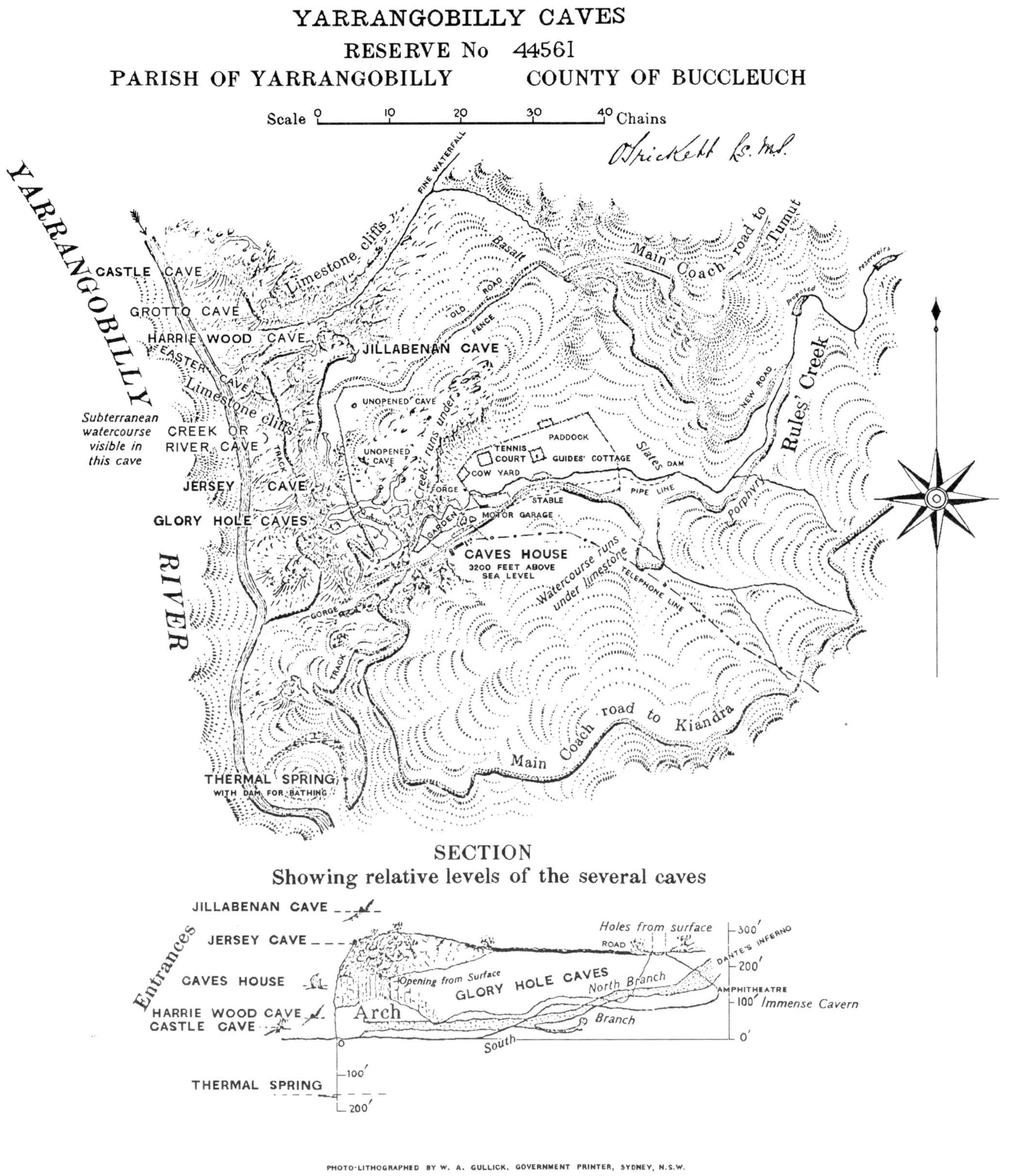

YARRANGOBILLY CAVES
RESERVE No 44561
PARISH OF YARRANGOBILLY   COUNTY OF BUCCLEUCH

SECTION
Showing relative levels of the several caves

Figure 61. Yarrangobilly Caves: Reserve No. 44561 (*ARDM* 1913 plan 4)

I completed the compilation of the geological map of the State, constructed a model of the Broken Hill silver lode, for the Panama Exposition, and brought up to date a model of this lode, which is on exhibition at the Mining Museum. An illustration of the model is attached. [Figure 92; and see Cave and Mine Models, pp. 107-113]

I also set out and supervised improvements which have been made for the convenience of visitors to the Caves. The work includes the opening of a new branch in the Castle Cave, Yarrangobilly Caves. (Trickett 1914a)

Also in 1914, Trickett contributed some notes on Jenolan Caves to a small publication put out by the British Association for the Advancement of Science for an excursion to the Caves following its 1914 meeting in Sydney (Trickett 1914b). These notes (two printed pages) covered caves in an international context, a brief description of the route from Mt. Victoria and brief notes on ten major caves and the three 'open' arches.

1915 Report

In his Annual Report of the Government Geologist for 1915, J.E. Carne, who had replaced E.F. Pittman in that post wrote, *inter alia*:

During the year the completed issue of the Geological map of New South Wales, compiled by Mr O. Trickett, L.S., M.S., was produced and favourably received.

Mr Trickett also prepared maps of the Adelong Gold Fields, Dubbo Coal Field, Limestone deposits of the State [for Carne & Jones (1919)], *Artesian Basin, and final plans of the Southern Coal Field, and numerous sections and diagrams.*

New geological surveys were recorded by him, and the register of mineral localities brought up to date.

In addition to the above works for the Geological Survey, Mr Trickett furnished reports on the caves for the Tourist Bureau, and designed and recommended improvements in them for the convenience of visitors, and for protection of the formations.

An enlargement of the bath at the Warm Spring, Yarrangobilly, was arranged for and completed. At the date of Mr Trickett's last visit, in December, 35,000 gallons of water per hour was flowing through the bath. To this flow an added 2,800 gallons per hour find their way through the strata surrounding the bath. Steps will be taken to determine whether any of the drainage from the swamp above the bath finds its way into it. [A plan of the pool by Trickett was appended - Figure 62.]

The model of the Broken Hill lode, prepared by Mr Trickett for the Panama-Pacific Exposition by direction of the Premier, was awarded a gold medal, and

another model is now being prepared by approval, which the Sulphide Corporation will present to the Museum of Technology, Melbourne.

With the assistance of Mr J.C. Wiburd, Mr Trickett made a survey of the Orient Cave, Jenolan, and has partly constructed a model from the survey.

In this connection he also designed an adaptation of the "Plane table", which was most useful in carrying out the survey. It will probably be found to be a convenience as an adjunct to the theodolite in the delineation of mine workings [Figure 63].

1916 Report

In his Government Geologist's report for 1916, Carne (1916) stated that Trickett was continuing to prepare plans, sections, etc. required by the Geological Survey, was making progress with the register of mineral localities and had designed and supervised the carrying out of improvements at Jenolan, Wombeyan and Yarrangobilly Caves. At Yarrangobilly the stairway near the entrance to the Jersey Caves was remodelled, reflecting "great credit on the workman (Leo Hoad)".

He also noted that Trickett had prepared another model of the Broken Hill lode for the Technical Museum,

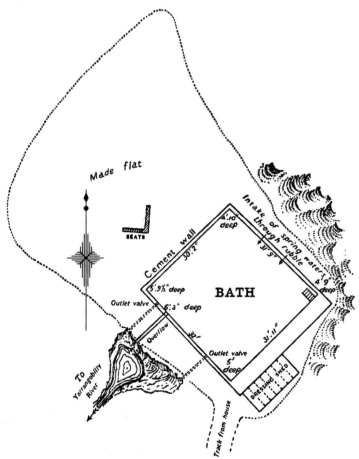

Figure 62. Plan by Trickett of thermal pool at
Yarrangobilly Caves
[From *Ann. Rep. Dept. Mines*, 1915, p. 190]

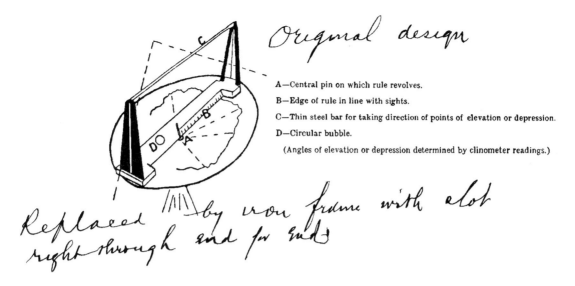

Original design

A—Central pin on which rule revolves.

B—Edge of rule in line with sights.

C—Thin steel bar for taking direction of points of elevation or depression.

D—Circular bubble.

(Angles of elevation or depression determined by clinometer readings.)

Replaced by iron frame with alot right through end for end

Figure 63. Diagram of plane table modified by Trickett for cave surveying
[From an original page of *ARDM* for 1915 (p. 190) with Trickett's notations by hand]

Melbourne and had completed a model of the Orient Cave, Jenolan. [See Cave and Mine Models, p. 111]

1917 Report

Carne's report for 1917 recorded further work by Trickett on plans and sections for the Geological Survey and completion of the register of mineral localities. Trickett continued to supervise work at the various caves and carried out a survey of the Jersey Cave at Yarrangobilly (Figure 64). A revised edition of his

guide to Yarrangobilly Caves was published with new plans and photographs. [See Cave Guidebooks, p. 88]

1918 Report

On Trickett's work in 1918, Carne (1918) reported:

The "Register of Mining Localities" by O. Trickett, L.S., M.S., has been handed to the Government Printer for publication.

Among other plans he completed for the Geological

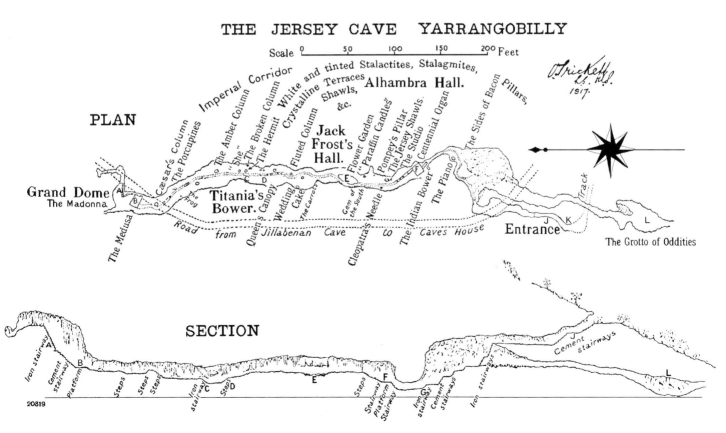

Figure 64. Plan and section of the Jersey Cave, Yarrangobilly (*ARDM*, 1917, p. 172)

Survey are those for the work on limestone now in press [Carne & Jones (1919)], *which include plans of cave limestones from his survey.*

During his spare time he completed models from his surveys of the Basin Cave, Wombeyan, and the Jersey Cave, Yarrangobilly [Figure 94], *both of which are now exhibited at the Mining Museum.*

He is now engaged similarly on a model of the Fig Tree and Creek Caves, Wombeyan.

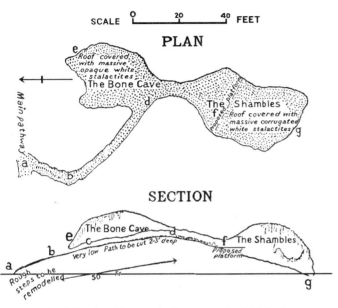

The following diagram indicates work which he has set out for attention in the Left Imperial Cave, Jenolan [Figure 65].

Figure 65. Plan of the Bone Cave and Shambles
Left Imperial, Jenolan
[From *Ann. Rep. Dept. Mines*, 1918, p. 16]

This diagram is the last cave plan of Trickett's to be published in the *Annual Report of the Department of Mines* and is probably one of the last cave plans he prepared. The 'work on limestone' referred to (Carne & Jones' *The Limestone Deposits of New South Wales*) was to be the definitive volume on limestone in New South Wales until the '2nd Edition' was published in 1986 (Lishmund, Dawood & Langley 1986). Trickett's plans

contributed greatly to the value of the book, particularly to cavers, as they showed where groups of caves were located and, in some cases, showed locations of particular caves. A selection of these plans is reproduced on pages 93 to 99, Figures 74 to 80. The originals were generally printed in two colours with the limestone deposits shown in green or blue shading.

1919 Report

The last reference to Trickett in the *Annual Report of the Department of Mines* is in Carne's report of 1919:

> *After an almost continuous service of over fifty years under the Governments of New South Wales and Victoria, since his appointment to the Mines Department of the latter State in 1865, Mr Trickett was retired from the Geological Branch in June last.*
>
> *During the year, in addition to his professional work in the Geological Branch, he completed surveys of the Kooringa and Wollondilly Caverns, Wombeyan Caves, from which he produced models in his private time. These models with others are on exhibition at the Mining Museum and will no doubt be found to be of considerable public interest.*

While there are reports of his official retirement *(Sydney Sun,* 8 July 1919, and *Mining Engineers Review,* 5 August - see p. 132) it appears that Trickett did not actually cease work on 30 June 1919. The *Government Gazette* of 26 September 1919 carried the following notice:

TRANSFER

DEPARTMENT OF MINES

> *HIS Excellency the Governor, with the advice of the Executive Council, and upon the recommendation of the Public Service Board, has been pleased to approve the transfer of*
>
> *Mr Oliver Trickett, Draftsman and Surveyor, Geological Survey Branch, this Department, to Draftsman and Surveyor, Relieving Staff, this Department, - such transfer to take effect from the 1st September, 1919.*
> *J.C.L. FITZPATRICK*

Annotated: Paper Misc. 19/7837/145 Misc. 20/ 8833/384

According to the Mines Department employment book (Table 2), Trickett's actual last day of service was 22 March 1920.

CAVE GUIDEBOOKS

Jenolan Guidebook, 1st Edition

1899 saw the publication, by the Geological Survey, of Trickett's first guidebook - to the Jenolan Caves (Trickett 1899d). There appears to be no information on who suggested the production of this guide (it may well have been Trickett's own idea); in any case it was a great success and the forerunner of a series, both for Jenolan and other tourist cave areas.

The guide is a skilful combination of scholarly work, both in relation to scientific aspects and history (sources are accurately referenced), and very readable descriptions, designed to appeal to the tourist (replete with the ever-popular 'Home of the Fairies', 'Fairies' Bower', 'Queen's Diamonds', 'Lots Wife', etc.). Trickett drew on the works of such luminaries as Charles Darwin, C.S. Wilkinson and Professor Edgeworth David for his descriptions of the surrounding country and was not afraid to quote from previous guides, especially Cook's (1889) and the Railway Guide of 1886. Although the reference is only brief, it is worthy of note that he starts the history section with a mention of the original owners, the Cox River Aborigines and their name for the place, *Binoomea*.

That Trickett was familiar with the international speleological literature of the day is demonstrated in the section on cave formation; he quotes examples from Mammoth Cave, Kentucky, Armand Cave, Southern France and Wind Cave, Missouri. He recommends, as additional reading, Dawkins' *Cave Hunting*, Hovey's *Celebrated American Caverns* and Martel's *Les Abimes*.

The major part of the guide is taken up with detailed and glowing descriptions of the known caves, including some unopened sections of the main system and notes on Bushrangers Cave, McKeowns Hole, Mammoth, Frenchmans and Glass Caves and the Bottomless Pit. Brief quotes will serve to illustrate the author's powers of description and his fascination with the myriad forms he carefully observed:

> *Under the ornamental roof formed by the Cascade is the Jewel Casket, one of Nature's treasure-houses. The Casket is contained in a small recess, and can be viewed by one person only at a time. ... The floor and sides sparkle with the light reflected from innumerable tinted crystals, which dazzle the eye with their splendour. Gems of all kinds, diamonds, agates, &c, appear to have been scattered about with a prodigal hand.* (Trickett 1899d, p. 35)

> *In close proximity are four smaller pillars, two of which are joined together near the top, and are known as the 'Giraffe's Fore Legs'. On the left is a formation named 'The Smoked Ox Tongue'. This is succeeded by the Mystery. This formation is not so large as the 'Mystery' in the left branch of the Imperial Cave, but it is decorated by similar fantastic and grotesque forms of lime deposits. Some of these are delicate and beautiful, but puzzle the spectator*

> *to account for the many peculiarities of shape which present themselves. Close to the 'Mystery' is the Battlefield. Here, in a diminutive and beautiful nook, are multitudes of curious forms, which are not unlike soldiers fighting in a field scattered here and there with war impedimenta and dead and dying warriors. A figure is seen like a stag leaping from a rocky precipice into space.* (Trickett 1899d, p. 48)

The multicoloured plan and sections of the caves which form the centre spread convey a remarkably clear picture of the extent of the various passages and chambers, as well as their relative positions (lower part of Figure 67). This five colour map (versions of which were a feature of all four editions of Trickett's guidebook) must have been a significant printing achievement in its day (though two and three colour maps were common in Geological Survey publications). Its standard has never even been approached in more recent guidebooks.

The 43 photographs which illustrate this edition Trickett attributed to "the artists attached to the photographic branches of the Government Printing Office and Public Works Department, Mr Cooke, photographer, of Jenolan [who was also the owner of the Kia-Ora Guest House], Mr Rowe, late of Jenolan, and Kerry & Co., of Sydney".

Appended to the cave descriptions are some details of unopened caves: the Red Cave and Alabaster Hall (branches of the Jubilee) and those more remote from the tourist area: Bushrangers Cave, McKeowns Hole, Mammoth Cave, Frenchmans Cave, Glass Cave and the Bottomless Pit. This edition also includes a page on Tuglow Cave, with Trickett's own photo of the since-destroyed 'Tuglow shawl', (Figure 66). Today this would not qualify as a 'tourist' cave—Trickett notes that rope is required for its descent—yet on page 7 he says that "Arrangements can be made with local residents for a visit to the Tuglow Caves". Presumably tourists became less adventuresome as reference to Tuglow Cave was omitted from later editions.

Figure 66. "Tuglow Cave" by Trickett
(showing the since-destroyed 'Tuglow shawl')
[From *Guide to the Jenolan Caves*, 1st Edn., p. 61]

The guidebook won immediate praise from the eminent botanist and Director of the Botanic Gardens, J. H. Maiden:

Botanic Gardens
Sydney, 7th Sept. 1899

Dear Sir,

Thank you for your kindness in sending me a copy of your booklet on Jenolan. It seems to me a model of what a guide book should be and the set-up is excellent. You should get much kudos from it and I trust something more substantial also.

Yours truly,

[signed] J.H. Maiden

O. Trickett, Esq. L.S.

Jenolan Guidebook, 2nd Edition

Trickett produced the second edition of his very popular Jenolan guidebook in 1905. Its price increased from two shillings to three shillings and six pence. There are at least four bindings of this edition, two with a green cover, one light blue and one grey. The frontispiece of the blue and grey versions is the same as that in the 1st edition: a photo (by Kerry) of the valley taken from an elevated point (presumably above the Grand Arch). This shows the old Caves House with its wide-verandahed north wing. One green version features the high-level Kerry photo and the other, a low-level photo (again by Kerry) of the approach to Caves House (in which Kerry's photographic kiosk is very prominent). The gable-roofed north wing of Caves House, completed in 1909 (Havard 1934, p. 46) is shown; hence this is a later printing. Another change in the green covered printings is the introduction of a colour frontispiece: "View from the Grand Arch looking east", a drawing by G. Rutherford[17]. Otherwise the four printings appear to be identical.

Trickett wrote his own introduction to the 1st edition, but E.F. Pittman, Government Geologist and Under Secretary for Mines got into the act for the 2nd. He wrote:

The success of the publication, for which great credit is, I think, due to the Author, Mr Oliver Trickett, has now rendered the issue of a second edition necessary; and owing to the very important caves which have recently been discovered by Mr Wiburd, the present Caretaker (also, to some extent, by Mr F.J. Wilson, his predecessor), and Guide Edwards, it will be found that much interesting matter has been added to the Guide-book, both as regards letter-press, plan, and photographic illustrations.

Certainly there were changes in the text, with extensive new descriptions of the "River Branches of the Lucas Cave": the River Cave, Mons Meg branch, The Temple

[17] Grace Rutherford, of Bathurst, was well known as a major artist-designer for Royal Doulton (Hamilton-Smith pers. comm.)

of Baal, the Orient Cave and the Skeleton [now Cerberus] Cave. There were also more photographs, including a number by Trickett, particularly in the new caves, and one purporting to show Trickett himself surveying (Figure 88).

The colour map, presented in a vertical format in the 1st edition, was completely redrawn in landscape format and, of course, new caves such as the River, Orient and Temple of Baal were added. This is reproduced, above the first edition version in Figure 67.

Advertisements in this edition give an interesting sidelight on transport competition at the time (between horse-drawn 'coaches' and cars). The advertisement for Cooper's Grand Hotel, Mt. Victoria, proclaimed:

The ONLY DAILY SERVICE to the Jenolan Caves is by Cooper's Coaches.

We recommend the Coaches as Cheaper, Safer, and More Reliable than the Motor Cars.

While the competition, the Medlow Bath Hydro, asserted:

To the Caves by Motor Car is the Proper Way to go.

You save one day's time! One day's expenses! And have a most enjoyable ride compared to horse-drawn vehicles. The motors are the biggest in Australia, 22 and 26 horse-power Daimler Cars. They glide along like railway trains, and your outing is more enjoyable.

Even if you have made the mistake of going otherwise, return by Motor Coach and visit Medlow Bath Hydro.

Yarrangobilly Guidebook, 1st Edition

Trickett's 1905 guide to Yarrangobilly Caves gives a detailed description of the access routes from Tumut and Cooma, as well as the caves themselves: Glory Hole Cavern (South & North Branches), Jersey Cave, Harrie Wood Cave and Castle Cave. Brief mention is also made of the River and Copper Mine Cave ("temporarily closed", page 6 – "with iron bars set in cement", page 28). The photos which illustrate the guidebook are mainly Trickett's own, though two (which he probably took anyway) bear the Government Printer's imprint. Of the two maps, the first (Figure 68) is an earlier version of Figure 55 with (in the original) the caves shaded light blue and the roads, brown. The second map is almost identical to Figure 53, except for the addition of the 'new road' to the latter, and is not reproduced here.

The writing clearly indicates Trickett's great attachment to the place. In the introduction he wrote:

The Caves contain treasure-houses which no dream of Eastern art can equal. The vastness of the Glory Hole Caverns; the mammoth stalactites of the Queen's Chamber; the weird and stupendous Cathedral Ruins; the exquisite forms and dainty colouring of the Jersey Cave; the richly-sculptured pillars of "The Temple of the Thousand Idols"; and the gorgeous drapery of King

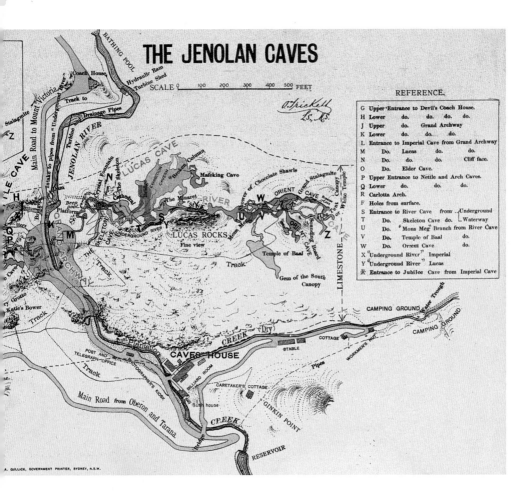

THE JENOLAN CAVES

SCALE 0 100 200 300 400 500 FEET

REFERENCE.

G	Upper Entrance to Devil's Coach House.		
H	Lower	do.	do. do.
J	Upper	do.	Grand Archway
K	Lower	do.	do. do.
L	Entrance to Imperial Cave from Grand Archway
M	Do.	Lucas	do. do.
N	Do.	do.	do. Cliff face.
O	Do.	Elder Cave.
P	Upper Entrance to Nettle and Arch Caves.
Q	Lower	do.	do. do.
R	Carlotta Arch.
F	Holes from surface.
S	Entrance to River Cave from Underground
T	Do.	Skeleton Cave do. Waterway
U	Do.	Mons Meg Branch from River Cave
V	Do.	Temple of Baal do.
W	Do.	Orient Cave do.
X	"Underground River" Imperial
Y	"Underground River" Lucas
※	Entrance to Jubilee Cave from Imperial Cave

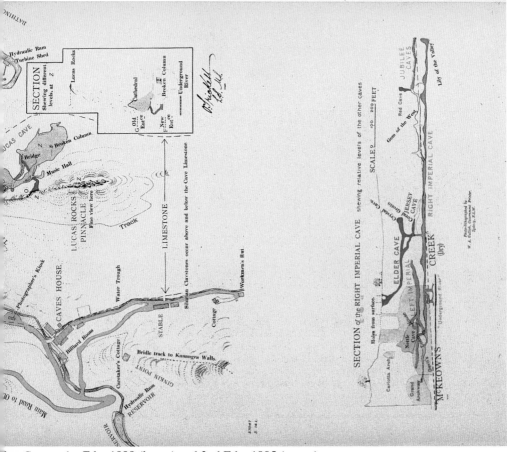

Jenolan Caves - 1st Edn. 1899 (lower) and 2nd Edn. 1905 (upper)

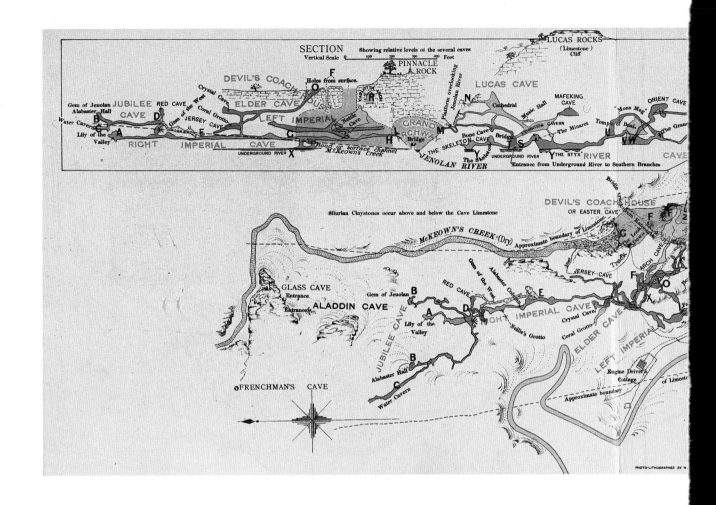

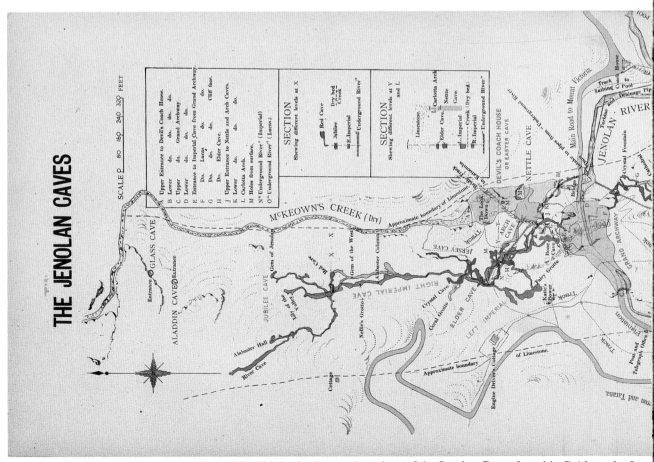

Figure 67.   Trickett's plans and sections of the Jenolan Caves from his *Guide to the Jeno*

81

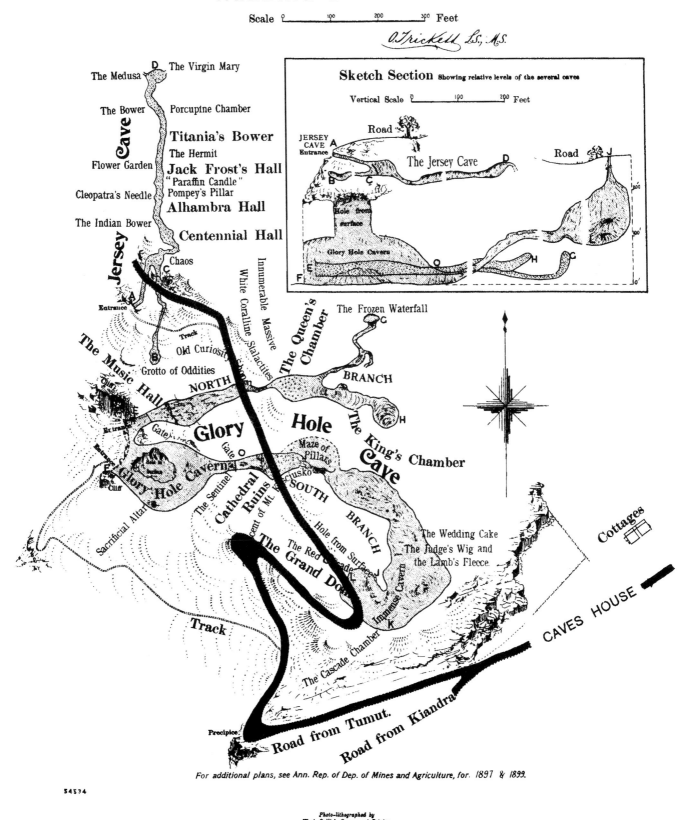

Figure 68. Yarrangobilly Caves - Glory Hole and Jersey Caves

(From *Guide to Yarrangobilly Caves*, 1st Edn., 1905)
[In the original the caves are shaded light blue and the road, brown]

Solomon's Temple unite in their grandeur and bewitching beauty to enthral all spectators. They occur in a belt of limestone from half a mile to one mile in width, and 6 or 7 miles long. The frontage of this belt to the Yarrangobilly River is singularly impressive. For miles precipices and battlemented outcrops dip their toes in the crystal waters of the rapidly-running river. They are weatherworn, carved here and there with grotesque shapes, scored and pitted with holes and crevices, many of which indicate the entrances to unexplored caverns with which the limestone is honeycombed. Two miles upstream from the Caves House the river has cut its way through the limestone, and now flows under it. Not very far away, but on top of the plateau, a curious weathering of the limestone has taken place, forming a labyrinth of huge pinnacled rocks, like tombstones marking the graves of a race of giants. (Trickett 1905c, p. 7)

The reference to the 'tombstones' is noteworthy, particularly as this is an area no tourist was ever likely to visit. It seems this was a place of particular interest to Trickett. As Anthony Bradley (a guide at Yarrangobilly between 1892 and 1911) recalled in 1970:

Every time, a week or two before he came to the caves, he used to send the word along to have the old grey mare ready. The old grey mare was by Goldsborough, a Melbourne Cup winner, and she was very flighty. He was an aged man at that time [in 1905 Trickett would have been 58] and we were always scared stiff of letting the old man get on this mare. Anyhow, he used to ride all over the place; between the hills, over the top there, all through the country. There's a place up there they call the Tombstones; he was fascinated with that area. He always used to go out of his way to ride through the Tombstones.

He was a very active old man. Even when he was 60 years of age he'd get hold of a broom handle and would jump through it standing up. He loved to go to Yarrangobilly and stop there for a week or more. (Middleton 1985a)

Possibly Trickett's favourite cave scene lies in the Castle Cave. He described it thus:

... the crowning glory of the Castle Cave is revealed to the spectator. This is KING SOLOMONS TEMPLE. From gracefully-rounded snowy-white ledges, rendered luminous by myriads of crystals, which sparkle like diamonds, hang gorgeous, orange-tinted shawls. Under the canopy thus formed are grottoes of exquisite beauty. No dream could conjure up any scene to outrival the splendour of this masterpiece of Nature's handicraft. (Trickett 1905c, p. 25) - see Figure 69.

In his own records he went even further; on a copy in his scrapbook of a plan of the Yarrangobilly limestone which he prepared for Carne & Jones (1919) he wrote the following:

Figure 69. Trickett's favourite cave scene: King Solomons Temple, Castle Cave, Yarrangobilly
(from *Guide to Yarrangobilly Caves*, 1st Edn., 1905)

The Castle Cave contains what is probably the finest specimen of limestone drip to be found anywhere in any cave in the world. Named King Solomons Temple - 17' across - varied in colour from the purest white to a rich fawn.

The following indicates that at about this time it was suggested that there be more advertising in Trickett's guidebooks:

> Government Printing Office,
> Sydney, 14th April 1905
>
> *Dear Mr Trickett,*
>
> *I have to thank you for yours of the 11th instant re Guide Book, which has come in very opportunely. I am pleased to tell you that the whole matter was placed in my hands for consideration this morning by our Under Secretary, and I shall be only too glad to let you know later on, what eventuates. It does seem to me, however, that your point is well taken. If the Government is going to advertise the Caves, they should do it properly and thoroughly, and I really believe that a good book, free to a great extent of interleaved advertisements, is more likely to be kept and become a standing advertisement, than one which it is a bother to read, and in which the real interest—the Caves themselves—is made subsidiary to the advertising matter. ... ...*
>
> *Yours faithfully*
> [signed] *W.A. Gullick*
>
> O. Trickett, Esq.
> Geological Survey Branch
> Department of Mines & Agriculture

Wombeyan Guidebook

In his introduction to the Wombeyan guidebook (Trickett 1906b), the Under Secretary of Mines, E.F. Pittman, makes it clear that it was produced as a result of the success of Trickett's guides to Jenolan and Yarrangobilly. He adds:

> *The Guide-book, which has been well prepared and illustrated by Mr O. Trickett, of this Department, will form an interesting souvenir for the visitor. Appended is a map [actually two] of the Caves, drawn from careful underground surveys by the same gentleman.*

The book follows the now familiar pattern of historical introduction, description of access routes (from Goulburn and Bowral) and detailed and imaginative descriptions of the various caves (Creek, Fig Tree, Basin, Wollondilly, Kooringa, Guineacor, Forest Creek and Tinted). Junction, Bullio, Shawl, Palace and Bouverie Caves, all then unopened, are also mentioned. Most of the 19 photos are by Trickett but four are attributed to Kerry & Co. Of the maps, the general location plan (Figure 70) appears to be new (or perhaps a major redrawing of Figure 21) but the cave plan is a simple redrafting of Figure 39.

This guidebook was also bound with those for Yarrangobilly and Jenolan (2nd Edn.); both blue and dark brown bindings of the combined guidebook are known (Hamilton-Smith pers. comm.).

Guidebooks to Abercrombie, Bungonia and Wellington Caves (1906)

These three guidebooks were unusual in at least three respects: they were the first to be produced by the Government Tourist Bureau (rather than the Geological Survey), they were in a much smaller size (160 mm x 100 mm as opposed to the earlier books' 250 mm x 180 mm) and they appear to be relatively rare (though Abercrombie and Wellington state "10,000 issued"). It is also notable that they carried more advertising than their predecessors. The covers are worthy examples of contemporary design (Figure 71). They follow roughly the pattern adopted for the earlier guidebooks, though the descriptions of the caves are not as detailed.

The Abercrombie guide (Trickett 1906c) concentrates on the Archway, with a brief mention of Grove Cave. It is notable as the only one of Trickett's published works to commit the ultimate sin of cave photo publishers: printing a photo upside down. Figure 72 shows the Pillars in the Hall of Terpsichore, as published. Although it carries the Government Printer's imprint it was probably taken by Trickett. The incorrect placing of the imprint on the photo no doubt led to the printer's mistake.

The map included is a direct copy (reduced) of Figure 38, omitting the sections and Trickett's signature[!].

In the case of the Bungonia guide (Trickett 1906d) only the Bungonia [Grill] and Drum Caves are described but the magnificent scenery of the gorge is emphasised (the quarry on the northern rim had not then commenced) and there is a full page devoted to an analysis of water from the Bungonia Natural Mineral Spring. No maps are included.

The guide to Wellington Caves (Trickett 1906e) refers to the Main, Gas-pipe and Water Caves, particularly the Alter, a large stalagmite in Main Cave, and the spectacular anticline in the roof of Water Cave (Figure 82). Over two pages are devoted to the giant marsupial fossils recovered from the Bone (or Breccia) Cave by Mitchell, Thomson, Krefft and others. The plan included is a copy of Mitchell's of 1838 as reproduced by Trickett in 1897 (Figure 23).

Jenolan Guidebook, 3rd Edition

Trickett produced the third edition of his Jenolan guidebook in 1915 and the price was reduced to just one shilling! There are at least two versions; one has a brown cover with gold lettering, the other blue on blue-grey. The frontispiece—for the first time a colour(ed) photograph—features, not a beautiful cave scene, but motor cars outside Caves House. This was the first edition to be produced by the Immigration and Tourist Bureau, and the introduction was written by its Superintendent, Percy Hunter.

For the most part the text and illustrations, including the multicoloured plan of the caves, are the same as the second edition. One addition concerns the origin of the name of the Imperial Caves, which Trickett says

Figure 70. The Wombeyan Caves (area plan)
(from *Guide to the Wombeyan Caves, NSW*, 1st Edn., 1906)

Figure 71. Covers of Trickett's 1906 guides to Bungonia and Abercrombie Caves
reproduced at actual size

Figure 72. "Pillars, Hall of Terpsichore" - a scene in the Abercrombie Archway, as published (upside down). (From *The Abercrombie Caves*, 1906, p. 8)

(without citing any authority) "were named after the Prince Imperial of France, the news of whose death in Africa reached Jenolan at the date of their discovery" (Trickett 1915, p. 57). Havard (1934, p. 21) refutes this, saying the French prince died on 1 June 1879, whereas Jeremiah Wilson had written a letter on 3 April 1879 saying he had named the cave the "imperial".

Yarrangobilly Guidebook, 2nd Edition

Trickett produced his second Yarrangobilly guide, this time published by the Immigration and Tourist Bureau, in 1917. The introductory sections were rewritten, though the cave descriptions are largely the same, with the major addition of a detailed description of the Jillabenan Cave.

In his introduction, Percy Hunter, Director of the Tourist Bureau, wrote glowingly of Trickett's work:

> *The Yarrangobilly Caves, in common with all the other limestone cave systems of New South Wales, which are famous throughout the world, owe a great deal to the zealous work of Mr O. Trickett, L.S., M.S., the author of this brochure; and particularly are these caves indebted to Mr Trickett for his happy inspiration in culling names from his vast fund of native lore. The points of interest in the recently opened cave, the Jillabenan, have all been identified by native names.* (Trickett 1917)

An interesting sidelight on the use of these Aboriginal names, particularly in the light of the above, was given by Leo Hoad (Yarrangobilly guide and later caretaker) in an interview with the present author in 1970. In relation to the naming of the Jillabenan Hoad recalled:

> *Kerry* [the renowned cave photographer of the day] *and Mr Trickett and Percy Hunter, who was Director of the Tourist Bureau, were having lunch one day and Trickett said "Hunter, you'll have to see about a name for that cave that Leo Hoad discovered". "Oh", Hunter said, I don't know, but I want a native name for it." Kerry said, "Oh, call it Jillabenan - it means a dark hole"* (Middleton 1985b).

Hardly surprising, then, that Hunter liked Trickett's 'happy inspiration' in using Aboriginal names!

[The story does not end there: the name Jillabenan had earlier been suggested for what became known as the Jersey Cave. In 1891 Anderson & Leigh had reported on 'newly discovered caves at Yarrangobilly Creek' and recommended

> *... that an aboriginal name be given to the "New Caves" .... One of the chief peculiarities of these caves is the amount of black-tinted stalagmite which covers the floors and sides. For this reason we would submit that they be known as the "Jillabenann Caves,"— "Jilla" being the words used by the Monaro tribes for black, and "benann" the word for hole or cave.* (Anderson & Leigh 1891)

This is not to say that it was not Kerry who originally put the name forward; he had been in what Anderson & Leigh reported was "the first party to follow these caves [the Jersey] to their present terminus" and had taken "numerous photographs of the interior". Since Anderson & Leigh were aware that some of these "have turned out very well" they were doubtless acquainted with Kerry. Who originally suggested the name, then, is not clear—except that it was not Mr Trickett, as Hunter implies.]

Where the Aboriginal names which Trickett applied to the Jillabenan came from is also not clear and there is no other suggestion that he actually possessed a "vast fund of native lore". Doubtless there were compilations of Aboriginal words available at the time and he simply drew on these. He was not concerned to keep to words of the local Monaro people, as he drew terms from all over NSW and acknowledged this in the text; eg 'kuttabul'—wonderful (Barwon people), 'turong'—water spirit (Illawarra), and 'kimberwalli'—star (Georges River). The names, incidentally, have not stuck, being replaced with more readily understood terms such as 'the Bath of Venus' and 'the Bottomless Pit'.

This guide is illustrated almost exclusively with Trickett's own photos, those of the Jersey and Jillabenan caves being extremely good. Two maps are included, both of which appeared first in *ARDM* 1913 (Figures 60 & 61) and a diagram of the thermal pool (or 'bath') which closely resembles that published in 1915 (Figure 62).

Jenolan Guidebook, 4th Edition

1922 saw the fourth and final edition of Trickett's Jenolan guidebook, with an increase in the price to two shillings and sixpence. The frontispiece has reverted to a black and white photo of Caves House to which, for some reason, an artist has crudely added a drawing of a car loaded with tourists. Mr J.S. Cormack, Director of the Government Tourist Bureau, contributed the introduction which commences:

> It is a glowing tribute to the author of this book, Mr Oliver Trickett, that a fourth edition of the work is necessary owing to the complete disposal of previous editions.

> The careful descriptions of what may be seen in the Jenolan Wonderland will stand through all editions just as the immutable and glittering formations of its splendid caverns will stand forever. (Cormack [in] Trickett 1922, p. 7)

There are, indeed, remarkably few changes in the text. Under 'Cave Improvements' the following is added:

> In 1917 the present power-station was erected, but fast as replacements are made, faster grows the demand for more power and light. The paths through the caves are lighted better than any city thoroughfare, and the marvellous formations which embellish the interior of the grottos, temples, chambers and caverns are brought out sometimes with dramatic effect, but at all times with a clearness overpowering and bewildering the beholder. (Trickett 1922, p. 33)

The double page multicoloured map of the caves was, for some reason not apparent, completely redrawn and not, possibly, by Trickett, for his familiar signature is replaced with "(Signed) O. Trickett L.S. M.S." The new lettering is inferior but the map appears to carry all the original information. Minor changes include the addition of the new exit from the Left Imperial (via

the Flitch of Bacon Cave), replacement of "McKeown's Creek" on the plan with "Head of Jenolan River" (though the section is still annotated "Flood or surface channel McKeown's Creek"), omission (presumably unintentional) of the letter 'J' on the plan to indicate the "Upper Entrance to Grand Archway" and alterations to reflect changes in the buildings.

About Trickett's care in writing, Bradley commented in 1970:

> The old man was very keen on being selective about his writings. When he was compiling his book on Jenolan he omitted to put in a little part in the Temple of Baal Cave. It's a little pocket only about an inch deep, and just like white enamel on the inside of it, with about 14 or 15 pebbles in it. The pebbles were about half an inch in diameter and kept smooth by dropping water. Anyhow, he'd forgotten to mention it so he wrote back to me at Jenolan and asked me if I could give him some sort of description so he could put it in with the rest of his writings. So I described it to the best of my ability and he wrote a very nice letter back, saying that he was extremely pleased with it but asking me not to let anyone know that I had assisted him in the work. (Middleton 1985a)

[This would have to refer to the 4th edition of the guidebook, since Bradley was not a guide at Jenolan until 1916, but there appears to be, in fact, no reference in the section on the Temple of Baal to the feature described.]

Acknowledgement to Printer

That Trickett was personally involved even with the printing of his guidebooks is shown by a photo and a note in his scrapbook. The photo shows Trickett, possibly after retirement, sitting with Mr W.E. Willcoxson in the backyard of Willcoxson's house in Ashfield (Figure 73). Trickett's note records:

> Mr Willcoxson, while in the Govt. Printing Office, NSW, was the Officer who was responsible for the fine way in which the maps and photos were produced in my guide books of the various caves of N.S.W.

Figure 73. W.E. Willcoxson (left), printer of Trickett's guidebooks, and Oliver Trickett.
[From an original photo in Trickett's Scrapbook]

A Tasmanian Connection

It is possible that Trickett contemplated writing more widely about Australia's caves, or he may merely have been seeking information to allow him to make more informed comparisons. Evidently Trickett wrote to the Tasmanian Government Geologist in 1917. Mr W. H. Twelvetrees replied:

Geological Survey Office,
Launceston, 18th June 1917

Dear Sir,

I have the pleasure to acknowledge receipt of your letter of the 12th instant asking for information about our limestone caves.

I am not certain what details are desired, but if they are for a guide book or of the nature of particulars such as are usually contained in guide-books, I think your best plan would be to write to Mr Emmett, the Secretary of the Government Tourist Bureau, Hobart. The caves, unlike those in New South Wales, are not under the control of the Mines Department and are outside my jurisdiction; consequently I do not know in what state they are or how far they have been developed, nor what facilities exist for visitors. The Tourist and Railways Departments cater for the visitors, and are constantly making improved arrangements for transport of passengers and accommodation, of which I am ignorant.

The caves are all I believe in a somewhat undeveloped state and most of them are on privately owned property. Baldock's caves at Mole Creek, however, are I believe vested in the control of the Northern Tasmanian Tourist Association. A letter to Mr L.S. Bruce, the Secretary of this Association, Launceston, would ensure reliable information being supplied as to these northern caves. The Ida Bay caves are on Crown Land.

I may mention that all these caves are in limestone of Silurian age; there are two groups, the northern and the southern, and they may be particularised as follows:-

Northern Group

1. The Chudleigh caves, about 60 miles from Launceston. These are known as the "wet" caves. They are on private property.

2. The Mole Creek caves, between 60 and 70 miles from Launceston. There are several in this district, viz. King Solomon's caves, Scott's caves (all on private property), and Byard's caves (vested in the Tourist association).

3. The Ulverstone caves at Gunn's plains, 16 miles south of Ulverstone; also on private property.

4. The Winkleigh caves, about 5 miles from Beaconsfield; on private property.

Southern Group

5. The Ida Bay caves, 4 to 6 miles from Southport, on land leased under the Mining Act; now vacant.

6. Junee caves, 5 miles beyond Tyenna, the terminus of the Derwent Valley line of railway (in National Park reserve).

7. Mount Field caves on Mt. Field West (Mt Humboldt). These exist on the reserve recently created for a national park.

I may mention that the only caves I have personally seen are those at Winkleigh, Gunn's Plains, Ida Bay and Junee.

The Winkleigh ones are at Flowery Gully, adjacent to the main road to Winkleigh, easily accessible by motor or carriage. Visitors have from time to time committed depredations and there is now nothing spectacular about them, but it is a good spot for pic-nics, and the caves can be followed into the body of limestone by exploratory works with a good chance of their developing into something better.

The Gunn's Plains caves are also easily accessible by excellent roads and likewise have pic-nic facilities. They are open into the limestone rock for a distance of about 3/4 mile and have lofty chambers. They have fine stalactites and blanket formations. They have not been fully explored.

Ida Bay: I have been in some of these caves but not the principal ones. They need exploratory and developmental work. Vehicles can travel along the main road to Recherche from Southport or Port Esperance to within about 4 miles of the caves, but the latter distance has to be traversed across the plains on foot or horse.

Junee: These caves are sadly in need of exploratory work. A cavity 20 feet in height forms the entrance, and the Junee River, a rapid stream, flows from it. A few stalactites still hang inside; the larger ones have been removed by visitors and others have been defaced. At about 50 feet from the entrance the subterranean river blocks further progress on foot, but it can be ascended a few chains further by means of a raft or boat. The only way to improve the cave is to open it up further by blasting down the roof in the end. The approach is highly picturesque, the banks of the stream being clothed with a luxuriant growth of tree fern and tall sombre myrtles.

Yours faithfully,
[signed] W. H. Twelvetrees
Government Geologist

Wm. [sic] Trickett, Esq.
Geological Survey of N.S.W.
Mines Department, Sydney

OTHER WORK

Plans for reports

Because of the wealth of published material available, it is easy to assume that Trickett's work, at least after 1896, mainly revolved around caves. This was probably not the case—caves were something of a sideline to his normal drafting and survey work. The following, from his papers, provides a rare glimpse into this area of his work.

GEOLOGICAL SURVEY, N. S. WALES
DEPARTMENT OF MINES & AGRICULTURE
SYDNEY, 8 March 1901

Dear Mr Trickett,

I still think that it would be advisable for you to run a theodolite traverse over those portions of the basalt-covered lead where no surveys have been made—Mr Andrews' letter refers to one break of 2 1/2 miles between old surveys and it is manifest that in view of the attraction mentioned by Mr A. it would be unsafe to traverse anything like this distance with no compass.

I should like you therefore to run a theodolite traverse wherever the old surveys are separated by any considerable distance of unmeasured country.

Yours very truly,
[signed] *Edward F. Pittman*

As part of his departmental duties Trickett worked for Professor T.W. Edgeworth David on a plan of the coalfields in the Hunter Valley. Apparently Trickett felt he was worthy of higher remuneration, and Professor Edgeworth David supported him in this:

The University of Sydney
09.05.1898

Dear Mr Trickett,

Understanding that you are applying to the Public Service Board for an increase of salary on the ground that your work comprises some of the duties of a surveyor as well as that of a 'Charting draftsman', I have much pleasure in bearing testimony to the value of your work in the field, of which I have had personal experience in connection with the map of the Coalfields in the Maitland and Newcastle District now in course of preparation by the Geological Survey and almost completed. For several years I was engaged from time to time upon the above geological map, and can speak in the highest terms of the valuable assistance you rendered me in the field in checking incorrect boundaries in some of the very old surveys and in mapping in with rapidity and precision the principal topographical features of the district which was being geologically examined.

I understand that in your capacity as Inspector of Caves you are from time to time engaged on underground and topographical survey work. Your ability as a surveyor as well as a draftsman make your services of real use and high value to the

Geological Survey, and I should be very pleased to hear of an increase of your salary being agreed to, if the Public Service Board can see its way to it.

Believe me. Yours very truly,

[signed] *T.W.E. David* Professor of Geology

Trickett later worked on other projects with Edgeworth David and they became lifelong friends.

In his introduction to Memoir 4, "Geology of the Hunter River Coal Measures, N.S.W.", David (1907), wrote:

Of my colleagues in the geological survey, I feel I owe more to Mr O. Trickett than to anyone else for the careful correlation of my many scattered notes, and the condensing of this information on to the geological maps and sections. He has, besides, constantly assisted me in the field with topographical surveys, and the running in some cases of geological boundaries. Whenever merit attaches to the finish of the geological maps and sections it is due to his skill and care as a draftsman, for he has throughout personally executed almost the whole of the drafting work. His services have been rendered in no perfunctory manner, and but for the many hours of overtime work which he has gratuitously given in the field and in the office, and the enthusiastic way in which he has laboured to reconcile apparently contradictory evidence, and to reduce it to a consistent whole, the information could not have been placed before the public except after further delay of some years.

The map which accompanied this report *(Geological map of the Hunter River Coal Field)* is of particular interest as it acknowledged Trickett's role in the geological fieldwork (rather than just the drafting). The 'credits' state: *Geologically surveyed by T.W.E. David, B.A., F.R.S., F.G.S., assisted by O. Trickett, L.S., G. A. Stonier, A.R.S.M., F.G.S., J.E. Carne, F.G.S., P.T. Hammond and W.S. Dun.*

Regarding Trickett's contribution to plans used in *Geological Survey Memoir 3*, J. E. Carne (1903) wrote:

The geological maps and sections have been most carefully prepared for photo-lithography by Mr O. Trickett, L.S., Draftsman to the Survey, to whom hearty thanks are due for zealous and valuable aid during the progress of the work. Mr Trickett is to be especially commended for rapidity of execution no less than for the artistic effort of his work." (p. xiv)

Likewise, in the introduction to *Mineral Resources* No. 14 (1911), Carne acknowledged:

To Mr O. Trickett, L.S., Draftsman to the Geological Survey, the writer is as usual, indebted for the preparation of the maps and sections, which exhibit his customary skill and care. In Mr Trickett, the Survey is fortunate in possessing a worker whose interest is not centred merely in artistic drafting, but in the adequate illustration of the geological features and correlation of mining details. (p. 3)

And in 1914 E.F. Pittman recorded, in the Annual Report of the Government Geologist:

> *The most important publication completed during the year was the new edition of the geological map of the State on a scale of 16 miles to an inch ... The new material was marshalled and drafted by Mr O. Trickett, L.S., who has long been utilising every available source of information with this end in view. The completed map is a record of his skill and patience.* (p. 182)

PLANS FOR CARNE & JONES (1919)

In 1919 the Geological Survey published a comprehensive survey of the limestone deposits of New South Wales, or at least all those known "within reasonable distance of rail and water carriage" (Carne and Jones 1919). Trickett was the obvious man to provide the necessary maps and, as Carne mentioned in his 1918 report, had been engaged in preparing "plans of cave limestones from his survey".

The Limestone Deposits of N.S.W. was a very significant work for its day and the maps were generally printed in two colours. There were 31 maps and Trickett seems to have prepared 28 of them. Only one, "Sketch shewing position of caves south of Braidwood" (facing p. 218) was taken directly from earlier published work (Figure 42 with the title changed). The plans are of two distinct types: those obviously drawn by Trickett, such as the Braidwood plan mentioned above, and those of Jenolan (Figure 74), Yarrangobilly (Figure 75) and Wombeyan (Figure 76), the latter two of which are actually signed by Trickett, and those that may have been drawn under his supervision, such as the limestone deposits in the Burrinjuck area (Figure 77), limestone deposits west of Kempsey (Figure 78), in the Marulan area (Figure 79) and those south of Cargo (Figure 80). These latter maps are much more formal-looking than those first listed above, which may be explained by their having been drawn by another draftsman (although only Trickett is acknowledged in the text). The fact that they are unsigned lends support to the view that they were not done by Trickett, though presumably under his supervision.

Trickett's maps, including those in Carne and Jones, have been invaluable in guiding speleologists to caves and to areas where they would be likely to find caves— usually. An exception was Henry Shannon in 1973:

> *My attempt to find a new Jenolan system foundered. I have long been intrigued by the words "limestone hereabouts" on Trickett's map of the Jenolan Limestone* [see NE corner of Figure 74]. *On the air photos there are bouldery outcrops in about the right place and the slate outcrop along the road looks very like the purple slate that overlies the limestone. However, the boulder outcrop is intrusive porphyry except for one area of conglomerate. I suspect the conglomerate occupies the stratigraphic horizon of the limestone* (Shannon 1973).

The book also contains numerous photographic illustrations of which eight were attributed to Trickett:

Limestone cliffs over Chalk Cave, Bungonia

Bedded Limestone above the "Look Down", Bungonia Creek

Cliff scene on track to Caves, Yarrangobilly

Entrance in Limestone Cliff to Glory Hole Caves, Yarrangobilly [Figure 81]

Gorge Track and Limestone Cliffs, Yarrangobilly [similar to Figure 87, but without the people]

Limestone Cliff over Grove Creek Archway, Abercrombie Creek

Anticlinal fold over Water Cave, Wellington [Figure 82]

Basin Formation, Wombeyan Caves

Figure 82. "Anticlinal fold over Water Cave, Wellington" [Photo by Trickett from *the Limestone Deposits of NSW*, opp. p. 340; also published in guidebook, *The Wellington Caves*, p. 5]

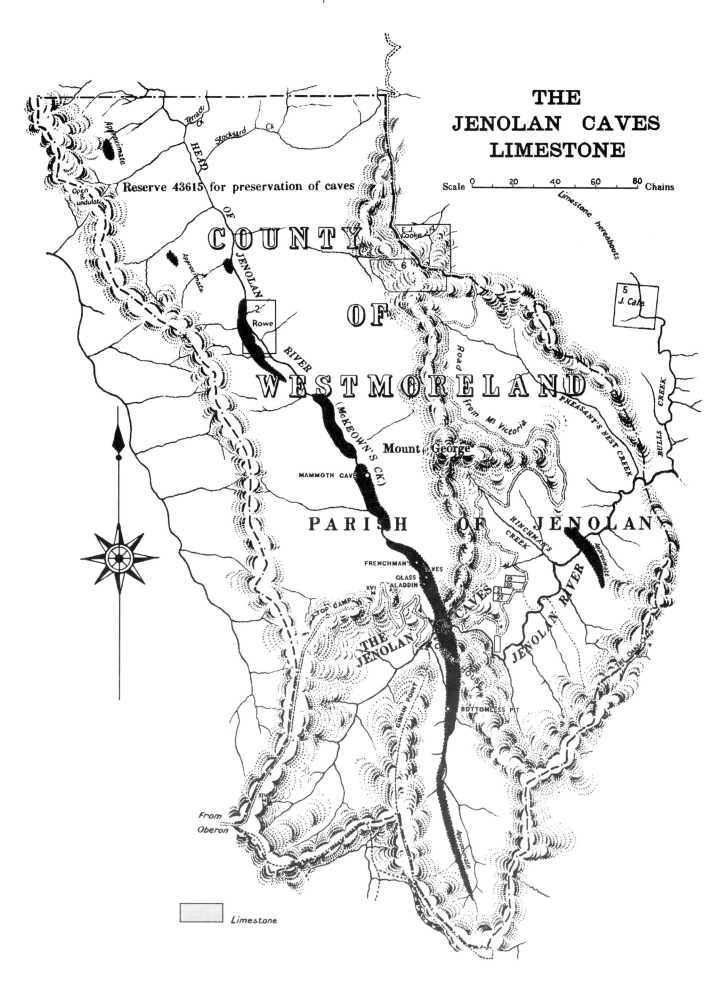

Figure 74. The Jenolan Caves Limestone
(from *The Limestone Deposits of NSW*, 1919, opposite p. 347)

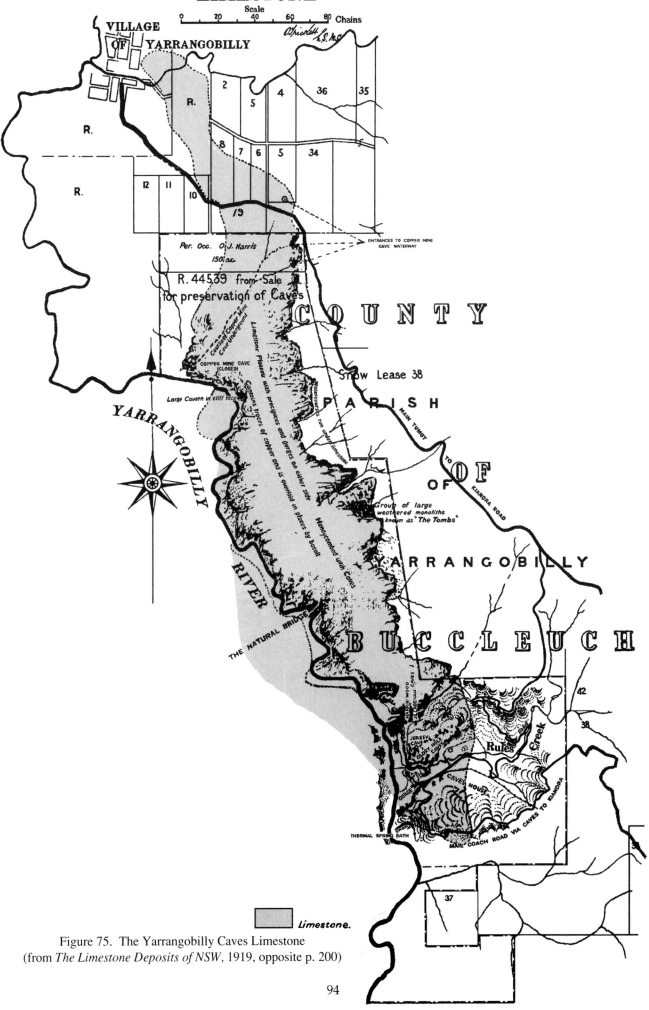

Figure 75. The Yarrangobilly Caves Limestone
(from *The Limestone Deposits of NSW*, 1919, opposite p. 200)

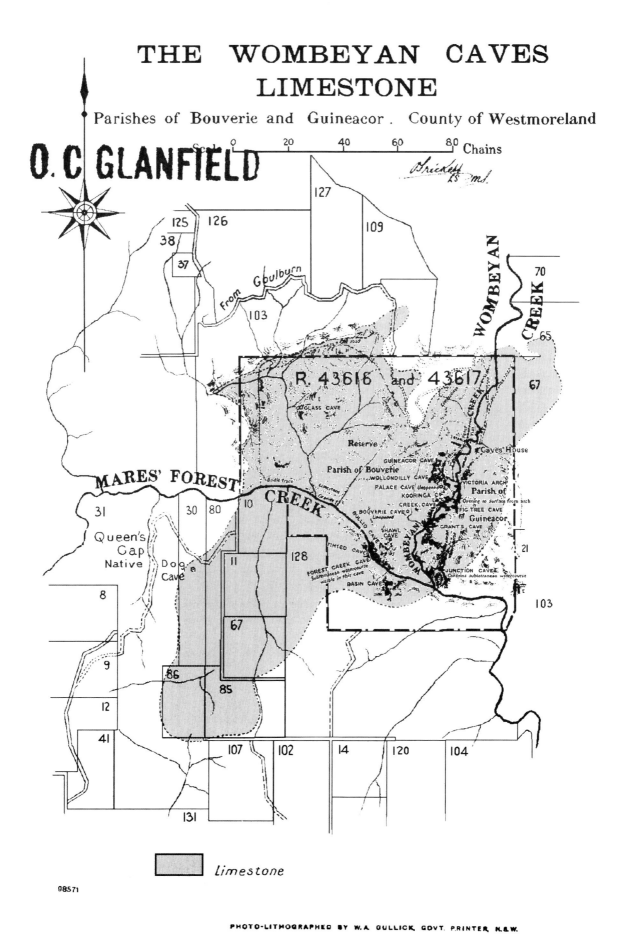

THE WOMBEYAN CAVES LIMESTONE

Parishes of Bouverie and Guineacor. County of Westmoreland

Figure 76. The Wombeyan Caves Limestone
[Slightly enlarged from *The Limestone Deposits of NSW*, opposite p. 344]
[From a copy of the book given to the author by Oliver Glanfield, hence the stamp]

95

Figure 77. Plan of the Limestone Deposits in the Burrinjuck Reservoir Area
(slightly reduced from *The Limestone Deposits of NSW*, 1919, opposite p. 209)

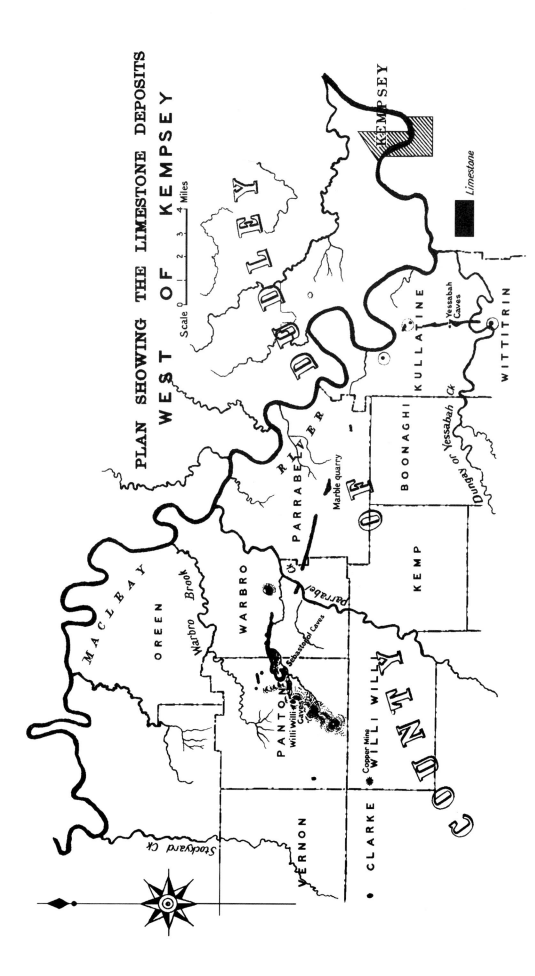

Figure 78. Plan showing the Limestone Deposits West of Kempsey
(from *The Limestone Deposits of NSW*, 1919, opposite p. 222)

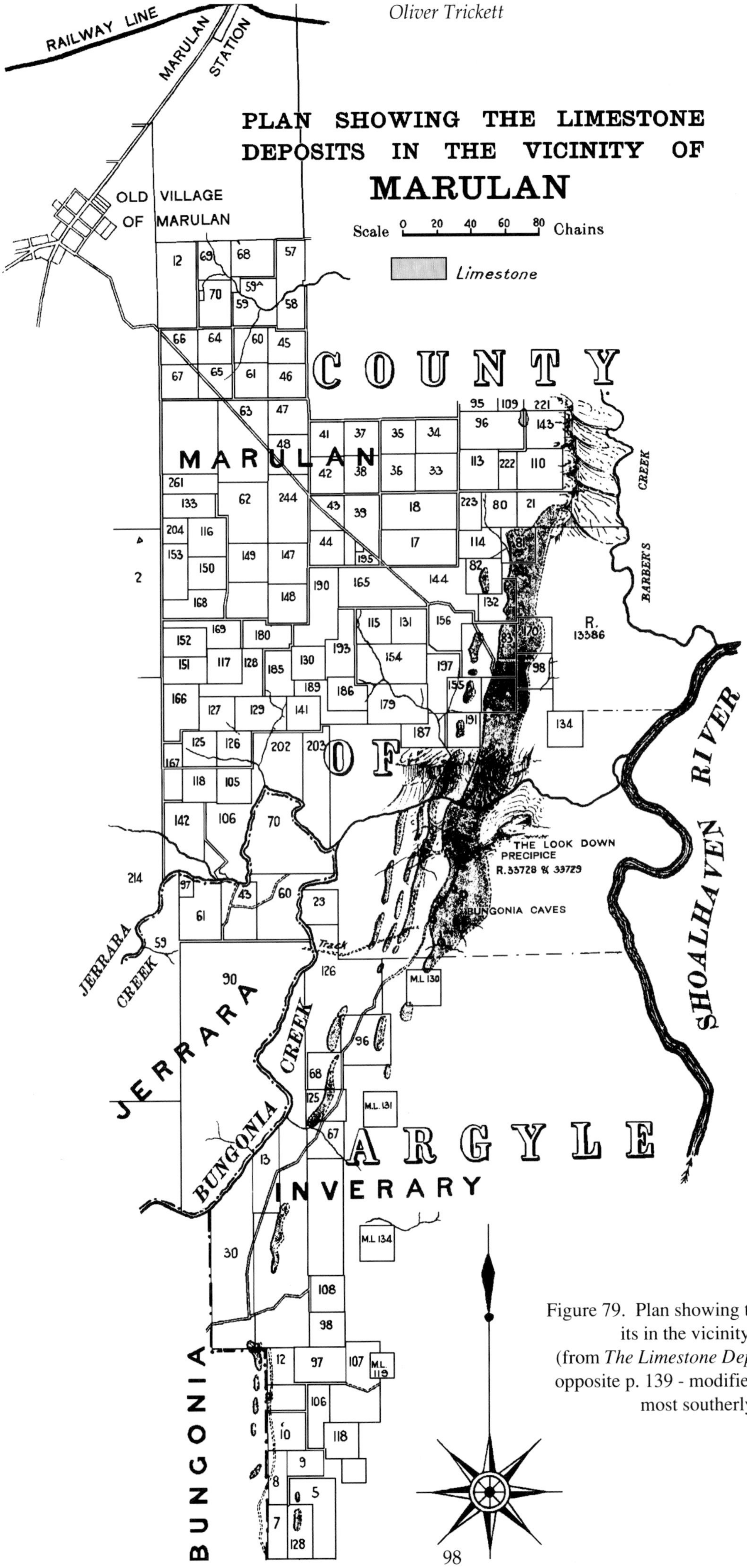

Oliver Trickett

PLAN SHOWING THE LIMESTONE
DEPOSITS IN THE VICINITY OF
MARULAN

Scale 0 20 40 60 80 Chains

Limestone

OLD VILLAGE
OF MARULAN

RAILWAY LINE

MARULAN STATION

COUNTY

MARULAN

OF

JERRARA CREEK

BUNGONIA CREEK

JERRARA

BUNGONIA

ARGYLE

INVERARY

BARBER'S CREEK

SHOALHAVEN RIVER

R. 13386

THE LOOK DOWN
PRECIPICE
R. 33728 & 33729

BUNGONIA CAVES

M.L 130

M.L 131

M.L 134

M.L 119

Figure 79. Plan showing the Limestone Deposits in the vicinity of Marulan
(from *The Limestone Deposits of NSW*, 1919,
opposite p. 139 - modified by omission of the
most southerly portion)

98

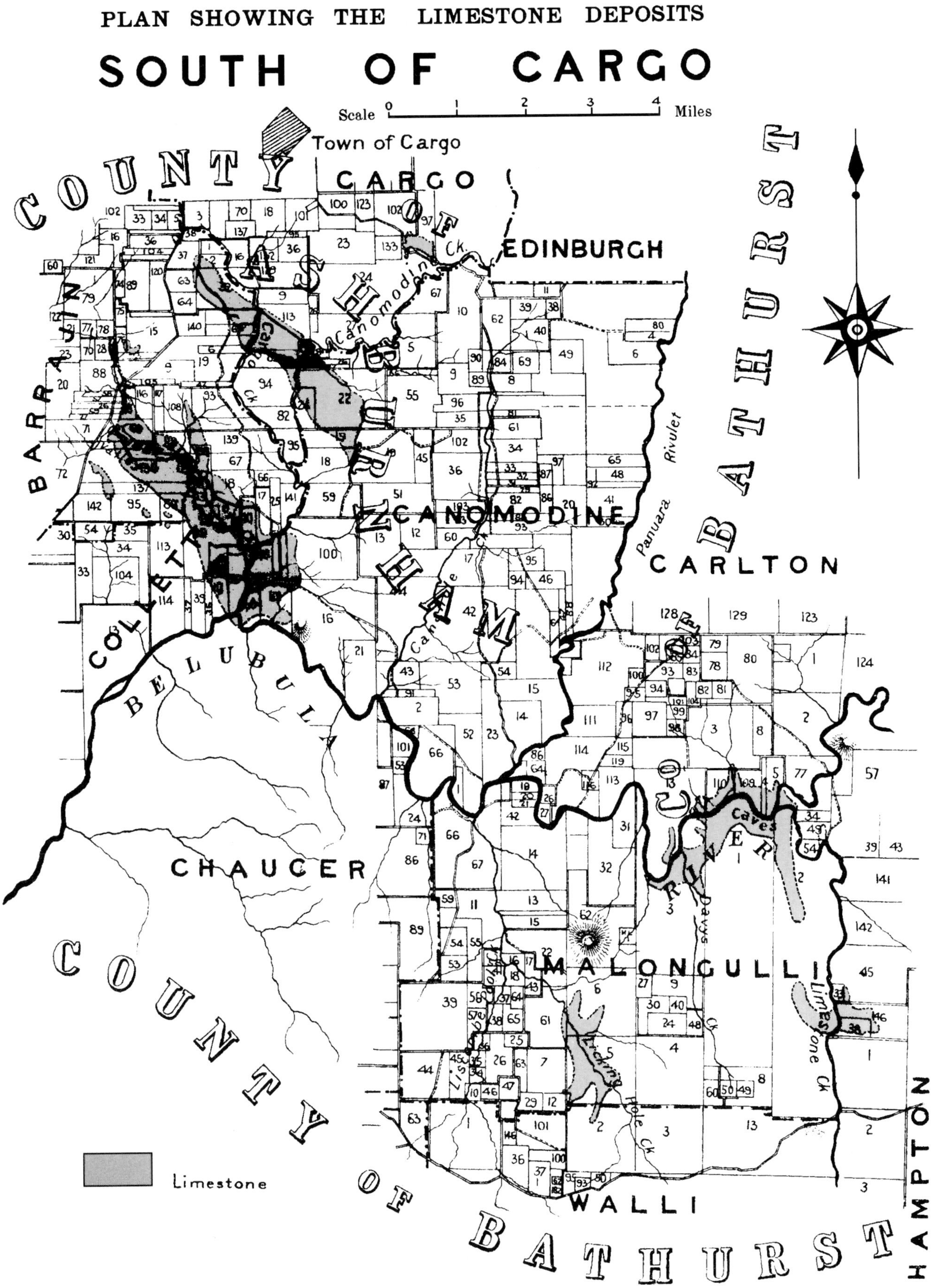

PLAN SHOWING THE LIMESTONE DEPOSITS

SOUTH OF CARGO

Figure 80. Plan showing the Limestone Deposits South of Cargo
(from *The Limestone Deposits of NSW*, 1919, opposite p. 163)

Figure 81. "Entrances in limestone cliff to Glory Hole Caves, Yarrangobilly"
[photo by Trickett from *The Limestone Deposits of NSW,* opp. p. 199]

BLUE MOUNTAINS MAPS

Trickett prepared at least three maps of the Blue Mountains. As Pittman (1908) reported:

In addition to current work for the Geological Branch, Mr Trickett produced during his own time an exceedingly good topographical map of the Blue Mountains, which is being reproduced as a geological map and, to a larger scale, as a topographical map. It is confidently believed that this map will be much appreciated by tourists.

Both versions were published in 1909, and covered the area Lawson to Lithgow. One, employing bright colours, showed topography and geology, at a scale of 1 inch to 1 mile (1:63,360) (dimensions 40 x 63 cm); it is reproduced in reduced form as Figure 83. On the reverse were printed detailed notes on the various attractions of the mountains of interest to tourists, notably, of course, Jenolan Caves. The other version was simplified to show only the topography and was published in fewer colours, at a smaller scale approximating 7/8ths inch to 1 mile (31.5 x 56 cm). Both maps included inserts depicting Caves House at Jenolan.

A third map of a somewhat larger area (Glenbrook to Lithgow) was completely different in its style and presentation, using much more sombre colours and relying on hill shading (hachures) to show relief. It is undated, but was printed by Alfred James Kent, who was Government Printer from 1923 to 1936, so must have been published in that period. It is reproduced, somewhat reduced, as Figure 84.

The original maps were regarded as very innovative for their day; they were widely distributed and attracted considerable critical acclaim. The following item appeared in *The Daily Telegraph* of 10 June 1910:

APPRECIATED ABROAD

The fine topographical map of the Blue Mountains, prepared by Mr Oliver Trickett, of the Mines Department, for the Government Tourist Bureau, which has proved so popular throughout Australia, has attracted favourable notice abroad. By the last American mail a letter came from Dr G.K. Gilbert, of the United States Geological Survey, containing a warm appreciation of the map.

The letter is then quoted. The original, in Trickett's papers, reads:

1919 16th St.
Washington City USA
March 8, 1910

Dear Mr Trickett,

I write to thank you for the map of the Blue Mountains. The notation for the relief is essentially novel and eminently successful. I doubt if any other map presents so vividly the relation of the physical forms to the geologic structure, and for a certain class of subjects your method can be followed with great advantage. I shall bring it to the attention of some of my colleagues whose work is likely to fall within its range of usefulness.

Very truly yours
[signed] *G. K. Gilbert*

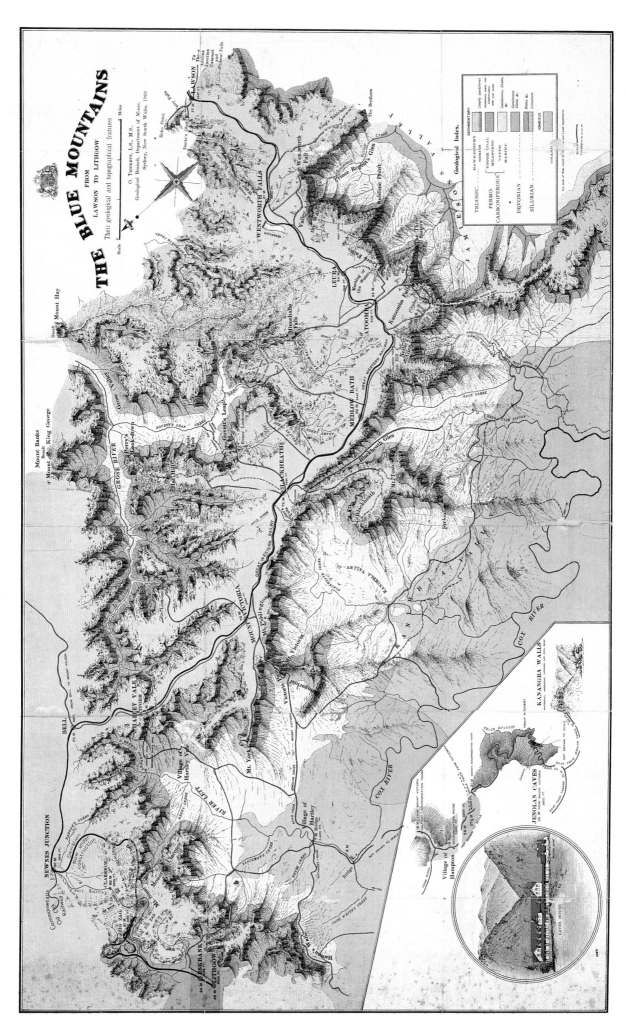

Figure 83. The Blue Mountains from Lawson to Lithgow, 1909 (reduced)

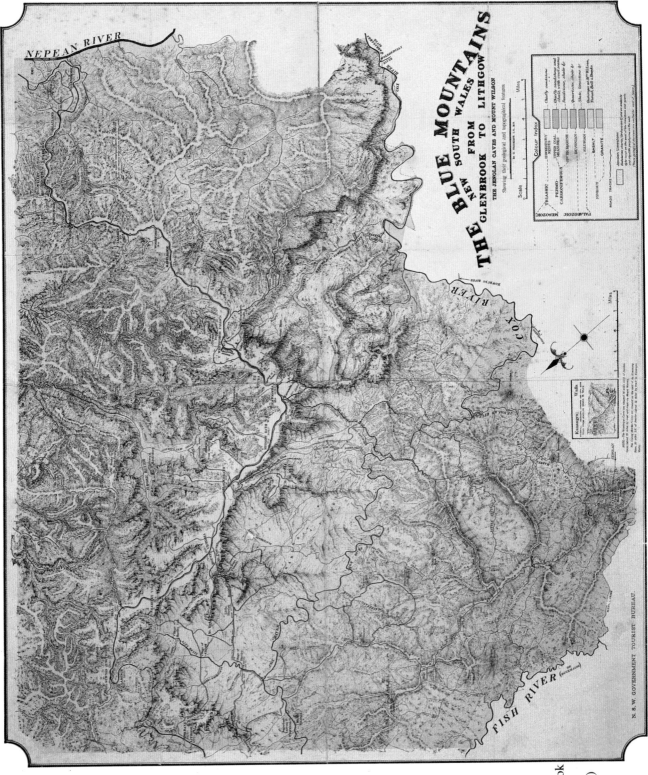

Figure 84. The Blue Mountains from Glenbrook to Lithgow (published between 1923 and 1936) (reduced)

On 8 October 1920 the Director of the Tourist Bureau, Mr E.H. Palmer, wrote, regarding Trickett's work:

> *No less an authority than Sir Ross Smith stated that the Blue [Mountains] map was the finest thing of its type he had ever seen for the use of aviation.*

Even as late as January 1933, Erwin Raisz, Instructor in Cartography at Harvard University, wrote to the Geological Survey seeking a copy of Trickett's map "showing the geology and a bird's-eye view of the Blue Mtns.". Having been sent a copy, Raisz responded:

> *Harvard University*
> *Institute of Geographical Exploration*
> *Cambridge, Massachusetts*
> *September 19, 1933*
>
> *Dear Mr Trickett,*
>
> *I think this map is a very important endeavour in physiographic drawing which method I am advocating in general maps of small scale. ... I agree with you perfectly that draughtsmen do not, as a rule, give sufficient prominence to physiographic features and I am in the hope that the method that you so successfully initiated will be a great help in this matter.*
>
> *Very truly yours*
> *Erwin Raisz*
> *Instructor in Cartography*

The map appears to have been reprinted a number of times but Trickett noted in his scrapbook: "State Railway Dept. wished to reproduce the map in 1933 publication - expressed disappointment that the block had been destroyed."

PHOTOGRAPHS AND POST CARDS

As noted in relation to the various cave guidebooks, Trickett was an accomplished photographer, at least as early as 1905 (when his own photos first appeared in the second edition of the Jenolan guidebook). It is not clear whether he received any payment for the photos used in the official guides (presumably he took the photos in work time), but he also had a small business going "on the side" publishing photographic postcards.

In his text to accompany an exhibit on *Australian Caves and Government*, featuring Australian cave post cards, Elery Hamilton-Smith (n.d.) noted:

> *Caves Superintendent Oliver Trickett was a fine photographer with unique opportunity for taking pictures of caves throughout N.S.W. However, he was probably prohibited, because of his position, from publishing them himself, so Kerry published for him.* (p. 7)

This may explain why a number of photos on cards published by Kerry appear to be Trickett's work and why the only recognition, when there is any, is a small "O.T." on some cards. Although Kerry is regarded as the authority on cave photography of that time, Hamilton-Smith (pers. comm.) suggests that Trickett was, in fact, more skilled at lighting his cave studies. An outstanding example is his photo of the Grand

Column in the Lucas Cave, Jenolan (Figure 85). The angle and strength of the side lighting gives real depth and contrast to this picture.

Figure 85. "The Grand Column", Lucas Cave, Jenolan [From *Guide to the Jenolan Caves*, 3rd Edn., 1915, p. 4]

Trickett's first post card was probably published in 1907; it featured his favourite cave scene, King Solomons Temple in the Castle Cave, Yarrangobilly (as Figure 69) (Ellis, Hamilton-Smith & Shaw, in prep.) He also produced a series of cards, all featuring scenes at Yarrangobilly, which were actual photographic prints, in about 1910. In about 1913 Charles Kerry produced a further series of cards using Trickett's photographs; they were printed in Germany. Kerry also published at least three of Trickett's Jenolan photographs as post cards. These featured The White Temple, Great Shawl, the Grand Column and the Grand Stalagmite, River Cave. Ellis, Hamilton-Smith & Shaw (in prep.) have deduced from two almost identical versions of the latter that Trickett and Kerry worked side-by-side to produce some of their photos.

The following are details of the known Trickett post cards of Yarrangobilly, as identified by Ellis, Hamilton-Smith & Shaw (in prep.):

"Graphic" Series (about 1907)

Published by Collins Bros. & Co., Great Britain
Printed in bluish-green with title in lower margin
  "King Solomons Temple," Yarrangobilly Caves, N.S.W. (as Figure 69)
  Mammoth Stalactites, Yarrangobilly, N.S.W.

Figure 86. An "O.T." photographic post card: Titanias Bower, Jersey Cave, Yarrangobilly

Figure 87. Trickett's photo post card of Bradley's path to the Glory Hole Cave, Yarrangobilly

Actual Photographic Prints (about 1910)

Presumably produced by Trickett himself
Photos have title, number and "O.T." superimposed
on print
   Flower Crystals, Jersey Cave, Yarrangobilly (#1)
   King Solomons Temple, Yarrangobilly (#8)
   Yarrangobilly Village (#22)
   Aladdin Cave, Yarrangobilly (#24)
   Indian Bower, Yarrangobilly (#25)
   Jack Frosts Hall, Yarrangobilly (#27)
   Titanias Bower, Jersey Cave, Yarrangobilly (#28)
    (Figure 86)
   Grotto, Jersey Cave, Yarrangobilly (#29)
   Wedding Cake, Yarrangobilly (#31)
   [Temple of a Thousand Idols, Harrie Wood Cave]
    (#32)
   Glory Hole Path, Yarrangobilly (#34) (Figure
    87)
   Glory Hole Path, Yarrangobilly (#36)
   The Burmese Temple, Yarrangobilly (?)

Kerry "Series 102 O.T." (about 1913)

Published by Kerry & Co. (though not identified on
   cards)
Printed in Germany by collotype
   Titanias Bower, Jersey Cave, Yarrangobilly
   Cathedral Ruins, Yarrangobilly
   Jersey Cave, Yarrangobilly
   King Solomons Temple, Yarrangobilly
   Temple of the Thousand Idols, Yarrangobilly

Whether Trickett made much profit from these post cards and how long they were on sale is not clear. There is no reference to them in his personal papers and, perhaps surprisingly, no copies of any of them.

Ellis, Hamilton-Smith and Shaw are continuing their studies of cave post cards and photos, and will no doubt identify more of Trickett's work in this field.

TRICKETT'S CAVE SURV-EYING TECHNIQUES AND THE ACCURACY OF HIS PLANS

We know little of the precise techniques used by Trickett to carry out his cave surveys and to prepare the resulting maps. It is clear, however, that he was a well-trained and experienced mining surveyor and had at his disposal the necessary equipment to carry out high grade surface and underground surveys. However, at least initially he had to make do with simple methods. In his second report (1896) he wrote:

> *I have commenced to define these channels, with the assistance of Mr Harper, Field Assistant, by making a compass survey of part of the Jenolan Caves, as indicated on plans herewith.*

> *I would have preferred to make a theodolite survey, to avoid errors of magnetic variation arising from the presence of the protecting ironwork and netting, but I should have required more time than I had at my disposal, and extra assistance.* [Trickett 1897a]

No doubt he preferred to use a theodolite, at least for major traverses, and he certainly went out of his way to give the impression that this was his usual practice, as a photo in the 2nd and later editions of the Jenolan guidebook attests (Figure 88).

Figure 88. "Surveying in caves" - a composite supposedly showing Trickett "at work"
[From *Guide to Jenolan Caves*, 2nd Edition, 1905, p. 22]

It doesn't require very close inspection of this photo to reveal that it has been 'manufactured' by superimposing a studio photo of Trickett with a theodolite (reproduced on the cover of this biography) on a suitable photo of a cave passage. As the studio photo of Trickett had been taken by Kerry, it seems likely that he would have made the montage.

Regarding Trickett's surveying at Yarrangobilly, Anthony Bradley confirmed that he used a theodolite. In 1970 he described: "I used to go ahead of him [Trickett] with a light and I'd hold the light while he pinpointed it, and measure the distance" (Middleton 1985a).

In the *ARDM* for 1915 Trickett illustrated his adaptation of the plane table for underground surveys (Figure 63) and in 1929 he delivered a short paper to the Institution of Surveyors, NSW, apparently on this instrument. The Scrapbook contains a typescript of this paper and it appears unlikely that it has been published. The official notice of the meeting (25 June 1929) advised that —

> *O. Trickett, Esq. will deliver a few remarks on his method of Caves Surveys*

The text of the paper read as follows:

AN INSTRUMENT FOR USE IN RAPID UNDERGROUND SURVEYS

> *The instrument I exhibit is simply an adaptation of the plane table but one which has the merit of giving results which closely approximate those of a Theodolite when applied to underground tortuous passages such as those of the Limestone Caves and the rapid delineation not only of direction but of the boundaries of those passages and of stopes in mines for which there is little space in a Surveyors field book.*

> *Its use on the surface would be limitated [sic] to the supply of details in congested areas[.] [F]or the angles of elevation or depression the use of a clinometer is added.*

> *When the horizontal distances are recorded each sheet one foot in diameter at the base of the table will contain a direct plotting of the area it represents in one tenth of the time a theodolite survey would take.*

> *Back and fore sights are carefully noted so that each succeeding sheet may be accurately fitted to the last as the traverse progresses.*

> *The comparative accuracy of this method of survey may be demonstrated by my survey of the Jenolan Caves in which 350 of the sheets were used. Several short spaces between Caverns were indicated and subsequently verified by cuttings rendering access easier.*

> *The plan showed that the return by Visitors of passages embracing some 170 steps from the Orient Cave could be avoided by excavating a tunnel which would give an easy graded pathway to near the Caves House. Owing to the expense of such an undertaking, i.e. 379 ft tunnel, the Surveyor (E. J. [W.L.?] Cooke) was authorised to determine the position of the tunnel by a theodolite traverse. The result (Figure 57, p. 72; see also p. 68) showed that the difference of level between the two surveys at their termination was nominal.*

Had I not designed the method of survey above described I should have had to depend entirely on compass bearings. The time at my disposal was strictly limited owing to the dual duties as an Officer of the Geological Branch of the Mines Department and as Superintendent of the Cave Systems of New South Wales.

On 15 September 1930 Trickett sent a copy of his map of Jenolan Caves to Oliver C. Farrington, Curator of Geology at the Field Museum of Natural History, Chicago. In an accompanying letter (a copy of which is among his papers) he wrote:

South of the Grand Archway the plan represents the result of survey by theodolite and level - North of the Archway a combined result of surveys by theodolite and level and the instrument of which I enclose a print [presumably Figure 63-GM]. Underground the latter gives results very nearly approximate to those of theodolite and level in some-thing like one tenth of the time or less, especially where narrow and tortuous channels are met with - both in survey and plan - and the surveyor can use untrained assistance. Otherwise, owing to the expense, I don't suppose that the plans of Jenolan, Wombeyan and Yarrangobilly, etc. caves systems would have been available to the public to the present day.

I think it will be evident that the method of survey which I have endeavoured to illustrate gives a direct and satisfactory representation of cave contours in a minimum of time and therefore of economy and in that respect may be of interest to you.

Assuming that the map referred to was Trickett's compilation published in 1925 (included in a pocket at rear), we have here a clear indication of the equipment used to carry out the surveys for this particular map.

The tunnel dug between two close sections of the Lucas Cave in 1900 to reduce the length of the return trip was, as described above in relation to the 1900 *ARDM* reports, made possible by a survey of Trickett's. Havard (1934) saw the success of this hole as proof of the accuracy of Trickett's surveys:

In 1900, there was considerable advance in making the caves more convenient for inspection. The accuracy of Trickett's work was shown when a drill hole, made where his survey indicated, showed two chambers about ten feet apart at the end of the cavern near the 'Crystal Fountain' in the Lucas Cave. This proved that a short outlet to the 'Balcony' was possible, obviating a return through the Lucas Cave. This improvement was completed in 1901. (Havard 1934)

And there was public acclaim for the feat. The *Daily Telegraph* of 23 May 1900 reported:

The accuracy of the survey of the caves made by Mr Trickett, of the Mines Department, and published in the Government Guide Book, has been demonstrated by Mr Caretaker Wilson. The Lucas cave survey showed two of the chambers coming within 12 ft of each other, and on the same level a hole was put through by

the aid of a drill, which came out in the middle of the other chamber through solid rock. When sufficiently opened for traffic this opening will be the means of making the Lucas Cave much easier to see. ...

Inspection of Trickett's map (Figure 44) shows that the distance which Trickett would have had to survey between the two points in order to discover their proximity is about 130 metres. It was therefore no great surveying feat to determine that they were just over 3 metres apart. Havard, however, commented:

Trickett's surveys, plans and models—wonderfully accurate—have contributed greatly to the successful development of the caves of New South Wales. (Havard 1934)

It is not clear whether Havard had any basis other than the 1900 survey for claiming 'wonderful accuracy'; he was not a surveyor and was probably not in a position to judge personally.

On the accuracy of Trickett's surveys, the 1967 *Handbook for Caves Guiding Staff* says:

Oliver Trickett, L.S., M.S., Superintendent of Caves in N.S.W. [he never had that title -GM], whose "plans have never since required amending", surveyed and modelled the new discoveries (p. 12).

Unfortunately the source of the quote is not cited.

Well known speleologist, Henry Shannon, has expressed the view —

nothing that was an improvement on Trickett appeared before I left Sydney in 1963, as far as surface was concerned. His underground mapping was aesthetically good, but overgeneralised as far as true depiction of passage shape was concerned. But again, nothing better was produced 'till the 60s, and still his portrayal of Jenolan gives a better 'feel' for the marvels of nature aspect than a modern style map. (pers. comm. 1989)

The high quality and great accuracy of Trickett's surveys became legendary in his own lifetime. Yet, apart from the fact that a couple of short tunnels designed by Trickett had broken through where expected, and that the finished maps have a neat and professional appearance, the legend appears to be based on little 'hard data'. As far as the writer is aware, apart from the one survey by Cooke, cited by Trickett (above) as showing the accuracy of his surveys, no one has deliberately set out to check the accuracy of any of Trickett's cave survey work.

The opportunity to do this systematically appears to be now at hand. A project to carry out a complete, high-grade survey of the main cave system at Jenolan is being undertaken under the auspices of the Jenolan Scientific Advisory Committee. Of Trickett's work the principals have written:

The first surveying in the Jenolan Cave system was by Oliver Trickett in 1897 and 1898. The published result (Trickett 1899d- Figure 67, lower) was a simplified plan and section of the main passages, which adequately represented the caves for the visitors and showed the relationship between the caves and the surface topography. From these surveys Trickett constructed an excellent three dimensional model of the caves which can be viewed in the Resource Centre at Jenolan Caves. Both the model and the "compass" surveys were incomplete and inadequate for scientific studies and cave development planning. (James, Martin & Tunnock 1988)

Unhappily, the results of this work have not become available in time to compare them with Trickett's and include here a rigorous assessment of the accuracy of Trickett's Jenolan plans. Hopefully this will soon be able to be done.

CAVE AND MINE MODELS

It seems logical that Trickett's interests in surveying and preparing maps of caves, together with his enthusiasm for increasing public understanding of them, should progress to preparing 'three dimensional maps'—models. His first model seems to have been of the Lucas Cave at Jenolan. It appears not to be mentioned in the official records, but the *Sydney Morning Herald* of 13 April 1906 carried the following small item:

> *Lucas Cave.—A model by Mr O. Trickett, L.S., showing the position of the recently-discovered branches of the Lucas Cave, at Jenolan, has been placed for public inspection in the Mining Museum, the Domain. These branches add something like half a mile of richly-decorated passages to the previously known caverns of the Jenolan wonderland and include novel features, such as conveyance in a punt over an underground pool, and in the floor of one of the caverns there are the remains of an aboriginal.*

His first officially-recognised model seems to have been of the Broken Hill Lode. Pittman (1909) recorded:

> *In response to a request for advice as to the best method of prospecting for a continuation of the deposits of ore in the Broken Hill Mines, it was decided to make a further examination of the workings of the big lode, and, as a preliminary, it was thought advisable to prepare a model of the ore deposit which has so far been disclosed by mining operations. With the consent and assistance of the various mine managers, copies of all the plans and sections of the mine workings were accordingly made by Mr Oliver Trickett, and from the information thus obtained, he has constructed as complete a model of the lode as possible on a scale of 100 feet to the inch. It is believed that this will be the source of useful information to persons interested in mining, and will enable the origin of the deposit and its possible extensions to be more clearly understood.* [p. 176]

Later in the same report Pittman added [p. 191]:

> *Towards the end of June* [1909], *he* [Trickett] *visited Broken Hill and obtained complete plans of the underground workings of the various mines; the Mining Managers and Inspectors of Mines are thanked for the cordial way in which they assisted him in the work. From the material thus obtained Mr Trickett has, as already mentioned, constructed a model of the Broken Hill Lode for exhibition in the Mining Museum.*

On 9 February 1911 W.E. Wainwright, the Honorary Secretary of the Broken Hill Mine Managers' Association, wrote to Trickett at the Geological Branch, advising —

> *that the model has been opened up, and found to have travelled in a very satisfactory manner. The members of my Association are very pleased with it and have voted you an additional £15 in connection therewith.*

This model appears not to be referred to in the official records. Evidently Trickett built it in his own time and was paid for it by the Mine Managers' Association.

It appears that Trickett's work as a model-maker was sufficiently highly regarded and his models of such interest that the Australasian Institute of Mining Engineers was prepared to publish a paper by him on the subject in its proceedings (Trickett 1912b). In this he pointed out the value of models of mines, not only to engineers, but to shareholders in a mine; he described the types of models: solid glass, solid wood, concrete, glass and skeleton forms and the methods he used, particularly to make the model of the Broken Hill silver lode. This was based on some 300 plans and sections and showed the lode for three miles. It was built at scale of 100 ft to 1 inch (1:1200), giving a length of 14 ft (4.3 m). He described in detail the steps used in its construction. Unhappily the paper says very little about cave models. In fact there is but one paragraph:

CAVE MODEL.

Plaster of Paris forms the floor of the larger caverns (See Plate VI). Covered wire was used for the pathways, even in the passages through which it is only possible to crawl. Perpendicular pieces of cardboard indicate the height of some of the caverns. This model was produced from surveys made by the writer to determine the form and extent of the Jenolan Caves. (Trickett 1912b)

The plate referred to is reproduced as Figure 89. A further plate from the paper (IV), showing stages in construction of the Broken Hill lode model is included as Figure 90. The fact that this model was built in Trickett's backyard is demonstrated by a photo from his scrapbook (Figure 91) which shows the larger picture, including the clothesline, fence and roof of the house next door!

In his report for 1914, Pittman recorded:

Mr O. Trickett, by direction of the Honorable the Premier, constructed a large model of the Broken Hill Silver-lead-zinc lode, embodying all the latest developments, for the Australian Pavilion at the Panama-Pacific Exposition, to be opened in February, 1915. On completion of this work he brought the model in the Mining and Geological Museum up to date. (p. 182)

Later in the *ARDM* for 1914 Trickett, himself, wrote:

In addition to the preparation of detail geological and mining maps, I completed the compilation of the geological map of the State, constructed a model of the Broken Hill silver lode, for the Panama Exposition, and brought up to date a model of this lode, which is on exhibition at the Mining Museum. An illustration of the model is attached. [Figure 92] (p. 212)

The following year, Carne (1915) was able to report:

The model of the Broken Hill lode, prepared by Mr Trickett for the Panama-Pacific Exposition by direction of the Premier, was awarded a gold medal, and another model is now being prepared by approval, which the Sulphide Corporation will present to the Museum of Technology, Melbourne.

The gold medal is illustrated in Figure 93.

Carne also make the first official reference to Trickett making a cave model (though the article cited above shows he had made one at least as early as 1906):

With the assistance of Mr J.C. Wiburd, Mr Trickett made a survey of the Orient Cave, Jenolan, and has partly constructed a model from the survey. (Carne 1915)

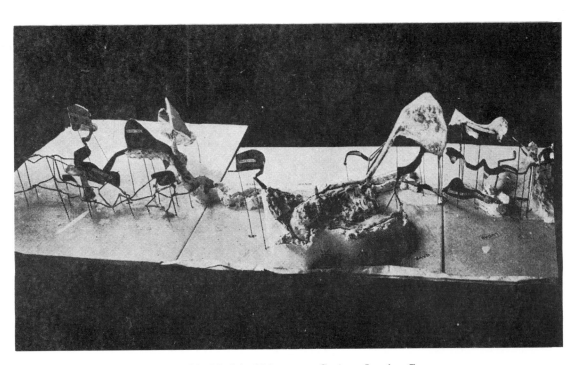

Figure 89. Model of Limestone Cave — Jenolan Caves
[From Trickett 1912b, Plate VI]

FIG. 1.

Skeleton formed of Cross Sections.

FIG. 2.

Skeleton formed of Cross Sections and Floor Levels.

Figure 90. Stages in construction of the Broken Hill lode model (illustrations from Trickett 1912b)

Part of Complete Model.

(Embraces Skeleton shown in Pl. IV., fig. 1.)

Figure 91. Early stage of Broken Hill model photographed in Trickett's backyard. [From a photo in the Trickett papers.]

Figure 93. Gold medal awarded to Trickett at the 1915 Panama-Pacific Exposition for his model of the Broken Hill lode. [From a photo in the Trickett papers]

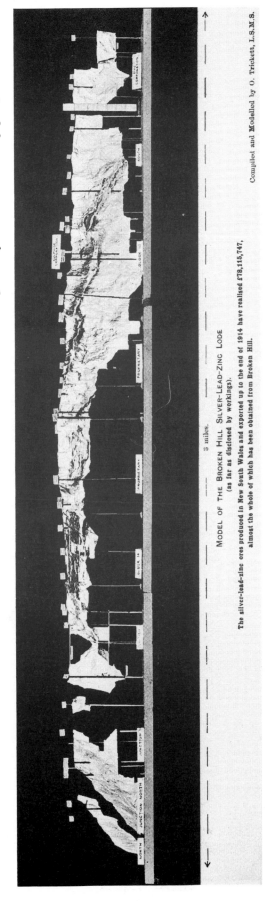

Compiled and Modelled by O. Trickett, L.S.M.S.

3 miles.

MODEL OF THE BROKEN HILL SILVER-LEAD-ZINC LODE
(as far as disclosed by workings).

The silver-lead-zinc ores produced in New South Wales and exported up to the end of 1914 have realised £78,115,747, almost the whole of which has been obtained from Broken Hill.

Figure 92. Model of the Broken Hill silver-lead-zinc lode by Oliver Trickett (1914) [From *ARDM* 1914, facing p. 212]

The following year Carne was able to report that Trickett had completed both:

*Mr Trickett prepared a model of the Broken Hill silver lode **during his private time** for the Technical Museum, Melbourne, and has completed a model of the Orient Cave, Jenolan. The objects of the latter model are threefold—first as an aid to exploration, secondly to indicate the advantage to be obtained from the construction of a route of exit by means of a tunnel, and thirdly to give visitors some idea of the shape of the cave caverns and passages.* (Carne 1916)

As will be seen below, Trickett thought there was a fourth reason: to inform the guides on the layout of the caves.

A letter from R. Henry Wallcott, Curator, Industrial & Technological Museum, Melbourne, dated 29.12.16 (in Trickett's Scrapbook) acknowledged the arrival of the Broken Hill model, and added it "will make an interesting and instructive exhibit, and we are very glad indeed to have it to add to our collection. I am pleased to have this opportunity of congratulating you upon the results of your work, and can fully appreciate the interest and labour it must have involved."

The Orient Cave model was given to the Tourist Bureau, as the following correspondence from Trickett's Scrapbook shows:

> Miscellaneous 1053/233
> 13 FEB. 1917
> *Dept. of Mines, N.S.W.*

Geological Survey, N. S. Wales
Department of Mines
Sydney, 12th Feb. 1917

Sir,

A model of the Orient Cave which I have constructed during my spare time will be handed to the Tourist Bureau on the 13th instant.

I beg to attach a letter of explanation addressed to the Superintendent of the Bureau.

> *I am your obdt Servant,*
> [signed] *O. Trickett*

Annotated:

Having seen the model I am of [the] *opinion that it will* [be] *of great value as a guide to further exploration and opening up of more accessible approaches to the caves from the surface. It will on this account be of great assistance to the Cave Staff.*

The attached letter might be forwarded to the Supt. Immigration and Tourist Bureau.

J.E.C. [Carne] *12.2.17*

[to] The *Under Secretary*

Annotated: *Approved R.H.C. [Cambage]*

Trickett conveyed the model with the following letter:

Geological Branch
Department of Mines
[12th February 1917]

Sir,

In handing over the model of the Orient Cave to the Tourist Bureau, I beg to inform you that it occupied my spare time during ten months, equal to a period of between three and four months of seven working hours per day and an outlay of £4 or £5.

It may be asked why I have considered the outlay of so much time and labour to be justified.

The reasons are fourfold:-

1st. Necessity for easy exit.
Ever since I made my first survey of the Orient Cave in 1903, [18] *I have recognised the ultimate necessity of a direct and easy exit by tunnel to the surface. The model indicates the advantage of such exit better than any plan or description. (Roughly estimated length of tunnel 300 ft: see* Annual Report Dept. of Mines *for 1911, p. 194)* [Figure 56]

2nd. Information for Guides.
Familiar as the Guides are with the Caves, they have no means of obtaining a correct idea of the ramifications of the River and Orient Caves and the manner in which the passages of the former underlie those of the Orient Cave. The model supplies this information.

3rd. Aid to exploration.
The model has already given Mr Wiburd an incentive to examine the passages which may lead from the Orient to the Mons Meg Branch of the River Cave. It will probably supply other hints for further exploration.

4th. Source of Interest to Visitors.
The Model will, I think, prove to be a continuous source of interest to visitors to Jenolan, supplying as it does the names of the various caverns and the position of the pathways and stairways which have to be traversed.

> *I have the honor, to be, Sir,*
> *Your obedient Servant,*
> [signed] *O. Trickett*

F.C. Govers, Esq.
Superintendent
Immigration and Tourist Bureau.

To which Mr Govers replied, inter alia:

Immigration and Tourist Bureau
Challis House
Sydney, 14th February, 1917

Dear Sir,

... The model has been placed in the Challis House window where it is attracting considerable attention.

---

18 In fact the cave was not discovered until 30th July 1904, according to Trickett's own report (1904). Hamilton-Smith and Ralston (pers. comm.) see this slip (?) as possibly supporting the theory that the cave was known before it was reported, in which case Trickett was siding with Wiburd et al. against the Wilsons (see 1903 Report, above, and Ralston 1990, p. 49).

I feel sure that not only will it be a source of interest to visitors but will also be a useful advertisement for the Jenolan Caves.

I am preparing a paragraph for the Press, and will also bring the matter officially under the notice of the Premier.

Yours faithfully,
[signed] Fred Govers
Superintendent

O. Trickett Esq.
Geological Branch
Department of Mines, Sydney

Trickett continued to work on cave models. In 1918, according to Carne (1918):

During his spare time he completed models of his surveys of the Basin Cave, Wombeyan, and the Jersey Cave, Yarrangobilly [Figure 94], both of which are now exhibited at the Mining Museum. He is now engaged similarly on a model of the Fig Tree and Creek Caves, Wombeyan.

And in 1919:

... he completed surveys of the Kooringa and Wollondilly Caverns, Wombeyan Caves, from which he produced models in his private time. These models with others are on exhibition at the Mining Museum and will no doubt be found to be of considerable public interest.

Trickett continued making cave models after his retirement in July 1919 as the following letters confirm:

"Thule"
103 Willoughby Road
CROWS NEST
September 20th, 1920

E.B. Harkness, Esq.,
Under Secretary,
Chief Sec. Department

Dear Sir,

I have completed a Model of part of the Jenolan Caves to the order of the Govt. Tourist Bureau of which fact you will no doubt be officially notified.

Pending its ultimate disposal it is at present on view at the Mining Museum, George St. North.

I have spent six months of unremitting work on its construction and the preliminary survey and as I understand the Hon. Mr Dooley takes great interest in the Caves I would esteem it a favour if the Minister and yourself could spare time to examine the model. I think it will be found to repay inspection and to warrant its construction.

Apart from the delineation of the wonderful way in which the caverns overlie one another, the model indicates the possibilities of forming new exits. For instance a short excavation would connect the 'Fairies Grotto' and 'Katies Bower' and a tunnel of about 80 ft would give access to the Grand Archway via the 'Flitch of Bacon Cave'.

Yours truly,
[signed] O. Trickett

103 Willoughby Road
CROWS NEST
September 20th, 1920

E.H. Palmer, Esq.,
Director,
Government Tourist Bureau

Dear Sir,

I have the honor to inform you that the Model of part of the Jenolan Caves is completed and is now at your disposal at the Mining Museum, George St. Nth.

It will, I think, be found to be of absorbing interest both to yourself and the general public as it shews the relation of the various caverns to each other.

I also venture to suggest that it will be of considerable service as it shews that a short excavation would connect the 'Fairies Grotto' with 'Katies Bower' [Left Imperial Cave] and that a tunnel of about 80 ft would give an exit from 'Katies Bower' to the Grand Archway via the 'Flitch of Bacon' Cave, the position of which is now indicated for the first time.

Working on an average of over 50 hours per week the survey and construction has taken me over six months to complete.

I think it will be recognised that I have spared neither time nor pains to supply information which will be found of considerable value in the future and to help visitors to a better understanding of the wonderful cave systems which could be obtained in no other way.

Yours truly,
[signed] O. Trickett

As late as 1927 Trickett was still maintaining his models.

Department of Mines
Sydney, 16th December 1927
27/16835 Misc.

Dear Mr Trickett,

I am in receipt of your letter of 12th instant advising the completion of the additions to the model of the Broken Hill Lode.

I desire to state that I greatly appreciate the splendid services rendered by you in bringing up to date this model, which besides being interesting will be most valuable for general educational purposes.

Yours faithfully,
[signed] F. S. Mance
Under Secretary

Most of Trickett's models appear to have been lost. Only one cave model (probably that made in 1920), depicting the Imperial Caves, is known; it is on display (1991) at the small visitor centre at Jenolan (Figure 95). Ralston (1990) records that this model was saved by guide John Poleson after a soulless manager of Caves House[19] had consigned it to the garbage truck!

---

[19] Hamilton-Smith (pers. comm.) is inclined to believe that the 'clean-up' was a head office idea.

David Branagan (pers. comm.) believes one of the Broken Hill lode models may still exist at Broken Hill.

Trickett's last model was probably that of the City of Sydney, constructed for the Harbour Trust—see pp. 116-117.

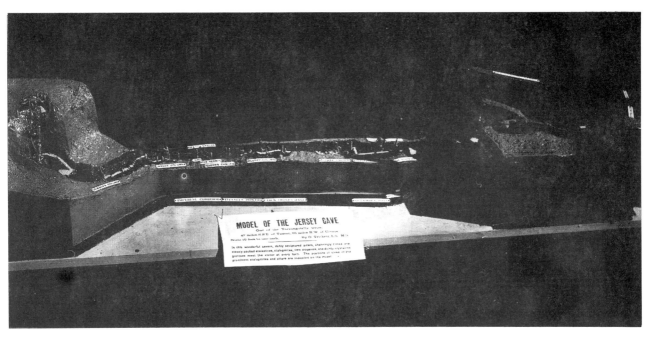

Figure 94. Trickett's model of the Jersey Cave, Yarrangobilly (1918)
[Original photo among Trickett papers]

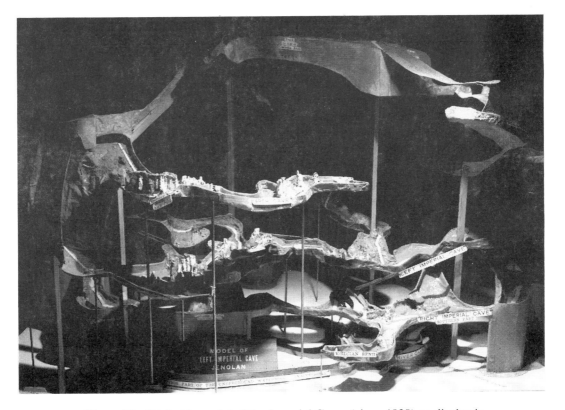

Figure 95. Trickett's model of the Imperial Caves (circa. 1920) on display in
the visitor centre, Jenolan Caves, 1989
[Photo: Stephen Babka]

POST-RETIREMENT: 1919-1934

Trickett officially retired from the Department of Mines on 30 June 1919 (with a temporary extension to 22 March 1920) after over fifty years in government service. But his work did not end there; during retirement he continued his strong interest in caves, producing the 4th edition of his Jenolan guidebook (see p. 89) and further cave and mine models, and he continued to provide advice to the government on cave management.

ENGAGEMENT ON SPECIAL PROJECTS

It appears that even before he retired officers of the Department of Mines had in mind continuing use of Trickett's services. The following is the surviving part of an undated, unsigned memorandum addressed to the Under Secretary:

> The most important work of the Geological Survey for some years is that which is now being carried out at Broken Hill, and has already occupied the greater part of two years. The importance is emphasised by the contribution of about £2,000 by the Mining Companies towards its completion. Illustrative models and sections are necessary which will require expert knowledge in their preparation. For similar work the Geological Survey has hitherto relied on Mr Trickett, and it will greatly help in carrying out the Broken Hill Survey to a satisfactory conclusion to have his assistance.
>
> I am not aware that any officer in the service has given any attention to the production of such models as are required and of which Mr Trickett has made a matter of special study.
>
> Mr Trickett has already made four models of the Broken Hill Lode which are of unique value and geological interest. Two of his models were prepared at the request of the Broken Hill Mine Managers Association. One model sent to Panama Pacific Exhibition was awarded a gold medal. He has a good knowledge of the Broken Hill Mines, having spent some time on the field, and at intervals since 1894 made plans and sections of same.
>
> I consider it most desirable that Mr Trickett's expert services should be retained by the Department in connection with the survey of Broken Hill now in progress, and as the Public Service Board has decided as a matter of policy that his services must terminate on the 30th June next [1919], I recommend that the Board be asked to approve of the Department employing him on fees or contract for this important work.
>
> The Under Secretary [Dept. of Mines]

A notice which appeared in the *Government Gazette* of 26 September 1919 (see p. 78) indicates that this move was successful and, as noted earlier, he was retained in a temporary capacity until 22 March 1920.

In July 1919, Trickett received the following letter from the NSW Premier:

> *Chief Secretarys Office*
> *2nd July 1919*
>
> *Dear Sir,*
>
> *I have your letter of the 30th ult. and am interested to know of the model of the Jersey Cave, Yarrangobilly which is to be seen in the Mining Museum.*
>
> *I congratulate you on your desire to continue in harness until the completion of the models of the Kooringa and Wollondilly Caves.*
>
> *Again thanking you,*
> *I am, Yours faithfully,*
>
> [signed] *George C. Fuller*
>
> O. Trickett, Esq.
> Geological Survey of NSW

In May 1920 Trickett wrote, regarding the possibility of further work:

> *"Thule"*
> *103 Willoughby Road*
> *CROWS NEST*
> *May 11th, 1920*
>
> The Chairman,
> Public Service Board,
> SYDNEY
>
> *I understand that application may be made for your approval of my employment on special work.*
>
> *I wish to bring under your notice some facts[20]*
>
> *I produced in my private time the following:-*
> Guide Book Jenolan Caves (Now in 3rd Edition.)
> " Yarrangobilly Caves (Now in 2nd Edn.)
> " Wombeyan Caves
> " Wellington Caves
> " Abercrombie Caves
> " Bungonia Caves
> Map of Blue Mountains (Several Editions)
>
> *Over 100,000 copies of the above have been issued by the Government and apart from their value in other respects have been largely used for the purpose of advertisement.*
>
> *I spent the whole of my leisure for nine months in the compilation of a Bibliograph[sic] of the Economic Minerals of N.S.W. which has recently been published for the Mines Department at a cost of £500. As the manuscript has been constantly used by Officers for the purpose of reference for 20 years, you can perhaps realize the very considerable sum in time which has been saved.*

---

20 The above is taken from the 'file copy' of this letter, on Geological Survey file GS 20/005; amendments in pencil have been incorporated. Another copy of the letter, dated the previous day and slightly differently worded, is included in Trickett's papers. The difference lies in the addition to the second sentence of: *which, added to my fitness, will I hope induce your Board to give my employment favorable consideration.*

It was no part of my duty to perform any of this work, neither the value nor the necessity for the above maps and compilation was recognised until I had produced them.

In my endeavour to further matters in connection with the Caves I have constructed the following models:-

Orient Cave   (On exhibition at Jenolan)

Jersey Cave   ("   "   Yarrangobilly)

Basin, Wollondilly, Kooringa, River and Fig Tree Caves, Wombeyan   (On exhibit at the Mining Museum).

I have received many compliments but no payment for anything I have done for the Government during my leisure except a bonus of £50 for the Orient model which in time and material represents a value of £150.

In all cases I have had a definite object in view. For instance, the Orient model shows the advantage of a direct exit by tunnel. Means of exit will inevitably be required in the future from the terminals of the various Caverns at Jenolan in order to cope with the ever increasing number of visitors to them. 900 people have been in the Luray Cavern near Washington at the same time. In some of ours only 16 persons or less, can be accommodated under the present conditions at one time.

Although you would find on enquiry that I am credited with rapidity in carrying out any work entrusted to me in the past, I was able to take very little advantage of annual leave as there always seemed to be some matter to be attended to which did not brook delay. Further I usually commenced my official duties at 8.30 am.

Had it not been for the War the Government might perhaps ere this have volunteered some recompense for my sacrifice of time in its service.

I have made no application for payment.

Yours truly,
[signed] Oliver Trickett

EX GRATIA BONUS PAYMENT

Whether this letter obtained for Trickett any further work is not clear (though he certainly did further work), but it evidently did not result in any payment as Trickett apparently later wrote and asked for monetary compensation. No copy of this letter is to hand but Trickett's papers contain the following copy of a memorandum which refers to it:

The statements made in paragraphs 1, 2, 3 of Mr Trickett's letter of the 20th inst. addressed to the Under Secretary which specially relate to the activities of the Government Tourist Bureau can be endorsed in their entirety and I have no reason whatever to doubt in any particular the statements made in paragraphs 4, 5, 6.

He has at all times been a tower of strength and his professional[ism] and skill were relied upon solely throughout the years the various cave systems have been in charge of this Bureau.

There is no doubt that in the very near future back doors must be constructed to some of the Caves so that the stream of traffic at present pulled up in a cul-de-sac may flow continuously onward and outward. The points where such exits may be cut with the least effort are clearly demonstrated on this remarkable model and the work may be carried out easily without any further survey.

The matters referred to in these paragraphs have undoubtedly created attention not only in this State but throughout many countries in the world. No less an authority than Sir Ross Smith stated that the Blue [Mountains] Map was the finest thing of its type he had ever seen for the use of aviation.

If I were called upon for a recommendation as to recognition I could not emphasise too strongly the fairness of a special bonus to Mr Trickett on this account.

[signed] E. H. Palmer Director 8/10/20

Annotated: Referred to U.S. for Mines
[signed] E.B. Harkness 25/10/20.

It is not clear whether it was solicited by Trickett or sought by the Board to help it determine this request, but there is among Trickett's papers a copy of the following memorandum in support of the bonus:

The models and maps of Mr Trickett's appear to have been very helpful to the public. In all these works carried out in his private time Mr Trickett has had a definite object in view namely that of offering the best means of access to caves through which very heavy traffic may be expected in the future.

With regard to his map of the Blue Mtns I may say that Dr G.K. Gilbert, perhaps the greatest American Geologist of the past generation, in a personal communication to me, stated that Mr Trickett's map showed such originality and usefulness in design in the matter of illustrating topographical features that he intended bringing it under the notice of the States Geological Survey.

If the Tourist Bureau has benefited by his models and his brochures as much as the Mines Department has by his Register of Localities then his work has been extremely valuable to them.

With regard to the Register, it may not be out of place to quote the following statement concerning it by Mr Pittman, Government Geologist at that time:

This Register, which has been compiled by Mr Trickett entirely in his private time, will be of very great value not only in connection with the mineral map of the Colony which he is compiling under my supervision but also for purposes of future reference. There is no other compilation from which reliable information can be obtained as to the localities of the various mineral deposits in New South Wales and enquiries are frequently made in this Office which shows the necessity for such a book of reference.

With respect to the models and publications which have been so much appreciated by the public it seems to me that this is a matter for consideration by the Department under which the Tourist Bureau comes seeing that this institution has made such extensive use of them.

[signed] *E.C. Andrews,*
Govt. Geologist
27 Oct 27

Evidently these approaches bore fruit, for there is a copy of part of Trickett's letter of 10 (or 11) May 1920 among his papers on which he has written: *Some of the particulars which led to £100 bonus in view of 27 years from 1892 to 1919.* However, this seems to have taken another decade to come about, as indicated by the following letter from the Director of the Tourist Bureau:

Government Tourist Bureau

Challis House, Martin Place, Sydney

9th January 1930

O. Trickett, Esq., L.S.M.S.
103 Willoughby Road
Crows Nest

Dear Sir,

I have pleasure in advising you that the Minister has approved of the payment to you of a cash bonus of £100 as an appreciation of the value of the work that you performed for the Bureau and Resorts during your period of service as a Public Officer.

If you will be kind enough to call at the Bureau at your early convenience the above amount will be made available.

With congratulations and cordial wishes,

Yours faithfully

[signed] *H. J. Lamble*
Director

Annotated: *Rec'd & acknowledged*

EXIT TUNNEL FROM LEFT IMPERIAL CAVE, 1922

As noted above under 'Cave and Mine Models', Trickett suggested, when submitting his model of Jenolan Caves (20 September 1920) that useful tunnels could be cut connecting the Fairies Grotto with Katies Bower (Left Imperial) and from Katies Bower to the Grand Arch through the Flitch of Bacon Cave. That this suggestion was taken up, that Trickett was still in government employ, and that Trickett was involved in supervising the work is indicated by the following letter in Trickett's papers:

Government Tourist Bureau
Challis House, Sydney

15th February 1922

Mr O. Trickett
Geological Survey Branch
Department of Mines

Proposed new exit from Left Imperial Cave
via Katie's Bower and Flitch of Bacon Cave.

Further to this subject and the supervision you have so kindly given to the attempt to cut an exit passage, I have to state that the Caretaker has expressed some doubt as to whether a cutting process is being conducted in the right direction.

I should be glad, therefore, if you can make it convenient to visit Jenolan at an early date and furnish a further report on the subject. Salary, travelling expenses and transportation will be allowed on the same scale as on the occasion of your previous visit. Kindly intimate the date you are likely to proceed, when arrangements will be made for rail and motor reservations.

[signed] *J. S. Cormack*

Acting Director

Unfortunately, the papers contain no further information on this project.

JENOLAN CAVES MAP, 1925

In 1925 the Government Tourist Bureau printed a large, multi-coloured map of the Jenolan Caves by Trickett. This appears to be a compilation from previous plans, with the addition of a diagram, based on a survey by W.L. Cooke, of a "Possible tunnel from Orient and Temple of Baal Caves to the surface" (Figure 57). A reproduction of this entire plan is included in a pocket at the back of this publication.

MODEL OF CITY OF SYDNEY, 1925

Perhaps Trickett's greatest achievement in retirement was to make a model of the City of Sydney (Figure 96). The following item on this appeared in *The Daily Guardian*, 30 April 1925:

HE BUILT SYDNEY IN 2 ¹/₂ YEARS
AND DID THE JOB IN THREE SECTIONS
MR. TRICKETT'S WORK

Just completed to the order of the Harbour Trust—a relief model of Sydney, showing every detail of layout, with harbour and wharves, complete.

Nothing like it has been made before in Australia. It took 2 ¹/₂ years to build, and is worth about £1000.

Mr Oliver Trickett, 77, used to be an officer of the Mines Department. His skill as a surveyor he showed when he built a model of Jenolan Caves, accurate in the most minute particulars.

He is the author of the newly finished Sydney. In a space of 11 feet by 10 feet, with Mosman at the north-

*east corner, Longueville at the north-west, the old
Victoria Barracks site at the south-east, and Lilyfield
at the south-west, he has modelled the harbour floor,
the foreshore (with each wharf and excavation), the
streets, and the city railway as it will run from Central
Station to Bayfield.*

*Beginning with 81 maps, the modeller gradually
amassed an enormous pile of information. In his 30
months of patient labour he made journey after journey about the city, verifying and correcting his data.
Most of his trouble was with grades and levels, over
which he took infinite pains.*

*The model was made in three equal sections— the first
one showing the foreshores, and the second and third
the southern and northern localities respectively.*

*Wood (for frame and foundation), paper pulp (for the
body), and drawing paper (for the surface) were the
materials Mr Trickett used. The model can be kept up
to date by excision of existing parts and insertion of
new ones as the city changes.*

*See it for yourself in the Mining Museum, George
Street North. That is where it lies, awaiting the
pleasure of the Harbour Trust.*

Trickett also made a model for the Shire of Hornsby,
for which he was paid, but the letter (dated 1 May
1923) which refers to delivery of it unfortunately does
not identify the subject.

Figure 96. Trickett's model of the City of Sydney, 1925
[from a photo in the Scrapbook]

ORIENT CAVE TUNNEL CONTROVERSY, 1927

Trickett never lost an opportunity to advocate the
drilling of a tunnel into the back of the Orient Cave to
facilitate tourist movement through the cave. At least
as early as 1911 he produced a diagram showing the
relationship of the Orient and Temple of Baal to the
surface (Figure 56). In the forth edition of his Jenolan
guidebook (1922), Trickett had written, with absolute
certainty, in his description of the western branch of
the Orient Cave:

*The descent of a short and final stairway ushers the
visitor into an interesting grotto from which an exit
will be constructed, giving a level and short passage
to the Caves House.* (Trickett 1922, p. 56)

And in his introduction to this edition of the guidebook,
J.S. Cormack, Director of the Tourist Bureau, wrote (no
doubt following Trickett's prompting):

*At present, a scheme of cutting exit passages from
the Caves is in hand. This will not only provide a
one-way stream of traffic, and make possible more
frequent inspections, but will add immensely to the
comfort of visitors. For instance a detailed survey
has shown that a level pathway can be constructed
from the Orient and Temple of Baal Caverns, which
will emerge in daylight within a few yards of Caves
House. It is also known that a cutting of less than
100 feet will admit of a passage from Katie's Bower
(at end of the Left Imperial Cave) to the Grand
Archway, through the comparatively level pathways
of the "Flitch of Bacon". ... Ventilation is still a
difficult problem and is the cause of restriction in
numbers and visits to some caves. This is
particularly noticeable in the Orient Cave.
Experiments in air-draughts cannot be carried on
owing to the danger of deterioration of formation, so
obvious in the older known caves, but the institution
of air-locked exits will afford some relief."* (Cormack
[in] Trickett 1922, p. 8-9)

Trickett again drew particular attention to the proposed
Orient Cave tunnel on his large composite map of 1925
on which he showed the route a tunnel could take and
included a small inset section (Figure 57), based on the
survey by Cooke. The proposal came to the fore in the
letters page of the *Sydney Morning Herald* early in 1927.
A writer complained of the difficulties of inspecting
the Orient Cave. This was responded to by a Mr
Larcombe on 15.2.27:

THE ORIENT CAVE—JENOLAN

*Sir,—In your issue of the 12 instant your correspondent
(A. Chas. Hake) rightly draws attention to the
difficulties surrounding the inspection of this glorious
masterpiece of Nature's handiwork. Every year there
must surely be some thousands of visitors to Jenolan
who for various reasons are unable to see the Orient
Cave. I am not familiar with the regulations to which
your correspondent alludes. They may or may not be
necessary. The important fact is that, whereas every*

possible facility should be afforded the public of seeing the Orient Cave, comparatively few are able to do so. The cave is difficult of approach. The underground track leading to it is tortuous and exhausting. To many it is dangerous and to not a few it is beset with impossibilities. By far the larger proportion of the time allotted to an inspection is taken up by the negotiation of this track going and coming. The question arises as to the possibility of avoiding this waste of time and energy, and I believe it can easily be done. My suggestion is that a direct passage or tunnel be put from the spot outside of the mountain nearest to the cave. It is a matter of only several hundred feet and it can be constructed in such a way as to prevent any possibility of injury to the cave or its specimens. I believe a prejudice exists on the part of the government authorities against the construction of such a tunnel, but I am convinced that with an impartial inquiry into the proposal the difficulties and dangers expected will vanish.

Should such a course be adopted, the Orient will become available to many times the number of visitors at present enjoying its beauties, including thousands of those who cannot by reason of physical disabilities surmount the existing difficulties of approach.

The financial aspect need cause no concern. The increased revenue will amply repay the cost. I am, etc.

W.F.A. LARCOMBE

8 Spring-street,
Sydney . Feb. 14

Which drew a defence of the cave from historian W.L. Havard on 18th:

Sir—Correspondence in the "Herald" re the Orient Cave includes the statement that "by far the larger proportion of the time allotted to an inspection is taken up by the negotiation of this track". This is rarely a fact. In a two-hours' inspection about 45 minutes are occupied in calmly moving to and fro. Extended time may be due to visitors who have not seen caves halting by the way to notice parts of the Lucas and River Caves. The passage to the Orient leads also to the Temple of Baal and River Caves, and there is no evidence, as readers of Mr W.F.A. Larcombe's letter will think there is, that the 'track' to these three caves is exhausting. And even if his direct tunnel (suggested and surveyed years ago) were cut the stairways and ladders in the Orient would still have to be negotiated twice—in and out by way of the tunnel.

The objection to a tunnel does not amount to a prejudice. It is the outcome of a sane desire to preserve unaltered the natural ventilation. There is good reason to believe that if the air conditions are changed deterioration will overcome the crystalline brilliance and dark colouring in and about the Orient Cave. Cave colours bleach where there is too much air; there are no intriguing helictites, nor could they exist, where the air supply is excessive; while cutting releases natural water valves and siphon systems and causes rapid and untimely flow over large areas. Discolouration instead of colouration is the result.

The tunnelling scheme savours very much of the position of a man who wishes to make an easy entry into a room in a strange house. Instead of seeking entrances (or exits) already provided, albeit partly concealed, the foolish fellow takes his pocket knife and laboriously gouges his way into solid wall. It is unreasonable blindly to tunnel blindly from the Orient Cave. In a descriptive booklet I have drawn attention to the existence of numerous unexplored openings in the caves. They lead into chambers into which hydrogen-filled balloons have been allowed to drift to considerable heights. The thorough exploration of these openings will reveal a new wonder-world and new passage-ways. In support may I bring before your readers the results of some exploration work recently carried out under the stimulating guidance of the caves' loving guardian, Mr J.C. Wiburd? From the Temple of Baal, which connects with the Orient, a narrow, low tunnel has been cut, not through rock but over the surface of consolidated river-drift. A cave was found and beyond it the little cut was advanced in the direction along which water sometimes comes from the hills outside. An advance of 60 feet has been made. A natural current of fresh air affords proof of the continuation of the partly-blocked passage. It is less than 150 feet to the outside world, and there is probably a cave in that stretch. The complete solution of the acknowledged difficulties of movement in some of the caves at Jenolan lies wholly in the outcome of an exploration of the old water channels and air vents developed by nature.

I am, etc.

W.L. HAVARD

Trickett naturally had to join the fray. His letter was published on 2 March.

JENOLAN CAVES TUNNEL SUGGESTION

Sir—In your issue of February 18 there are remarks by W.L. Havard on a proposed tunnel to the Jenolan Caves, which are either inaccurate or based on opinions which have no sufficient warranty for the views they express with as much confidence.

It may be necessary to give some particulars of my acquaintance with the caves in order to give weight to anything I may write.

I have surveyed, modelled, and photographed the majority of the known caves of New South Wales. This work was carried out originally under the direction of the geological branch of the Department of Mines and afterwards of the Tourist Bureau, which have published my plans and guide books. I was also closely associated with the construction of the pathways which render the caves accessible to the public.

Firstly, I may state that there would be no steps to retrace if the proposed tunnel was constructed, because it would start from the end of the Orient Cave. There are one or two short stairways to branch caverns which have to be traversed twice, but they can be shown on the way to the end. The immense advantage to the public of a tunnel giving a short and almost level outlet to the Orient and Temple of Baal caverns must be obvious.

When I found from my surveys that such a tunnel was possible the Government sent a party of surveyors to verify my work.

It may be asked why I did not press the construction. First, the cost of construction had to be considered. Secondly, there were the views of Mr J.C. Wiburd, who, since his appointment many years ago, has given his life and energies to the opening up of the Jenolan caverns, and to exhibit the beauties they contain to the best advantage. His opinions naturally command respect.

But I do not know of any instance where air has done any damage. Even in the wind-swept Grand Arch I have seen vivid tints apparently unchanged by time.

As years roll on fragile beauties which decorate caverns with limited air currents will probably deteriorate from the tramping of the feet of thousands of visitors as they move along the pathways. This may be the greater danger.

Finally, if an air current has objectors, the closure of a tunnel exit by a door would shut out any draught. [21] *I am, etc.,*

O. TRICKETT

103 Willoughby-road, Crow's Nest, Mar. 1

Havard's response was published on 7 March 1927:

JENOLAN CAVES TUNNEL SUGGESTION

Sir—Mr O. Trickett's letter in your issue of March 2 recalls the fact that his cave work warrants comparison with the similar work of Dawkins in England, Martel on the Continent, and Hovey in America. These names are very prominent in cave literature.

A tunnel serving the Orient Cave could be used in two ways, viz., (1) by visitors traversing the existing pathway, inspecting the cave, and passing out through the tunnel; (2) by entering through the tunnel, inspecting the cave, and returning through it and the tunnel. Mr Trickett's scheme would find consummation in the former. As Mr Larcombe (S.M.H., 15/2/'27) wished to avoid the "exhausting" track and waste of time and energy (still partly involved in Mr Trickett's scheme) he suggested a tunnel from outside the mountain, in order to "surmount the existing difficulties of approach." I took this, and still take it, to mean that he would advance and retreat by way of his tunnel. I replied accordingly (S.M.H., 18/2/'27), and made no reference to the alternative method, not being then concerned with it. This advertent omission does not justify Mr Trickett's assumption that I am ignorant of the alternative. Also I sought to show that the objection to a tunnel does not amount to a prejudice. But Mr Trickett would have your readers believe that my opinions are unwarranted. Am I, therefore, to take it that there is a prejudice? If so, then Mr Larcombe is justified, on that score, in suggesting an impartial inquiry. It is implied also that the tunnel does not find favour with the Superintendent of Caves. His opinions do command respect, and it would interest the public to know them.

The factors operating to decorate or damage our caves have received no thorough investigation. Though developed as commercial assets, Australian caves have been neglected scientifically.

It is astonishing that your correspondent does not know of any instance where air has done any damage. By damage I understand a destructive change in the pristine colour and form of cave decorations. For considerable distances the caves leading from the Grand Arch are bleached, decomposed, and rugged, and in marked contrast with chambers nearer the heart of the hills. Prolonged attacks by air, irregularly moist and dry, have damaged the original, undimmed calcium carbonate crystals into the dull, soft bicarbonate form. The illusive "vivid tints" in the Grand Arch and Coachouse are due more often to plant forms than to mineral matter, which produces the warm and concentrated colours of the remote caves. Before the limestone collapsed, and formed the Grand Arch, the caves about it treasured colours and delicate forms similar to those of the Orient Cave. There are vestiges of splendour in the Nettle Cave and the Architects Studio. After the collapse it is believed that many of the cave streams were blocked with silt, which, in turn, sealed many air vents in the remote parts of the cave system. This caused large volumes of air to stagnate, and favoured the development of exquisite cave forms. In the vicinity of the Arch, however, the collapse exposed numerous vents, and so, under the new conditions of circulating air, these exquisite caves deteriorated into their present condition. They are criticised in cave literature as being "monotonously white." The damage caused by excessive air is therefore just as real as the decoration effected by limited air. Our most beautiful caves are characterised by a limited air supply; where there is freely-circulating air our caves are rugged, and more or less devoid of mineral colour.

It is claimed that a gate will control the passage of air in a tunnel. That must be on the assumption that no (!) intermediate vents will be unsealed along the 379 feet of the cut. Even one very small hole (eight inches in diameter in the famous Wind Cave in South Dakota) may admit a strong and destructive draught. Furthermore, the researches of Banta, and subsequently of Eigenmann, have modified the theory commonly held concerning the movement of air in cave passageways and entrances.

Grave danger exists in disregarding the cave axiom never to cut "blue rock" (limestone). This rock forms the natural framework of any cave system, and any interference with it tends to weaken the whole structure.

Though I repeat that it is unreasonable to tunnel blindly from the Orient Cave—blindly, because I understand nobody knows anything definite concerning the nature of the rock along the line of the survey—I doubt not the mathematical accuracy of Mr Trickett's scheme. By exploring the openings that lead off from the end of the Orient much valuable information might be obtained and arising out of this some

---

21 When the tunnel was eventually built, a door to control draught was, in fact, fitted.

well-considered scheme could be devised. By the exploration of some openings in 1903-1904, Mr Wiburd and his assistants discovered the wonder world which is the admiration of everyone who has been fortunate enough to view it.

If the outcome of this correspondence is a vigorous policy of exploration and internal development of the caves, in order to make them more easily accessible to greater numbers of visitors, it will have served its main purpose. This development would likewise serve to place a coping-stone on Mr Wiburd's patriarchal rule over caves which he has established as Australia's greatest scenic asset. History often repeats itself. The real Jenolan the world admires to-day was unknown before the exploration.

I am, etc.

W.L. HAVARD   *Katoomba, March 5.*

The tunnel was eventually dug in 1953 (Driscoll 1977), fulfilling Trickett's idea of 1911 and his prophesy of 1922. The tunnel was, as stated on the plaque at the entrance, seen as a commemoration of Trickett's work.

PLAQUE IN GRAND ARCH, JENOLAN, 1929

An event which must have been a highlight of Trickett's later life took place at Jenolan on 23 February 1929. It was the unveiling, by Sir Edgeworth David, of a plaque in the Grand Arch commemorating the explorers who discovered the major caves, and Oliver Trickett, L.S., M.S., "whose surveys and plans have contributed so much to their development". The plaque is shown in Figure 97.

The idea of commemorating the early explorers of Jenolan seems to have originated with the historian Ward L. Havard. A memorandum in the files of the NSW Government Tourist Bureau reads as follows[22]:

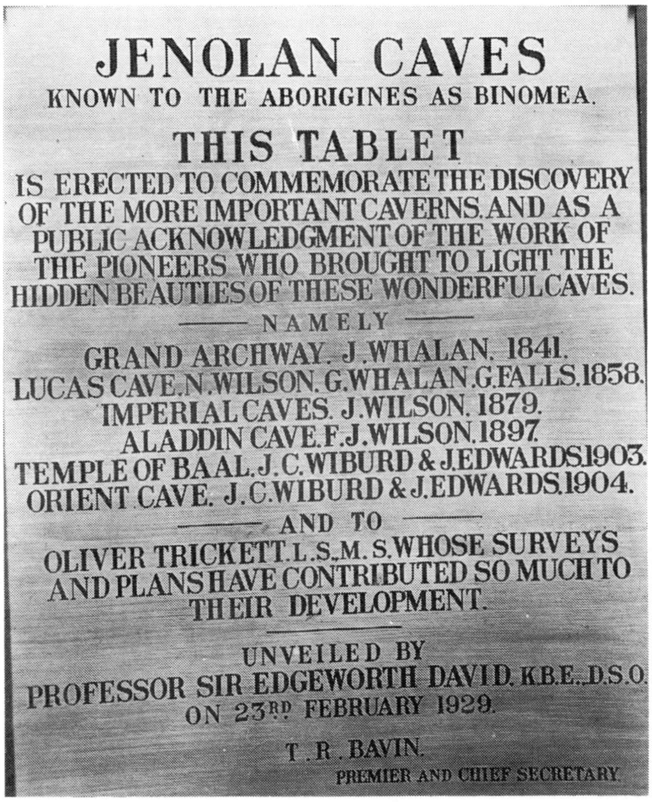

Figure 97. Plaque commemorating the discoverers of the major caves and Oliver Trickett, their surveyor, Grand Arch, Jenolan.

From   *31st August 1928*
The Superintendent of Caves,
Jenolan Caves   Memo to
                                The Director
                                Government Tourist Bureau,
                                Sydney

Subject: Imperial Cave in answer to 28/1733

I may say that February 1929 will be the anniversary of the discovery of part of the Imperial Cave, and I do not think there are any alive today who would be interested in a commemoration of the 50th anniversary of its discovery.

The 50th anniversary of the Lucas Cave was well commemorated by the finding of the River Cave, Baal, Skeleton and Orient Caves in 1904[23]. The only item I would suggest would be a Wireless talk from one of the Wireless Stations or from Jenolan. There is no way at present that I could suggest of commemorating the discovery to cause the people to take an active interest in it. The usual way of commemorating things is to give a dinner or have a ball, and if a dinner is given there would be any amount to commemorate so long as it was free, and a grand ball would be on similar lines no matter if it was held to commemorate a funeral or a wedding it would be patronised by a commemorating crowd who always seem to be on hand to commemorate anything and to give a speech on something they know nothing of.

Perhaps Mr Havard has some scheme at the back of his head which he would like to put forward or suggest to you in the way of commemorating the event. I would suggest that Mr Havard be written to for his idea of commemorating and it may be considered if not carried out.

[signed] *J. C. Wiburd*
Superintendent of Caves

At the foot of this is written:

Mr Havard might be advised that the Bureau will co-operate in every possible way in the production of the article on the Imperial Caves, and that if he has any suggestion with a view to commemoration of the anniversary it will receive due consideration.

J.G.C[ocks] 4/9

---

22 The author is indebted to Ross Ellis who provided access to the following quoted documents, copies of which were obtained by Ben Nurse from the Tourist Bureau some years ago.

23 This is incorrect; the Lucas Cave was actually discovered in 1860 (Ralston 1989, p. 12).

In November Mr Cocks, Assistant Director of the Bureau, wrote to the Director:

N.S.W. Government Tourist Bureau

Commemoration of the 50th Anniversary of the discovery of the Imperial Cave.

Mr Havard called at the Bureau yesterday on the above subject and enquired if anything was proposed to be done in connection with the above anniversary. He considers that a tablet should be erected with an inscription similar to the following:-

"This Tablet is to Commemorate the Discovery of the Imperial Series of Caves by   on the   day of February 1879. Erected in Commemoration of the 50th Anniversary of the Discovery by Alfred Bruntnell, Chief Secretary."

In reviewing the report of the Superintendent dated 31st August, I am not inclined to agree with his opinion. If it cost the Bureau £50 to stage a small ceremony of this nature the publicity value would be considerable. Though there are probably not many alive today who are directly interested in a commemoration of this nature, it will have a practical interest for quite a number and a news interest practically the world over. At the present time there is no commemoration tablet publicly acknowledging the exploration done or the discoveries made by Mr Wiburd.

I desire to recommend the erection of a tablet at a place to be selected, that the Minister be invited to erect the tablet and that on the occasion of this ceremony he be accompanied by the Under Secretary and a number of the public officials who have been immediately interested in the Caves. Invitations might be limited.

Jenolan is in great need of publicity and I think it will be found that a small function of this nature will help business materially.

As Mr Wiburd says, the 50th Anniversary of the Lucas Cave discovery was commemorated by the finding of the River Cave, Baal, Skeleton and Orient Caves in 1904. This brings us to the fact that the 25th Anniversary of the discovery of the Orient also occurs next year.

[initialled] *J.G.C.*
Asst. Director 8/11/28

At the foot of this memo is written:

Some recognition of the exploratory work of Messrs Wiburd & Edwards and the surveys of Mr Trickett should be provided at the Caves.
(Initialled) *H.J.L*[amble] *13/11/28*

Mr Cocks replied to Mr Wiburd, for the Director, on 23 November:

The Superintendent of Caves
JENOLAN CAVES

Subject: Commemoration of the 50th Anniversary of the discovery of the Imperial Cave.

Referring to your communication of 31st August on the above subject, it is considered that probably a better plan will be to commemorate the discovery of the River, Baal, Skeleton and Orient Caves by the erection of a small tablet which will have the effect of giving official and public recognition to the exploration work carried out by Edwards and yourself [and] *also the surveys conducted by Mr Oliver Trickett.*

The erection of a tablet as suggested, will have great publicity value as attention will thereby be drawn to the Caves in the press probably throughout the world.

It is thought that probably the position for a tablet of this nature could be found on a wall in the vicinity of the river but perhaps you may have some better position to suggest. Illumination would be desirable so that the attention of every visitor passing by would be drawn to the tablet.

I shall be glad to know the exact date of the finding of the caves mentioned, so that suitable arrangements may be placed in hand.

Director
23/11/28

The Superintendent replied on 3 December:

Subject: Commemoration of the Discovery of Imperial Caves

With reference to the finding of the Baal, River-Skel[eton] & Orient Caves, I think the best plan would be to see a report sent in by Mr O. Trickett, Mines Dept. of the year 1904 which would give an accurate account of it and the different dates of discovery of each cave.

The erection of a tablet would have great publicity if erected in a place where most people would see it. Of course a small tablet of marble could be put in the River Cave at the exact spot where the explorers came into it first. But as a place where most visitors would see it would be in the Lucas Cave near the Broken Column right at the spot we started from. There would be plenty of standing room and it could be well illuminated.

I would suggest that you write to Mr O. Trickett and he could give you the reports or the date of them and you might also ask his opinion of the most suitable spot for the erection of the tablet, naming the spots suggested.

[signed] *J. C. Wiburd*

The suggestion was obviously taken up as there follows a note (undated) by Trickett, who was evidently asked his opinion:

My dear Cocks

I know you wish to recognise J.C. Wiburd's invaluable services but I take it that the tablet confines itself to discoveries. I do not know when Wiburd became Superintendent, this title preceded the Director and had a different significance. (Perhaps Caretaker or Senior Guide until my retirement 11 years ago from control.)

I took charge of the caves 1896 and continued under the Geol. Branch of the Mines Dept. until the advent of the Intelligence [Department] and then the Tourist Bureau - under which I was requested to continue. I haven't kept any record of this arrangement (made with consent of Mines Dept.) Perhaps there are two letters which might throw some light on this, vis:

*11 May 1915 Tourist Bureau to Public S. Board
22 April 1918 " " "*

If you still wish to record Wiburd's services you could have a second tablet or a blackboard (white lettering on black) somewhere near the tablet. Or simply prepare something for the reporters — in the latter case I have prepared particulars you might like to have.

[signed] O. Trickett

THE JENOLAN CAVES

Known to the Aborigines as Binomea

THIS TABLET

is erected to commemorate the discovery of the more important caverns and as an acknowledgement of the debt the public owes to the pioneers who brought to light the hidden beauties of these marvellous caves

namely

GRAND ARCHWAY *by* J. WHALAN 1841
LUCAS CAVE N.WILSON, G.WHALAN & G.FALLS 1858
IMPERIAL CAVES J. WILSON 1879
ALADDIN CAVE & MAFEKING F.J.WILSON 1897, ~~1900~~
TEMPLE OF BAAL J. C. WIBURD & J. EDWARDS 1904
ORIENT CAVE J. C. WIBURD & J. EDWARDS 1904

T. R. BAVIN
Premier & Chief Secretary

I would prefer to leave out Mafeking if [sic?—unless?] I knew which was 1897 and which was 1900 (perhaps I can find out but the time is short). Also word caves, i.e. IMPERIALS, L. and R. and lumping Also thus

RIVER BRANCHES—TEMPLE OF BAAL & ORIENT
J.C. WIBURD & J. EDWARDS 1904

The most important item is Whalan 1841 and I do not know that the months are important. R.I. Bailey occupied no more important position than those who assisted J. Wilson who have been ignored and are not now known.

It is not easy — alter or amend the above any way you think best.

As Figure 97 shows, the Tablet was made almost as Trickett proposed (some words were changed and recognition of his work added). Unfortunately some

of it is incorrect; 1841 should probably be 1836, 1858 should be 1860 and, according to Ralston (1989, p. 12) the discoverers of the Lucas were G. Whiting and N. Irwin. Ralston feels that Bailey's contribution was underrated by Trickett (pers. comm. and 1989, p. 50). Even Trickett, in the second edition of his Jenolan guide (1905, p. 22) acknowledges that Wiburd and Edwards were "assisted by R.I. Bailey" in their discoveries of 1903-04.

Invitations to the unveiling ceremony were evidently sent out in January 1929; Trickett replied:

*Thule
103 Willoughby Road
Crows Nest
27.1.29*

Dear Mr Cocks,

Thanks for your invitation. My daughter, Lily, may like [the] trip.

Would it be any use my giving 1/2 hour at Caves House? If so, I would like enlarged photo: Mystery— Ribbon branch—Orient Cave, large basin, Wombeyan Caves, Warm Bath Yarrangobilly, also trial photo Blue Mountains, Caves and Blue Mountains maps.

Yours truly,

[signed] O. Trickett

Evidently Mr Cocks did not like the prospect of Trickett giving a lecture; he replied:

N.S.W. Government Tourist Bureau

30th January 1929

Dear Mr Trickett

I have to thank you for your memo of 27th instant and for your suggestion concerning the half hour at Caves House.

It is the official desire that there shall be no ceremony other than the unveiling. There will be a large number of guests in the house over the weekend and although those officially invited and perhaps a few of the guests would be very interested, the greater proportion of those present will desire to dance in the evening, and there will be no opportunity.

I will suggest the matter and see if some special arrangement can be made, letting you know the result a little later.

There has been an amendment to the original suggestion in view of the 50th Anniversary of the discovery of the Imperial Caves, occurring on 15th February, and it has therefore been proposed to include Jeremiah Wilson's name on the tablet and instead of erecting it in the Exhibition Chamber in the Lucas Cave and to place it in the Grand Arch. This has the endorsement of Mr Wiburd.

I am glad to know that your daughter will accompany you on this occasion.

With kind regards,

Yours faithfully,

Asst. Director

Not to be easily put off, Trickett wrote back:

Thursday [no date]

Dear Mr Cocks,

Naturally your arrangements for making a success of the forthcoming function would make the trip a most enjoyable one to the guests.

I would not venture to address a crowd—my idea was a round table chat to a dozen or more with the table littered with maps and plans. It might interest some of the visitors and the photos I asked for would be of use to you later on.

Personally I would rather remain in the background.

Yours truly,

[signed] *O. Trickett*

The event went ahead on 23 February 1929 and by all accounts was a great success; there does not appear to be any record of Trickett having his discussion over a round table littered with maps and photos but he did speak at the official ceremony (Figure 98).

"The Government," said Sir Edgeworth, "is warmly to be congratulated on the way it has kept these crown jewels of the Commonwealth, and our thanks are due to the pioneers who have helped to keep these jewels undimmed."

Some of the figures quoted by Sir Edgeworth David caused a murmur of amazement. During 1928 78,000 people, he said, visited the Caves. Since the time when Jenolan was opened to inspection, more than 1,000,000 people had been guided through scenes of mystery and grandeur that could not fail to be a joyous memory and a source of inspiration for the remainder of their lives.

Among other speakers at the ceremony were the Minister for Mines (Mr Chaffey), representing the Government; Oliver Trickett, whose surveys of the Caves have proved models of thoroughness; Mr J.C. Wiburd, chief guide and one of the early explorers of Jenolan; and Mr Lambell [sic–Lamble], of the Tourist Bureau.

Figure 98. Trickett addressing the guests in the Grand Arch prior to the unveiling of the plaque by Sir Edgeworth David
[From a photograph in the Scrapbook]

The *Sydney Morning Herald*, 25 February 1929, described the event thus:

TABLET TO DISCOVERERS

UNVEILED BY SIR EDGEWORTH DAVID

In the cathedral light of the Grand Archway leading to the Jenolan Caves, Sir Edgeworth David on Saturday afternoon unveiled a brass tablet in memory of the discoverers of the Caves. Several hundreds of tourists attended.

The item was accompanied by Figure 99 which shows some of the official party leaving the Grand Arch.

The *Guardian* saw it more as a social event:

POPULAR CAVES HOUSE

The always-delightful Caves House at Jenolan echoed with even more than usually happy sounds all the week-end, for a particularly interesting party arrived at midnight on Friday, after a thrilling descent for the unveiling of the caves-discovery tablet by Professor Sir Edgeworth David; and there was

Figure 99. The official party leaving the Grand Arch after the unveiling ceremony (left to right): J.C. Wiburd, H.J. Lamble, Sir Edgeworth David, O. Trickett and F. Chaffey, MLA.

never a dull moment. Director Lamble, of the Tourist Bureau, with his charming wife; Mr and Mrs Cocks; and Mr Casey, led the party, which included Mr Chaffey, with his wife and kiddies; Mr Ryan M.L.C., and Mrs Ryan; Mr Grove, Assistant-Government Architect, and his wife; and the wife and daughter of the Minister for Health. One of the most popular girls at the Caves was Lily Trickett, who it is said "knows Jenolan backwards", for her father, the veteran of the party, was the surveyor who, with explorer Wiburd, has made the Caves his life work. It must have been a proud occasion, too, for Mrs Wiburd and her daughter, for the silvery-haired explorer-guide was the hero of the day, the admiring crowd of visitors listening raptly to his tales of his wonderful work in revealing the beauties of the Caves.

Whatever its success, the cost of the event rather exceeded the £50 suggested by Mr Cocks. The tablet itself, engraved on 14 gauge brass by Messrs Edgar Kemp (Engravers) Ltd of 49 Clarence Street, Sydney cost £22/10/-, a tourist coach (Sydney-Jenolan & return): £45, meals and accommodation for the official party: £73/12/11, asbestos cable and insulators [?]: £1/2/6; a total cost of £143/5/5.

PROPOSED ROAD THROUGH DEVILS COACHHOUSE, 1929

Trickett's continuing involvement in the management of Jenolan is amply illustrated by the following letters which survive among his papers.

Main Roads Board of New South Wales
Sydney
17 APL 1929

Dear Mr Trickett,

Will you please accept my sincere thanks for your letter of 16th April in which you have been good enough to say that you would assist the Board in connection with the matter of locating a road at the Jenolan Caves.

Mr Down, the Divisional Engineer, has the matter in hand, and will see you this morning with a view to making all necessary arrangements.

The position is that in consideration of making an improved route of access to the Caves, the most suitable route would appear to be one that will pass through the Devil's Coach House. Mr Wiburd is concerned that some damage may occur to the Caves if the road is constructed in that location, and with a view to either supporting his objection or removing his fears, it was thought, after conversation with Mr Mance, that if you could see your way clear to visit with one of the Board's Engineers, meeting Mr Surveyor Middleton on the ground, the Board would be taking the proper action.

We realise that even if not immediately then at no distant date, improved access will be called for, but we do not wish to do anything that would jeopardise the Caves in any way. Should you be able to see your way clear to visit and advise the Board, we will gladly make any arrangement that would be for your comfort and convenience, and I think possibly the better way would be to drive from Sydney to Jenolan, thereby avoiding changes en route. Any arrangement that you can make with Mr Down will be suitable to the Board.

Again with many thanks.

Yours faithfully,

[signed] *H. H. Newell*

O. Trickett,. Esq.
"Thule"
103 Willoughby Road
CROW'S NEST, N. SYDNEY

While there is no indication of when any visit took place, or of what transpired, Trickett subsequently wrote to the Board:

103 Willoughby Road
Crow's Nest
3rd May, 1929

H.H. Newell, Esq.
Main Roads Board, Sydney
Dear Mr Newell,

<u>Re Road through the Devil's Coach House,
Jenolan.</u>

In the first place strong opposition is made to the proposal by responsible officers of the Tourist Bureau, accentuated perhaps by the construction of a roadway to the Abercrombie Caves by the Public Works Department, where it is asserted that much of the attractiveness of the approach was destroyed quite unnecessarily. I do not endorse their opposition, although the removal of rocks and debris—the evidence of ancient floods—would obliterate points which are of interest to many tourists. It is difficult to forecast what might happen by the construction of a roadway unless ample provision were made for flood water.

There is not sufficient record on which to base an estimate of the height an abnormal flood might reach. There are ripple marks which appear to me to be above the level which any future flood might attain, owing to the scouring of the channel as time went on. The present floor is formed of water-worn stones and debris, dotted here and there by huge rocks which have fallen from the roof and sides of the arch. This waste has a depth of say 15 to 20 feet above the base of the channel. That there is such a base is evidenced after a flood by the disappearance of the water as it recedes in three different places.

Mr Wiburd, who is able to supply data of flood waters during the past forty years, thinks any interference with a free flow might result in flooding some of the caves. He may be right, but it is quite problematical. The eastern side of the arch is fairly stable, but on the western side the rock near its base is fractured and honeycombed by crevices which connect with the caves. Both sides are undercut slightly.

In any case, at small expense, these crevices could be stopped in such a way as not to be unduly visible.

Since the caves were discovered I think I can say no rocks have fallen from the sides or roof of the arch, but to the casual observer there is the appearance of insecurity. This could be remedied by a bessemer tie

at A[24], for which there is perhaps no necessity. Any fall which might occur in future would be ascribed to road operations.

The whole question appears to rest on the Tourist Bureau's attitude on any tampering with the floor of the cavern, and the provision for flood waters— a somewhat costly undertaking.

Yours truly,

[signed] *O. Trickett*

It appears that Wiburd's objections, or perhaps the cost, stopped the project, since no road was ever built through the Coachhouse; it certainly was not due to Trickett, who appears to have found the idea acceptable.

UNPUBLISHED [?] NOTE

Among Trickett's papers there is a single typewritten page which appears to have been originally drafted as a letter to the Editor of the *Sydney Morning Herald* in response to an item by W.L. Havard on the Orient Cave. It has been altered subsequently to make it less specific but whether it was in fact published is not known. Its title would indicate that it was intended as a more significant piece than it appears to be, but the fact that it is signed at the foot of the page gives the impression that it is, in fact, complete. It is not dated but was probably written in the early 1930s.

Exploration of the Cave Systems of the Commonwealth

with Special reference to Jenolan Caves

With reference to a recent article in the Sydney Morning Herald by W.L. Havard on the discovery of the Orient Cave, Jenolan, by J.C. Wiburd whose son, Captain Dr Wiburd, gained distinction in the Great War, and J. Edwards, one is apt to forget those early explorers, Messrs Blaxland and Wentworth, who in 1813, two years before the Battle of Waterloo, paved the way not only for the Great Western Road and Railway but for the road to the Jenolan Caves through the Blue Mountains, a Tourist's Paradise of Forest, rock, dainty wooded glens and waterfalls, which culminates in the Great Esplanades of precipices which overlook from Wentworth Falls to Mount Victoria, the Kanimbla and other valleys, 2,000 feet below.

Returning to the Orient Cave which is one of the beautiful branches of the River Cave, the difficulty of exploring this River area was brought vividly under my notice when before survey, an inspection, including a precarious passing over the pool known as the Styx in a box floated by kerosene tins, occupied our time from 11 a.m. to 3 a.m. next morning.

These attractive caverns are on the south side of the Grand Archway. The earlier discovered caves on its north side all speak eloquently of Natures master

---

[24] Presumably a plan with a point marked 'A' was included with the original letter; there is no plan attached to the copy in Trickett's papers.

hand. What could be more beautiful than the Gem of the West in the Right Imperial Cavern?

None of the Jenolan Series should be missed by those who have time to spare. There are caves of much greater size in other countries. The Mammoth Caves of Kentucky total 200 miles and are massive and inspiring rather than delicate or beautiful in their sculpturing and in their waterways and cascades. It may be stated that for a combination that includes easy access, handy and comfortable accommodation and continuous unbroken arrays of delicately moulded forms, translucent and fragile lime sprays, all well lighted, the Jenolan, Wombeyan and Yarrangobilly Caves in New South Wales and with few exceptions those of the rest of Australia, of Tasmania and New Zealand stand unrivalled in their attractions for the visitor.

[signed] *O. Trickett*

COMMEMORATION IN GEOGRAPHICAL NAMES

Since Trickett was heavily involved with exploration, surveying and maps it is not surprising that his name should have found its way into the gazetteer of Australian place names. The first time this happened, however, was long before he rose to prominence as a surveyor and promoter of the limestone caves of New South Wales. It arose, in fact, from his rowing days. The *South Australia Advertiser* of 5 February 1873 carried the following item:

MR ERNEST GILES'S EXPLORATIONS TO THE WESTWARD

October 17.—Mr Giles and Mr Carmichael started to-day with a week's supply of rations, to the S.W., intending to reach the high mountain previously noted.

[The article describes the area passed through by the party in some detail, then under "November 1" the article records, in part:]

*Followed this creek down further, thinking it would lead into the Finke, and, in three miles, found it emptied itself into a much larger stony mountain stream. Called this **Trickett's Creek**; and the range which they had followed so long was named George Gill's Range, after Mr G.D. Gill, of Melbourne. "The country round its foot is the best I have seen in this region, and no doubt before many years pass it will be part of a stocked run. The new creek we had just discovered had a large stony waterhole immediately above and below the junction of Trickett's Creek, and as we approached the one below the junction I noticed three or four native wurleys, just deserted, whose owners had fled at our approach ..."*

[The article concludes:]
They were sixty-four miles from the main camp, and had been most successful in finding a route by which Robinson could return, for there seemed little

doubt that this creek would reach the Finke—a surmise, however, which afterwards proved to be incorrect. Turned their horses heads for home, and camped at the Stokes, having travelled forty miles.

A hand-written annotation by Trickett, beside this cutting in the Scrapbook, reads:

Tricketts Creek named after O. Trickett by Carmichael, an assistant of Giles and brother of Carmichael who won the Challenge Pair oar race at the Melbourne Regatta twice with O.T. [This was in 1871 and 1872—GM]

Confirmation of this is found in Giles' published account, *Australia Twice Traversed* (p. 112)

Following it three miles farther we found that it emptied itself into a much larger stony mountain stream; I named this Trickett's Creek, after a friend of Mr Carmichael's.

The Place Names Committee of the Northern Territory has confirmed that the name is still in use and that **Trickett Creek** appears in the Henbury 1:250,000 sheet at Lat. 24°27', Long. 132°04'. G. Tutty, for the Board advised (6 April 1987):

*A trigonometrical station was established in the vicinity of the creek in September 1963 which also appears on the map as **Tricketts Bluff**.* [744m asl]

A well made road runs from Wallera Ranch to Kings Canyon, running parallel for some of the way to the George Gill Range, so the area around Trickett Creek is in constant use by the travelling public.

In New South Wales three features have official geographical names which are likely to have been given in honour of Oliver Trickett but the Geographical Names Board of NSW is unable to confirm this. The **Parish of Trickett** lies in the County of Bourke, Narraburra Shire at Lat. 34°31', Long. 147°17' (Barmedman 8329 1:100,000 sheet) and a **Trickett Trig. Station** occurs nearby, at Lat. 34°31', Long. 147°18' at a height of 371m asl (Coolamon 8328N). These names were gazetted on 16.8.74 and 18.10.74, respectively, though they have probably been in use much longer. It is possible that Trickett worked in this region in the 1880s, or that a surveyor colleague used his name when establishing a new parish and trig. station.

[It is also possible, of course, that these were actually named after another famous Trickett, Edward (1851-1916), the Australian champion sculler who won the World Sculling Championship on the Thames in 1876, or William J. Trickett (1843-1916) who was a Sydney solicitor and politician].

Mount Trickett (1360m) stands in the Great Dividing Range in the Oberon Shire nearly four kilometres south-west of Jenolan Caves at Lat. 33°50', Long. 149°59'. The name was gazetted 10 October 1969, but it may have been in use long before then. Without any doubt it commemorates the contribution of Oliver Trickett to the understanding and management of the nearby caves.

There are at least three other geographical features in NSW bearing Oliver Trickett's name, though these are not (yet) approved by the Geographical Names Board.

At Yarrangobilly, a cave shown by Trickett on his 1897 map (Figure 20) as "Large cave in cliff face" has become known as **Tricketts Cave** (Figure 100). This may have originated with Rose (1964) who referred to it as "Trickett's" Cave and mentioned that it was 'shown on O. Trickett's area plan as "large cave in Gorge"'. The cave is listed as Trickett's Cave in *Australian Karst Index 1985* (Matthews 1985, p. 2-63) is numbered Y13 and has a length of about 200 metres (80% mapped). Tricketts Cave was surveyed in 1973 by Andrew Pavey of UNSWSS, and others; the result is reproduced as Figure 101 (Pavey 1973).

At Abercrombie there is a cave known as **Tricketts Hole** which connects with the main Abercrombie Arch. It may well have been given this name because it is one of the entrances shown by Trickett on his 1897 (Figure 24) or 1899 (Figure 38) plans. Its cave number is A34.

Some five kilometres south-west of Tuglow Caves, in a cave area known as Jaunter, there is a large limestone arch which spans a tributary of the Tuglow River. This is known as **Tricketts Arch**, having been shown by Trickett on his 1897 plan (Figure 28) as "Limestone Creek passing under arch hereabouts", though he did not mention it in his report (1897c). Matthews (1985, p. 2-33) lists 'Southern Trickett's Arch' (JA1, an active inflow cave) and 'Northern Trickett's Arch' (JA2, an active outflow cave), both of which are said to have a length of about 50 metres (and presumably connect).

Matthews (1985, p. 2-13) also lists **Tricketts Mystery Cave** (BC2) in the Billys Creek cave area. However, there seems no real justification for including 'Tricketts' in this name. Trickett showed it as 'Mystery Cave' on his map of 1899 (Figure 37) but he did not discover it (the cave was shown to him by a Mr W.L. Gaudry). In any case, there are grave doubts as to whether this cave has been re-located since no cave has been found in the area with the 'oval and symmetrical bunch of the "mystery" type of dripstone formation' described by Trickett as being 1.5 feet long by 1 foot in diameter and 'the most wonderful network of lime sprays and stalactites which I have seen' (Trickett 1899b).

TRIBUTES TO TRICKETT'S WORK

Many complimentary comments in relation to Trickett's work are recorded in items mentioned in the foregoing. There are, however, a number of items which specifically record tributes to his efforts; some of these are reproduced below. As early as 1892, a glowing personal testament to Trickett's work was provided by R. Etheridge, Curator of the Australian Museum:

The Australian Museum

Sydney, May 2nd. 1898

It affords me great pleasure to bear testimony to the admirable and methodical manner in which Mr Oliver Trickett (Draughtsman to the Geological Branch, Department of Mines and Agriculture) has, in addition to performing the current, ordinary, draughting duties appertaining to the Branch,

Figure 100. The entrance to Tricketts Cave, "large cave in cliff face", Yarrangobilly
[Photo: Ross Ellis]

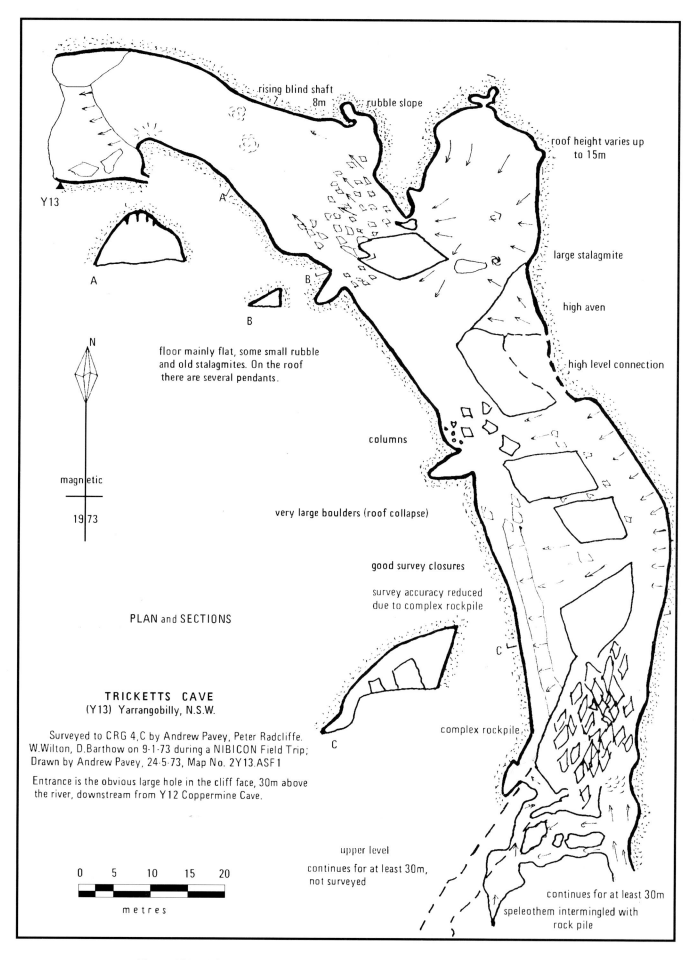

Y13

rising blind shaft 8m

rubble slope

roof height varies up to 15m

large stalagmite

high aven

high level connection

A

B

N

magnetic

1973

floor mainly flat, some small rubble and old stalagmites. On the roof there are several pendants.

columns

very large boulders (roof collapse)

good survey closures

survey accuracy reduced due to complex rockpile

PLAN and SECTIONS

C

TRICKETTS CAVE
(Y13) Yarrangobilly, N.S.W.

Surveyed to CRG 4,C by Andrew Pavey, Peter Radcliffe. W.Wilton, D.Barthow on 9-1-73 during a NIBICON Field Trip; Drawn by Andrew Pavey, 24-5-73, Map No. 2Y13.ASF1

Entrance is the obvious large hole in the cliff face, 30m above the river, downstream from Y12 Coppermine Cave.

complex rockpile

upper level continues for at least 30m, not surveyed

0   5   10   15   20

metres

continues for at least 30m

speleothem intermingled with rock pile

Figure 101. Tricketts Cave, Yarrangobilly - Plan and Sections by Pavey et al., 1973
[Reproduced from *Spar*, #30:7]

reduced to order a very large mass of old Records, Notes, and Field Books, thus rendering them available for use at any moment. As a former Officer of the Mines Branch, I can speak with certainty on this subject, for this collated information was on many occasions of great use to me in my own work. He has further devoted himself to acquiring such a knowledge of the Geological and Mineral data of N.S.W. as enables him to save much time to the Government Geologist and his Officers.

Mr Trickett has also a matured reputation as a surveyor, both in N.S.W. and Victoria;- with regard to the latter Colony, both Mr Trickett and myself had the honor, many years ago, to be Officers of the same Department (Department Mines) in the Victorian service, and the experience thus gained enables him to be of great service to his present Branch, when the Surveyor's field notes or sketches of underground workings, and surface features require delineation.

[signed] R. Etheridge

T.W. Edgeworth David's tribute to Trickett's work as published in the introduction to his 1907 "Geology of the Hunter River Coal Measures" is quoted on page 91, as is his letter supporting Trickett's application for a pay rise in 1898. The next year, in a letter to Trickett, David wrote:

University of Sydney
Feb. 9, 1899

My Dear Trickett,

The more I use your index, and those plotted traverses, the more lost I am in admiration at your enormous patience in reducing such a mass of chaos to law and order.

Believe me, Yours sincerely,

[signed] T.W.E. David

As noted under the 1907 report of the Dept. of Mines (above), Trickett ceased to have actual responsibility for the limestone caves from that year. The occasion did not pass unnoticed, however. His fellow workers presented him with a silver tea and coffee service (Figure 102) and an illuminated scroll (Figure 103). The *Town and Country Journal* of 4 September 1907 reported the occasion thus:

Figure 102. Silver tea and coffee service presented to Trickett by the caves staff in 1907.
[Photo by Kerry & Co., Sydney]

Figure 103. Illuminated scroll presented to Trickett by the caves' staff in 1907.
[Reduced from the original in the scrapbook; shaded areas were purple]

PRESENTATION TO MR O. TRICKETT

Mr Oliver Trickett, who for more than 11 years has held the responsible position of inspector of caves in New South Wales, in conjunction with the office of Geological Surveyor, has relinquished the former post, all the caves in the State now being under the supervision of the Government Tourist Bureau. During Mr Trickett's term of office as inspector he worked extremely hard, effecting numerous improvements, and making many alterations, with the result that the caves have become ever so much more popular with the public, and of recent years the number of visitors yearly has increased by thousands. Mr Trickett had sole control of the caves, and never spared himself in carrying out his work, which at times was most difficult.

While Mr Trickett was inspector a number of very important discoveries were made, a notable one being the river cave at Jenolan, which is declared to be one of the most remarkable and wonderful caves in the world. Mr Trickett is the author of the very excellent guide books that so beautifully illustrate and describe the caves of New South Wales. He also undertook the difficult and laborious task of making underground surveys of the caves, from which maps have been compiled, showing the situation of the different caverns. These maps find a place in the guide books.

Mr Trickett was held in high esteem by the employees at the caves, who very much regret the change that has taken place. They all speak of their late chief as a "white man", and as a fitting appreciation of his kindness to them decided to make a presentation to him. It was impossible for all the men employed in the four caves districts to be present at the ceremony, however much they would like to have been. So it was decided that the presentation, in the form of a handsome silver tea and coffee service and tray, should be made by Mr J.C. Wiburd, who is caretaker of Jenolan Caves. The presentation, which was quiet and informal, took place in Mr Trickett's office at the Mines Department, Sydney, on August 30. Mr H. Benyon, of Jenolan Caves, was present at the ceremony. The presentation came as a great, but pleasant, surprise to Mr Trickett, who much appreciated the kindly feelings and goodwill which actuated the gift.

The presentation was inscribed, the inscription on the tray reading: "To O. Trickett, Esq., as a token of esteem, from the caretakers, guides, and engineers of Jenolan, Yarrangobilly, Wombeyan, and Abercrombie Caves.

Mr Trickett has not altogether severed his connection with the caves, but will see to their underground requirements.

This item, from the Trickett Scrapbook, is illustrated with a photo of the tea and coffee service by Kerry (Figure 102); Trickett has written in the margin: "By permission of Mines Dept. Inspector continued under Tourist Bureau up to 1917".

The Intelligence Department was most appreciative of Trickett's efforts and its Director wrote in 1907:

Intelligence Department
30th July 07

Sir,

In connection with the transfer to this Department of the administration of the Caves, I desire to express my high appreciation of the admirable reports submitted by Mr O. Trickett, respecting the various caves. These reports show abundant evidence of the great pains Mr Trickett has taken to make a permanent record of all matters of interest in connection with the various caves. The information is complete and well arranged, and will prove invaluable to this Department.

[signed] H.C.L Anderson
Director

The Under Secretary for Mines

The Mines Department also acknowledged the value of Trickett's work:

I do not know where I could obtain another officer to replace him (Mr Trickett) in the Geological Survey Branch. Ordinary Surveyors' Draftsmen are not capable of performing his duties. The cave work was taken up by Mr Trickett as an addition to his other duties after the PSB was instituted, but I do not consider it was by any means his most important work.

[signed] E.F. Pittman
10 Sept 07

After the control of caves passed from the Mines Department to the Immigration and Tourist Bureau (initially known as the Intelligence Department) in 1907, an arrangement between these agencies enabled Trickett to continue working with the caves. This arrangement was renewed from time to time, as indicated by the following extract from a report by the Director of the Immigration & Tourist Bureau to the Under Secretary for Finance & Trade, 8 August 1911:

The services of Mr O. Trickett L.S., M.S., of the Mines Department were made available for the supervision of the interior work [in the caves].

The great value of Mr Trickett's services in this connection has been deeply appreciated, and his long experience and intimate knowledge of all matters relating to the caves, as well as his keen personal interest in them and his ready co-operation with the Bureau cannot be too gratefully acknowledged. I trust that the arrangement may be continued as long as he is able and willing to carry on the work.

It appears that in January 1912 the Government Geologist of Western Australia sought details of the drafting staff employed by the NSW Geological Survey (perhaps he was trying to justify more staff). In his reply (17.1.12) E.F. Pittman, Under Secretary of Mines and Government Geologist stated:

The drafting work of the Geological Survey of New South Wales is all done by one man, viz Mr O. Trickett, and he is graded as "Draftsman and Surveyor". It is recognised that this Officer's salary is higher than that of an ordinary draftsman, the reason being that he possesses quite exceptional qualifications. While it cannot be said to be a sine quâ non that the draftsman should also be a licensed surveyor, it happens that he is one, and his services have been specially useful on that account. For instance, he has, on numerous occasions, assisted the Geological Surveyors in their field work, and he has made all the underground surveys of the limestone caves, besides taking numerous photographs of them; he designs all improvements to the caves, and supervises the work of construction. He has also made (unassisted) a very valuable model of the Broken Hill Lode.

In regard to his drafting work, the plans and sections are for the most part prepared from those handed in by the Geological Surveyors, though he also makes frequent use of their field books. The plans so prepared are reproduced by photo-lithography by the Government Printer. In exceptional cases, maps, such as the Geological Map of the State are compiled entirely by Mr Trickett, and transferred to stone (in the Lithographic Branch of the Lands Department).

Mr Trickett possesses much originality as a draftsman, and is exceptionally rapid in his work, so much so that it would be unjust to compare his salary with that of an ordinary surveyor's draftsman.

After he turned 65 (1912) Trickett's continuing employment had to be reviewed each year. Although he worked in the Geological Survey, his efforts were greatly appreciated by the Tourist Bureau, after it took over the running of the caves. The Superintendent wrote to the Public Service Board in 1915, as follows:

> *Immigration and Tourist Bureau*
> *Challis House*
> *Sydney, 11th May 1915*

Sir,

As it is not unlikely that the Public Service Board will shortly again give consideration to the question of concurring in the continuance in the Public Service of Mr Oliver Trickett, Draftsman and Surveyor in the Geological Survey Branch of the Department of Mines, now over 65 years of age, it will not, perhaps, be considered out of place if I record the appreciation of this Department of the invaluable services rendered to it by Mr Trickett, whose long association with, and active control of the development of the limestone caves of New South Wales has done so much, not only to open up these wonder caverns, but to obtain for them pride of place amongst the tourist attractions of the world. The work that Mr Trickett continues to do for this Department is carried out with unflagging energy

and enthusiasm, and the withdrawal of his experienced help would mean a severe loss to the Department.

I should be glad if these representations could be placed before the Board.

> *I have the honor to be, Sir,*
> *Your Obedient Servant,*
> *PERCY HUNTER*
> *Superintendent*
> *per E. H. Palmer*

The Secretary
Public Service Board

And again in 1918:

> *Immigration and Tourist Bureau*
> *Challis House*
> *Sydney, 22nd April, 1918*

Sir,

I understand that the case of Mr Surveyor O. Trickett will shortly be reviewed by the Board.

I would like to record this Bureau's appreciation of the services Mr Trickett continues to render this Department. He has, during the past year, carried out a considerable amount of work in making further surveys - some of them in his own time - of certain caves at Jenolan, Wombeyan and Yarrangobilly, and certain self-appointed tasks of considerable benefit to the Bureau in this direction are not yet complete. For instance he is making a model of the Jersey Cave at Yarrangobilly, similar to that which he made and presented to the Government of the Orient Cave at Jenolan.

So far as I am aware, there is no officer in the Public Service competent and available to discharge for this Bureau the special duties which, since its inception, have devolved upon Mr Trickett.

> *I have the honor to be, Sir,*
> *Your Obedient Servant,*
> *[Percy Hunter]*
> *Superintendent*

Secretary, Public Service Board
Hunter Street, Sydney

On Trickett's retirement, the *Mining Engineers Review* of 5 August 1919 reported:

Mr Oliver Trickett, surveyor and draftsman in the geological branch of the N.S.W. department of mines, has retired after some 27 years' service. Mr R.H. Cambage, under secretary for mines, on behalf of his fellow officers, presented Mr Trickett with a gold watch as a token of esteem and regard. In making the presentation, Mr Cambage spoke in high eulogy of Mr Trickett's valuable services, more particularly in regard to his work in surveying the Jenolan caves and making plans and models in connection therewith. He also alluded to Mr Trickett's unique model of the Broken Hill lode, for which he received a gold medal at the San Francisco exhibition.

A similar report had appeared in the Sydney *Sun* of 8 July.

In 1933 Havard wrote:

> The surveys and maps of the caves systems of New South Wales are those of Oliver Trickett, who voluntarily took up the work. The major part of the survey was undertaken during his leisure; the whole of the maps, reduced from these surveys, and all his guide books, were similarly the result of his sacrifice of private time. Trickett's surveys, plans and models—wonderfully accurate—have contributed greatly to the successful development of the caves of New South Wales. (Havard 1933)

As Havard pointed out, the amount of work Trickett carried out in his own time, particularly in relation to caves, was clearly remarkable. At least as early as 1895 he was referring to preparing at home most of the then 500 page reference work on the mineral deposits of NSW which was published as the *Bibliography of Economic Minerals of NSW* in 1919. Certainly the models were made in his own time, as, apparently, were the guidebooks, and the Blue Mountains maps. The £100 'bonus' which he was eventually paid in 1930, although an official recognition of his efforts, was hardly fair compensation for this work.

Trickett's professional contributions were acknowledged in an official *History of Geological Mapping, NSW Department of Mines* (Lucas 1974), published by the Department to celebrate its centenary. This brief sketch mentions Trickett on three occasions:

> During the early years of the Geological Survey maps were drawn by the geological surveyors (e.g. C.S. Wilkinson) or by draftsmen (e.g. O. Trickett) who were attached to the Charting Branch of the Department. (p. 2)

> 1893   A new edition of the geological map of the Colony. (Drawn by O. Trickett) (p. 3)

> Another interesting facet of the Survey's work in these early years was the exploration and mapping of limestone caves, and their opening to tourists. Maps and brief reports were prepared by W.S Leigh to 1896 and subsequently by O. Trickett (in addition to his duties as draftsman to the Geological Survey). Trickett prepared a guidebook to the Jenolan Caves, used for many years by tourists. (p. 3)

The booklet also includes a photo of Trickett, the only officer of the Department to be so honoured.

Trickett's work has been recognised internationally. In his *History of Cave Science* [to 1900], T.R. Shaw (1979) wrote:

> Many of the reports were accompanied by accurate plans of the caves as well as detailed descriptions. They culminated at the end of the century in the work of Oliver Trickett who was a licensed surveyor but not a professional geologist. He produced innumerable plans and, besides publishing lengthy reports in official publications, he also wrote popular guide books of good quality on serveral of the main cave areas. (p. 77)

Although most of those who have benefited from his maps, reports and other cave publications sing Trickett's praises, not everyone who has studied his work has been complimentary about him. A critical note creeps into the observations by Ralston (1990) on Trickett's comments on the efforts of explorers at Jenolan, which Ralston feels were less than generous. Of Trickett's comments on the exploits of Wiburd, Edwards and Bailey in discovering the River Cave and the Temple of Baal in June-August 1903, Ralston says "Oliver Trickett could have been more enthusiastic too about this dangerous journey. 'Their energy is appreciated' he reported" (Ralston 1990, p. 42). In fact Trickett was extremely enthusiastic about the discovery; he twice said it was 'the most important event at Jenolan of recent years' and his description is peppered with terms like 'endless variety of beautiful formations', 'highly decorated chambers', 'many grand caverns', 'superb', 'charming', 'rich fringes', 'truly marvellous collection' and 'unrivalled collection' [of helictites] (Trickett 1903b). This was very great praise from Trickett, who had seen just about all the State's then known caves. And of the deed, he in fact said "Considerable credit is due to the guides for the unflagging energy with which they carried out the work of exploration". This is fulsome praise for an official report in 1903.

Ralston also implies criticism of Trickett for saying he found his ten and a half hour visit to the River Cave hot on the heals of Wiburd and Edwards 'troublesome', whereas 'Wiburd and Edwards had been doing the same thing many nights running, as well as carrying out their normal guiding duties by day' (1990, p. 43). Although I have been unable to locate the quoted complaint I don't find it difficult to envisage that Trickett, at 56 years of age, might have found ten hours of crawling around in newly-discovered passages 'troublesome'.

Ralston has also related another, previously unpublished, incident involving Trickett which he gleaned from papers found in the State Archives in 1968:

> When Wiburd went to live in the Senior [Guide]'s cottage vacated by Fred Wilson after only three years from new, he found it so bad that he wanted to repaint the interior, and I think the post office as well. He sent an estimate to the Mines Dept. of £30 and asked for permission. Not getting a reply, he went ahead and sent an account for £26/4/8. Trickett recommended that Wiburd not be recompensed as he had not waited for permission. Wiburd offered to pay £5 himself, which the Dept. accepted. This was after he had found the River and Skeleton Caves. (Ralston, pers. comm.)

This would appear to indicate that Trickett was a good public servant, if somewhat a stickler for the rules.

FRIENDS AND ASSOCIATES

During his declining years Trickett seems to have revived his associations with a number of former associates and colleagues. This is inferred from the large number of letters from such people from the late 1920s among his papers. Of course it is possible that the contact was continuous through his life and only the letters of later years were retained. In any case there are letters from :

Sir Frank Gavan Duffy, a judge of the High Court, with whom Trickett had rowed in the Civil Service Rowing Club in Melbourne (1868-76)—31.7.22, 24.12.27, 29 11[?] 28, 27.12.29, 7.6.31, 7.6.33

John William Colville, first Secretary of the League of Nations Union, Victorian Branch and another former CSRC member—8.1.29 [died 10.11.29]

F. G. Finley, fellow surveyor with Trickett in 1879-83 [and who perhaps carried out early surveys of the Jenolan district ca. 1867-70 (Dunkley 1988 p. 40)]— 26.3.29

Frank Chaffey, Chief Secretary of NSW, former Minister for Mines—17, 24.2.30, 13.4.31

F. S. Mance, Under Secretary for Mines—3.1.30

J. A. Reid—26.4.30

Professor T.W.E. David, Professor of Geology at Sydney University and former colleague of Trickett's at Mines Department—15.6.28, 24.2.30, 1.6.31, 25.6.31, 24.5.33, etc

These letters give some indication of the depth of feeling which existed between Trickett and his colleagues. Edgeworth David's letters are good examples:

The University of Sydney

June 15, 1928

My dear Trickett,

(1) Herewith please find your two sets of notes with your small sketch plan, I have tried to answer your questions.

(2) I need, please, at your earliest convenience, a map drawn to show the Nullagine (Newer Proterozoic Areas) on same scale *as map supplied to you and showing same information as the smaller map. Editor of A. & S. volume, at Hobart, has just telegraphed for this.*

(3) I omitted to wish you many Happy Returns of your Birthday on May 29. Please let me do so now. May you live many happy years yet!

(4) I enclose a cheque for £5-0-0 on account.

Yours very sincerely,

[signed] *T. W. Edgeworth David*

and

UNIVERSITY CLUB
SYDNEY

February 24th, 1930

My dear Trickett,

Please accept my hearty gratitude for your kind thought in presenting me with the photographs of yourself, 1875 and 1929, together with those of the many trophies you have so well and worthily won. I am particularly touched by the kind words of your dedication on the back of the photograph. You are good enough to speak about my "many kindly acts in the past to one who will always keep them in remembrance".

Thank you so much, dear friend, for those words which I know come from your heart, and from the heart I say that as long as one is spared to live, one will ever treasure a happy memory of your many kindly services to myself rendered not only from a sense of duty, but as I am convinced, also from motives of personal esteem and, may I presume to add, affection.

You yourself little realise in what truly affectionate regard you are held by all those who have the privilege of your friendship. I wish, please, to take this opportunity of thanking you from my heart for so much invaluable help in the past. H.E.C. Robinson and I were only a couple of days ago, recalling your excellent and original methods of showing the cliff escarpments of the Blue Mountains. Those maps of yours will long live. With all good wishes and renewed thanks for your welcome gift.

I am, Yours very sincerely,

[signed] *T.W. Edgeworth David*

Again in 1931, Edgeworth David wrote:

The University of Sydney

June 1st 1931

My dear Trickett,

I ought to have written before to wish you, my dear friend, "Many Happy Returns of your Birthday". I was sorry that I was not at the Geological Branch when you called last week, so that I could have given you my congratulations personally.

All health and happiness to you, old friend and comrade! Yours very sincerely,

[signed] *T. W. Edgeworth David*

And again on 25 June 1931:

Oliver Trickett, Esq., L.S.
"Thule", 103 Willoughby Road
CROWS NEST, N. SYDNEY
25th June, 1931

My dear Trickett,

Many thanks to you for your kind letter of June 3rd.

Most certainly I endorse, with emphasis, the statement in the "Daily Telegraph" of May 29th, that you are a grand old sportsman, many thanks too for sending me a copy of the verses by Sir Henry Parkes which I think are very good.

With all good wishes from your old comrade,

Yours very sincerely.

[signed]T. W. Edgeworth David

David's letter of September 28, 1932 shows Trickett was still actively thinking and writing about geological matters:

"Coringah"
49 Burdett Street
Hornsby
Sept. 28, 1932

My dear Trickett,

Please forgive me for delay first in thanking you for your kind letter of 30.8.32 enclosing those very interesting lines by Sir Henry Parkes, and secondly for delay in acknowledging your letter of 16.9.32 ...
...
I find it difficult to answer your letter of 16.9.32.

In regard to D. J. Mares supplying half a page on "the Ice Ages causes of appearance and breaking up" I think that even the most concise account would need at least three pages to get in anything worth while on such an intricate subject.

Again "Why the Sea is Salt" really is a far from simple problem, and there is still some difference of opinion on the subject.

I would, my dear friend, like to help you, but I much regret that I can't see my way clear to do it in this case. I can see that it would be very difficult for me. You will, I am sure not misunderstand me under the circumstances. If you could have a good talk with W.S. Dun on the subject I should like to hear what his opinion is.

Yours very sincerely,

[signed] T. W. Edgeworth David

And in 1933:

University, Sydney
May 24, 1933

My dear Trickett,

I was delighted to get your most kind and generous letter of congratulation.

I feel I owe it not a little to the invaluable assistance of your good self that one has been enabled to accomplish such geological work as one has been spared to do, and I shall never cease to be grateful to you for your collaboration and comradeship.

Yours sincerely

[signed] T. W. Edgeworth David

Trickett's former colleague, F.G. Finley, wrote:

15 Wyalong Street
Burwood
26th March 1929

Dear Trickett

I have just heard from Mr Hodgson, J.P., who witnesses my signature for superannuation – of your address and I hasten to write to you a few lines to express my pleasure of the fact of knowing where you are. You have often been in my mind as I well remember that there was always peace and harmony between us in our official days. Of course I knew you were still on the earth's surface and I saw a photo of you the other day in connection with the Caves Memorial business. I wrote a short article to the 'Herald' about the Caves in the old days [published 2.3.29] and as Mr Hodgson saw it I suppose you did? But they curtailed the account I gave a great deal and left out some other particulars.

I would much like to meet you again before I 'go west'. I am now 85 and pretty good at that age. The photo I saw of you was not a darned bit like the Trickett I knew! I see you are at "Crows Nest", a place I know nothing about, but I suppose it is not difficult to find.

I have not been to Jenolan for a good few years and I just missed you when I made the visit.

If you let me know of any time and place where I could see you I will be there and have the pleasure of shaking hands with an old and esteemed official friend.

Yours sincerely,

[signed] F. G. Finley

And in one of his many letters, Sir Frank Duffy wrote:

AUSTRALIAN CLUB

June 7, 31

My dear Trickett,

Thanks for your kind congratulations which reached me on my way to Brisbane where we sit on Thursday. In return let me join Sir Edgeworth David in affectionate congratulations on your birthday.

Yours sincerely,

[signed] Frank Gavan Duffy

Mr J.A. Reid wrote:

MILLIONS CLUB OF N.S.W.
CR. PITT AND ROWE STREETS
SYDNEY. N.S.W.

April 26th 1930

Dear Mr. Trickett

I have just returned after a week's sojourn on the mountains, where I spent a very enjoyable time; wood-chopping, gardening and I could see the North Shore Bridge, with and without field-glasses (approx.

air-line 45 miles) at 5 pm, in a fading light so my eyesight is still fairly good.

Thank you very much for the Print of the Jenolan Caves. I will look through it with pleasure. Hope you liked Sir Henry's poem "70". I copied it out of a book of Australian verse. There are also some more of his poems in the book.

Hoping you are well,

Sincerely yours,

[signed] J.A. Reid

P.S. I only got your letter and Print this morning, hence the delay in acknowledging them.

It is evident that Trickett did, indeed, like Sir Henry's poem, for he wrote it out and sent copies to Sir Edgeworth David (see acknowledgement above), his sister, Ellen, Walter Hoad, former caretaker at Yarrangobilly Caves, and perhaps others. The poem expresses a very positive attitude to old age and no doubt appealed to him, as an active octogenarian. It began:

SEVENTY

Three score and ten, — the weight of years
Scarce seem to touch the tireless brain;
How bright the future still appears!
How dim the past of toil and pain!

FAMILY

There is little in Trickett's papers concerning his family. Mention is made of his parents only in the autobiographical note mentioned on page 2. There is a photograph of his mother, Henrietta, and a published obituary notice (source not identified). This states she was born in Edinburgh of Baptist parents; her mother's early death left her in the care of a deeply religious elder sister; she married the Rev. Edward Trickett at Bridlington, Yorkshire, and later came to Australia. Her husband predeceased her and she died in 1907.

Among the papers there is a photo of Oliver's younger brother, Arthur, and two newspaper items about his sister, Ellen Agnes. One of these, published in 1932, is mentioned on page 2. Apart from the fact that she lived in a house on the corner of Albert and Lansdowne Streets, East Melbourne, this indicates she was an art teacher for fifty years. The other item, published in *The Herald*, 7 May 1925, states that she was a teacher at the Presbyterian Ladies College from 1877 and that she taught Latin. There is no photo of Oliver's wife (though there is one thought to be of her mother) and her name, Elizabeth Anne, is only known from a death notice which appeared in the *Sydney Morning Herald* of 2 February 1933. It is believed her maiden name was Collins.

Elizabeth and Oliver had six children: Ruby (who married George Carroll), Lily (who accompanied her father to the 1929 plaque unveiling at Jenolan),

Gwendoline, Oliver William, Arthur (known as "Joe", who married Amelia (known as "Millie") and had children Gwen, Oliver and Pamela) and Margary (who married Jerry Selmes). A newspaper cutting indicates Oliver William owned a clothing factory in Wentworth Avenue, Sydney, which was severely damaged by fire on 21 June 1931. Another item states that Arthur ("Joe") Trickett was re-elected Secretary of the Northern Suburbs Hardcourt [tennis] Association on 24 January 1933.

Figure 104 is a family tree showing four generations of Tricketts.

CONCLUSION

Trickett was a man of prodigious energy and great determination. His productivity, even well after middle age, was staggering. It is evident, from the places that he got to and the work he carried out that he enjoyed field work—he was no arm-chair caver. And yet he also produced the necessary bureaucratic paperwork, detailed reports on his inspections, and his ubiquitous cave maps. His outstanding contribution was his documentation of the caves which recorded, interpreted and promoted them—through detailed maps, precise reports, guidebooks and models. His interest in caves must at times have amounted to an obsession but we unfortunately do not know the origins of this. It is not even clear whether he had any active role in cave conservation, though some of his reports indicate he was concerned about this and the creation of cave reserves soon after some reports (eg Colong) seems to indicate he played an active role.

Trickett clearly had the confidence of his superiors – he seems to have been given a virtually free hand in the administration of the caves – yet he did not progress to the upper echelons of the Public Service. His position remained virtually the same for 21 years. This may have been because he lacked appropriate education or background, because he was happy in his job, or simply because opportunities did not arise. In any case he was obviously very popular with his colleagues and was highly regarded by those who worked for him (especially the caves' staff) and by a number of prominent citizens. Despite his devotion to his work he retained contact at the personal level with his staff and friends. His contribution to the knowledge, protection and promotion of the limestone caves of New South Wales is unmatched.

Oliver Trickett died at his home, "Thule", in the northern Sydney suburb of Crows Nest on 31 March 1934. The following obituary appeared in the *Sydney Morning Herald* on 3 April 1934:

TRICKETT FAMILY TREE

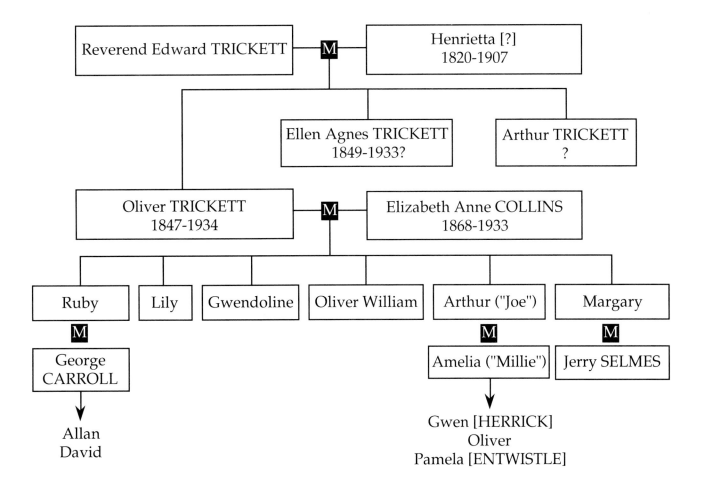

Figure 104. Trickett Family Tree showing four generations of Oliver's family

MR O. TRICKETT

Mr Oliver Trickett, whose funeral moved yesterday to the Northern Suburbs Cemetery, was 86 years of age, and retired from the Mines Department about 20 years ago.

As a young man he practiced as a licensed surveyor and mining surveyor, and on joining the Public Service rose to the position of Chief Draftsman of the geological survey branch of the Department of Mines, which he held for about 20 years. He carried out a number of notable works. The most arresting was a plaster of Paris model of Sydney Harbour, which was executed under a commission from the Sydney Harbour Trust. He did valuable work on the preparation of Sir Edgeworth David's maps of the Maitland coalfields, and of maps showing the disposition of metals in the Barrier mining field.

His guide books on the limestone caves of NSW are well known, as are his models of the Jenolan and Yarrangobilly Caves.

The large gathering at the funeral included Messrs F.S. Mance (Under-Secretary for Lands [sic–Mines?]), L.S. Harper (Government Geologist), John Mingaye (formerly Chief Government Analyst), Robert Vale (chief draftsman of the Lands Department), and M.J. Meldrum (draftsman of the geological survey branch of the Mines Department).

And so passed a man who had done more than anyone before him (and arguably, since) to document, develop, protect, present and promote the limestone caves of NSW.

REFERENCES

[A note on references to the *Annual Report of the Department of Mines, NSW* — ARDM
Since many of Trickett's reports and maps were published in this serial, it is frequently mentioned in the text and below. Strictly speaking, a report for a particular year would have been published in the following year and thus any item published, eg in the 1899 report, should be cited as 1900. This is likely to cause confusion, so for the sake of simplicity the year to which the report relates is referred to as the date of publication. Also, in some years the actual title was *Annual Report of the Department of Mines and Agriculture*; however, for simplicity, 'and Agriculture' has been omitted.]

ANDERSON, RONALD 1956 Cave areas of New South Wales *Communications*, Vol. 2:24-56

ANDERSON, W. & LEIGH, W.S. 1891 Report on newly-discovered caves at Yarrangobilly Creek *Ann. Rep. Dept. Mines NSW* 1891 pp. 249-252

BRADLEY, A.H.M. 1972 Recollections of the early history of Yarrangobilly Caves. *J. Syd Speleol. Soc.*, 16(6):162-164

CAMPBELL, W.D. 1899 Aboriginal carvings of Port Jackson and Broken Bay *Memoirs of the Geological Survey of NSW; Ethnological Series No. 1*

CARNE, J.E. 1903 Author's preface [to] The Kerosene Deposits of NSW, *Geological Survey Memoir* 3, p. xiv

CARNE, J.E. 1911 Introduction [to] The Tin Mining Industry and the Distribution of Tin Ores in NSW. *Mineral Resources* No. 14 Department of Mines Geological Survey : Sydney p. 3

CARNE, J.E. 1915 Annual Report of the Government Geologist *Ann. Rep. Dept. Mines NSW* 1915 p. 190

CARNE, J.E. 1916 Annual Report of the Government Geologist *Ann. Rep. Dept. Mines NSW* 1916 p. 218

CARNE, J.E. 1917 Annual Report of the Government Geologist *Ann. Rep. Dept. Mines NSW* 1917 p. 172

CARNE, J.E. 1918 Annual Report of the Government Geologist *Ann. Rep. Dept. Mines NSW* 1918 p. 166

CARNE, J.E. 1919 Annual Report of the Government Geologist *Ann. Rep. Dept. Mines NSW* 1919 p. 178

CARNE, J.E. & JONES, L.J. 1919 The limestone deposits of New South Wales. *Mineral Resources* No. 25 Department of Mines Geological Survey : Sydney 411 pp.

COOK, SAMUEL 1889 *The Jenolan Caves : an excursion into Australian wonderland* Eyre & Spottiswoode : London 192 pp

DAVID, T.W. EDGEWORTH 1907 Geology of the Hunter River coal measures, N.S.W. *Memoirs of the Geological Survey of NSW, No. 4* Government Printer : Sydney

DRISCOLL, IAN 1977 The Binoomea Cut - Jenolan Caves *Jenolan Caves Historical & Preservation Society Occ. Pap. #4* 16 pp

DUNKLEY, JOHN R. [1988] *A Bibliography of the Jenolan Caves – Part 2: Literature* Speleological Research Council Ltd: Sydney 45 pp

ELLIS, R., HAMILTON-SMITH, E. & SHAW, T. in prep. *Australian caves on post cards 1900-1939*

ETHERIDGE, R., Junr. & TRICKETT, O. 1904 The discovery of a human skeleton at Jenolan Caves. *Rec. Geol. Surv. NSW*, VII(4):325-328 + photo + plan

FOSTER, J.J. 1890 *The Jenolan Caves* Government Printer : Sydney 96 pp

HAMILTON-SMITH, ELERY n.d. Australian caves and government (unpublished MS.) p. 7

HARPER, L.F. 1930 The Yerranderie silver field *Mineral Resources* No. 35 Geological Survey of NSW : Sydney [includes Trickett 1899b as an appendix]

HARVEY, R.W. & TRICKETT, O. 1889 *Handy register of mining companies ... in the Australian colonies.* Messrs Harvey & Trickett : Sydney.

HAVARD, W. L. 1934 The romance of Jenolan Caves. *J. & Proc. Roy. Aust. Hist. Soc.*, XX(1):18-65 [Reprinted as a monograph with pages numbered 1 to 48.]

JAMES, J.M., MARTIN, D.J. & TUNNOCK, L.K. 1988 The Jenolan Cave System surveying project. Part 1 - history, organisation and assessment [in] *Preprints of papers for the 17th Biennial Conference of Aust. Speleol. Fed. (Tropicon)* ASF Tropicon Subcommittee : Cairns pp. 25-31

JAQUET, J.B. 1894 Geology of the Broken Hill lode and Barrier Ranges mineral field, New South Wales. *Memoirs of the Geological Survey of NSW. Geology, No. 5* Government Printer : Sydney

LACHLAN, D.C.W. 1898 Under Secretary's Report: Limestone Caves *Ann. Rep. Dept. Mines NSW* 1898 p. 192

LANG, JOHN 1919 *The Victorian oarsman with a rowing register 1857 to 1919.* Massina & Co. : Melbourne pp. 128-136, 217

LEIGH, W.S. 1888 Appendix No. 7 to Wilkinson, C.S., Geological Survey of NSW: Report of progress for 1888 *Ann. Rep. Dept. Mines NSW* 1888 p. 200

LEIGH, W.S. 1893 Appendix 9B (Report on new cave (Jubilee), Jenolan Caves), *Ann. Rep. Dept. Mines NSW* 1893 pp. 140-142

LISHMUND, S.R., DAWOOD, A.D. & LANGLEY, W.V. The limestone deposits of New South Wales. *Mineral Resources* No. 25 2nd Edition Department of Mineral Resources Geological Survey : Sydney 373 pp.

LUCAS, R.R. 1974 *History of geological mapping, New South Wales Department of Mines, centenary 1874-1974.* The department : Sydney 12 pp

MATTHEWS, P.G. 1985 *Australian karst index 1985.* Australian Speleological Federation : Melbourne

MIDDLETON, G.J. 1967 An historical background to Colong Caves. *Communications Occasional Paper* No. 2, pp. 1-10

MIDDLETON, G. 1985a An interview with Anthony Harris Mobsby Bradley on Yarrangobilly *J. Syd. Speleol. Soc.,* 29(4):59-66

MIDDLETON, G. 1985b An interview with Leo Hoad on Yarrangobilly Caves. *J. Syd. Speleol. Soc.,* 29(8):145-154

MIDDLETON, G.J. 1988 Index to references to caves in three NSW government publications 1870-1919. *S.S.S. Occ. Pap.* #9 22 pp

MIDDLETON, G. 1990 Jubilee/Slattery Cave, Jenolan: an historical insight. *J. Syd. Speleol. Soc.,* 34(9):169-175

NSW DEPT. OF TOURIST ACTIVITIES 1967 *Handbook for Caves Guiding Staff.* The Department: Sydney 68 pp [Largely prepared by B. T. Dunlop]

OSBORNE, R.A.L. & BRANAGAN, D.F. 1988 Karst landscapes of New South Wales, Australia [in] Firman, J. (Ed.) Landscapes of the Southern Hemisphere *Earth-Sci. Rev.,* 25:467-480

PAVEY, ANDREW 1973 Yarrangobilly Seminar *Spar, #30:7*

PITTMAN, E.F. 1893 Progress report for 1893 by the Government Geologist *Ann. Rep. Dept. Mines NSW* 1893 p. 105

PITTMAN, E.F. 1896 Progress report for 1896 by the Government Geologist *Ann. Rep. Dept. Mines NSW* 1896 p. 97

PITTMAN, E.F. 1897 Progress report for 1897 by the Government Geologist *Ann. Rep. Dept. Mines NSW* 1897 p. 134

PITTMAN, E.F. 1900 Geological Survey of NSW : Progress report for 1900 by the Government Geologist *Ann. Rep. Dept. Mines NSW* 1900 p. 175

PITTMAN, E.F. 1901 Geological Survey of NSW : Progress report for 1901 by the Government Geologist *Ann. Rep. Dept. Mines NSW* 1901 pp. 176-177

PITTMAN, E.F. 1908 Annual Report of the Government Geologist *Ann. Rep. Dept. Mines NSW* 1908 p. 172

PITTMAN, E.F. 1909 Annual Report of the Government Geologist *Ann. Rep. Dept. Mines NSW* 1909 p. 191

PITTMAN, E.F. 1911 Annual Report of the Government Geologist *Ann. Rep. Dept. Mines NSW* 1911 pp. 193-194 (incl. section)

PITTMAN, E.F. 1914 Annual Report of the Government Geologist *Ann. Rep. Dept. Mines NSW* 1914 p. 182

RALSTON, BASIL 1990 *Jenolan: the golden ages of caving* Three Sisters Productions : Winmalee, NSW 64pp.

ROSE, P.V. 1964 An introduction to Yarrangobilly Caves, NSW, Australia. Part I *Cave Science* (BSA, UK), #36:203-216

SHANNON, HENRY 1973 A.S.F. field trips – Jenolan. *Down Under,* 12(1):17-19

SHAW, Trevor R. 1979 *History of Cave Science: The scientific investigation of limestone caves, to 1900.* Anne Oldham: Crymych, Wales 490 pp. + 88 figures

TRICKETT, O. 1896 Progress report on the caves for the year 1896. *Ann. Rep. Dept. Mines NSW* 1896 pp. 148-149

TRICKETT, O. 1897a Appendix 29 - Caves - Progress and other reports on the limestone caves for the year 1897 [in] Progress report for 1897 by the Government Geologist *Ann. Rep. Dept. Mines NSW* 1897 pp. 202-205

TRICKETT, O. 1897b Appendix 30 - The Grove Cave (Abercrombie Caves) *Ann. Rep. Dept. Mines NSW* 1897 p. 205 + plan

TRICKETT, O. 1897c Appendix 31 - Tuglow Caves, Tuglow River *Ann. Rep. Dept. Mines NSW* 1897 p. 205-206 + plan

TRICKETT, O. 1897d Appendix 32 - New Cave, Jenolan Caves *Ann. Rep. Dept. Mines NSW* 1897 p. 206

TRICKETT, O. 1897e Appendix 33 - Mutilation of the Copper Mine Cave, Yarrangobilly *Ann. Rep. Dept. Mines NSW* 1897 p. 207

TRICKETT, O. 1898a Appendix 31 - Caves - Progress and other reports on the limestone caves for the year 1898 *Ann. Rep. Dept. Mines NSW* 1898 pp. 192-193

TRICKETT, O. 1898b Appendix 29 - The Junction Cave—Wombeyan Caves *Ann. Rep. Dept. Mines NSW* 1898 pp. 193-194 + plan

TRICKETT, O. 1898c Appendix 30 - Limestone cave at Limekilns *Ann. Rep. Dept. Mines NSW* 1898 p. 194 + plan

TRICKETT, O. 1898d *Notes on the limestone caves of New South Wales with plans.* Dept. of Mines & Agriculture : Sydney 17 pp [reprinted from Trickett 1897a, incl. 13 plans, 2 from *ARDM* 1900]

TRICKETT, O. 1899a Caves - Progress and other reports on the limestone caves for the year 1899 *Ann. Rep. Dept. Mines NSW* 1899 pp. 210-211 + plan

TRICKETT, O. 1899b Report on Colong Caves. *Ann. Rep. Dept. Mines NSW* 1899 pp. 211-212 + plan [reprinted as an appendix to Harper 1930]

TRICKETT, O. 1899c Report on the Wyanbene Cave. *Ann. Rep. Dept. Mines NSW* 1899 p. 213 [plan published 1900]

TRICKETT, O. 1899d *Guide to the Jenolan Caves, New South Wales.* Geological Survey of NSW : Sydney 64 pp, 43 photos, 2 maps

TRICKETT, O. 1900a Progress and other reports on the limestone caves for the year 1900 *Ann. Rep. Dept. Mines NSW* 1900 pp. 196-198

TRICKETT, O. 1900b Report on Bungonia Caves *Ann. Rep. Dept. Mines NSW* 1900 pp. 198-199 + plan

TRICKETT, O. 1900c New chamber off the Jubilee Cave, Jenolan Caves *Ann. Rep. Dept. Mines NSW* 1900 p. 199 + plan

TRICKETT, O. 1900d New passage, Lucas Cave, Jenolan Caves *Ann. Rep. Dept. Mines NSW* 1900 p. 199 + plan

TRICKETT, O. 1900e New branch of the Lucas Cave, Jenolan Caves *Ann. Rep. Dept. Mines NSW* 1900 p. 199 + plan

TRICKETT, O. 1900f Wellington Caves *Ann. Rep. Dept. Mines NSW* 1900 p. 200

TRICKETT, O. 1901 [Report on the limestone caves for 1901] *Ann. Rep. Dept. Mines NSW* 1901 pp. 176-177

TRICKETT, O. 1902 [Report on the limestone caves for 1902] *Ann. Rep. Dept. Mines NSW* 1902 p. 129

TRICKETT, O. 1903a Report on the limestone caves *Ann. Rep. Dept. Mines NSW* 1903 pp. 135-136

TRICKETT, O. 1903b Discovery of new branches of the Lucas Cave, Jenolan *Ann. Rep. Dept. Mines NSW* 1903 p. 136 + plan

TRICKETT, O. 1903c Bouverie Cave, Wombeyan Caves *Ann. Rep. Dept. Mines NSW* 1903 p. 136 + plan

TRICKETT, O. 1904 [Report on the limestone caves] *Ann. Rep. Dept. Mines NSW* 1904 p. 148

TRICKETT, O. 1905a Caves *Ann. Rep. Dept. Mines NSW* 1905 p. 158

TRICKETT, O. 1905b *Guide to the Jenolan Caves, New South Wales.* Geological Survey of NSW : Sydney 2nd Edition 82 pp, 63 photos, 2 maps

TRICKETT, O. 1905c *Guide to Yarrangobilly Caves, NSW* Geological Survey of NSW : Sydney 30 pp, 19 photos, 2 maps

TRICKETT, O. 1906a [Report on the limestone caves] *Ann. Rep. Dept. Mines NSW* 1906 p. 173

TRICKETT, O. 1906b Guide to the Wombeyan Caves, NSW Geological Survey of NSW : Sydney 36 pp, 19 photos, 2 maps

TRICKETT, O. 1906c *The Abercrombie Caves* Government Tourist Bureau : Sydney 12 pp, 3 photos, map

TRICKETT, O. 1906d *The Bungonia Caves* Government Tourist Bureau : Sydney 8 pp, 3 photos

TRICKETT, O. 1906e *The Wellington Caves* Government Tourist Bureau : Sydney 12 pp, 3 photos, map

TRICKETT, O. 1907 Limestone caves - report by O. Trickett, L.S.M.S. *Ann. Rep. Dept. Mines NSW* p. 174

TRICKETT, O. 1908 Report of the Cliefden Caves, warm spring and fossil hill, Belubula River *Ann. Rep. Dept. Mines NSW* 1908 p. 172

TRICKETT, O. 1910 Report on caves *Ann. Rep. Dept. Mines NSW* 1910 p. 182-183 + 3 plans

TRICKETT, O. 1912a Limestone Caves *Ann. Rep. Dept. Mines NSW* 1912 p. 193

TRICKETT, O. 1912b The construction of mine models *A'asian Inst. of Mining Engineers Proc.*, Supp No. II New Series #6:1-5, 6 plates

TRICKETT, O. 1913 Limestone Caves *Ann. Rep. Dept. Mines NSW* 1913 pp. 185-186

TRICKETT, O. 1914a Report by O. Trickett *Ann. Rep. Dept. Mines NSW* 1914 pp. 212-213 + plate

TRICKETT, O. 1914b Notes on the Jenolan Caves [in] *Notes on Excursion to the Jenolan Caves* British Association for the Advancement of Science 1914 Meeting, Sydney pp. 12-13

TRICKETT, O. 1915 *Guide to the Jenolan Caves, New South Wales.* Immigration and Tourist Bureau : Sydney 3rd Edition 88 pp, 64 photos, 2 maps

TRICKETT, O. 1917 *Guide to Yarrangobilly Caves, NSW* Immigration & Tourist Bureau : Sydney 2nd Edition 44 pp, 38 photos, diagram, 2 maps

TRICKETT, O. 1919 Bibliography of the Economic Minerals of New South Wales *Mineral Resources* No. 28 Department of Mines, Geological Survey : Sydney

TRICKETT, O. 1922 *Guide to the Jenolan Caves, New South Wales.* NSW Government Tourist Bureau : Sydney 4th Edition 90 pp, 63 photos, 2 maps

TRICKETT, O. & ETHERIDGE, R. 1903 Report on the discovery of a human skeleton in a branch of the Lucas Cave, at Jenolan. *Ann. Rep. Dept. Mines NSW* 1903 pp. 137-138

WILKINSON, C.S. & DAVID, T.W.E. 1895 *Geological Map shewing the principal stanniferous leads in the Tingha and Elsmore Districts.* Dept. of Mines & Agriculture : Sydney

APPENDIX 1
The Limestone Caves of New South Wales

[Part of Trickett's progress report on caves for the year 1897, *Annual Report of Dept. of Mines,* 1897, pp. 203-205; re-published by the Dept. of Mines and Agriculture as *Notes on the Limestone Caves of NSW - with plans* in 1898. This probably constitutes the first published bibliography of Australian caves. It has been edited only in that the caves have been rearranged into alphabetical order and some additional information has been added, in square brackets.]

THE control of the [limestone] caves [of NSW] was transferred from the Lands Department to the Mines Department in 1879 (M.79/8,989) Between 1st January 1883 and July 1897 the sum of £23,131 had been expended on the care and improvement of the caves. Particulars of earlier expenditure are not readily available.

Probably as much more has been expended on the roads to the Jenolan, Yarrangobilly and Wombeyan Caves.

The Jenolan and Yarrangobilly Caves have telegraphic communication.

There is a post office at Jenolan and a postal receiving office at Wombeyan.

The eastern portion of the Colony contains numerous deposits of limestone, many of which are unexplored. Wherever the limestone occurs in mountainous or rugged country it has been found to contain caves, which, from their grandeur and the richness and delicacy of their ornamentation, have been termed the "Australian Fairy Land".

The causes which have led to the formation of the caves have been explained by the late C. S. Wilkinson, Geological Surveyor in Charge, in a paper published in the Railway Guide, 1886, and by Professor T. W. E. David in his report on the Wombeyan Caves, 22/6/85.

The limestone in which most of the caves are situated is of Upper Silurian or Lower Devonian age; but I am informed by Mr W. S. Dun, Assistant Palæontologist, that the Yessabah Caves are probably in limestone of Permo-Carboniferous age, while the Isis River Caves [Timor] may be in Carboniferous rocks [actually Middle to Upper Devonian].

The caves have been the subject of the following descriptions and reports:—

ABERCROMBIE CAVES.
C.S. Wilkinson, 1877, Annual Report of Department of Mines for 1877, p. 206.
C.S. Wilkinson, 26th November, 1879, Proceedings of the Linnean Society of N.S.W., for 1879, p. 460.
W.S. Leigh, 6th March, 1894, Annual Report of Department of Mines and Agriculture for 1894, p. 157.
O. Trickett, 7th January, 1897, M. 97/560.*
O. Trickett, 25th September, 1897, Annual Report of Department of Mines for 1897 [p. 205].

ARRANARRANG CAVES (Mongola Creek, a tributary of the Tumut River).
Clarke's "Southern Gold Fields," 1860, p. 106

BELUBULA CAVES (10 m. E. of Canowindra).
C.S. Wilkinson, 26th August, 1876, *T. and C. Journal,* 9th September, 1876.
C.S. Wilkinson, 26th August, 1876, Records Geol. Survey, N.S.W., 1892, iii, Pt. 1.
Parliamentary Paper, Exploration of Caves and Rivers of N.S.W., 1882.

BENDITHERA CAVES.
W.S. Leigh, 29th April, 1890, Annual Report of Department of Mines for 1890, p. 310.
O. Trickett, 27th February 1897, M. 97/5,029.*

BIG HOLE (South of Braidwood).
E.J.H. Knapp, 1874, Misc. Lands, 74/2,986.

BORENORE OR BOREE CAVES (between Molong and Cudal).
M. 90/23,126; Misc. Lands, 95/9,442.

BUNGONIA CAVES.
W. Anderson, 25th June, 1889, Annual Report of Department of Mines for 1889, p. 232.
W.S. Leigh, 5th August, 1889, Annual Report of Department of Mines for 1889, p. 251.
W.S. Leigh, 28th October, 1891, Annual Report of Department of Mines and Agriculture for 1891, p. 281.
O. Trickett, 5th May, 1897, M. 97/9,965.*

CAVE FLAT CAVES (Junction of Murrumbidgee and Goodradigbee Rivers).
R. Etheridge, Junr., 6th July 1888, Annual Report Trustees Australian Museum for 1889.
Parliamentary Papers, Exploration of Caves and Rivers of N.S.W., 1882

COODRADIGBEE (See "GOODRAVALE").

COOLEMAN CAVES (Cooleman Creek, Goodradigbee River).

W.S. Leigh and R. Etheridge, Junr., Annual Report of Department of Mines and Agriculture for 1893, p. 134

GOODRAVALE CAVES (Goodradigbee River).

Clarke's "Southern Gold-fields," p. 105.

R. Etheridge, Junr.—1892 Records Geol. Survey N.S.W., 1892, iii, Pt. 1, p. 37

ISIS RIVER CAVES (near Crawney).

W.E. Abbott, 6th May, 1896, G.S., 96/706.

JENOLAN CAVES

(Originally known as the Fish River or Binda Caves. Name altered to Jenolan by *Gazette* Notice, 19th August, 1884.)

Sydney Morning Herald, 5th June, 1863.

J.E. Richter, *Scientific American,* 1884, No. 15.

Sydney Morning Herald, a series of articles published in 1886.

S. Cook, The Jenolan Caves, an Excursion in Australian Wonderland, 1889.

C.S. Wilkinson, Railway Guide, 1886.

W.S. Leigh, 11th June 1888, Annual Report of Department of Mines for 1888, p. 202.

W.S. Leigh, 24th March, 1893, Annual Report of Department of Mines and Agriculture for 1893, p. 140.

W.S. Leigh, 6th March, 1894, Annual Report of Department of Mines and Agriculture for 1894, p. 156.

Foster's Guide Book, published by the Government Printer in 1890. This book contains a description by C.S. Wilkinson and L.H.G. Young.

A. Tissandier, Bull. Soc. Spéléologie, 1895, I, No. 2, pp. 50-56.

O. Trickett, 3rd January, 1897, M.97/674.*

O. Trickett, 6th December, 1897, Annual Report, Department of Mines and Agriculture for 1897. [p. 206]

JERRARA CAVES. [subsequently destroyed by mining]

W.S. Leigh, 26th November, 1890, Annual Report of Department of Mines for 1890, p. 311.

KYBEAN CAVES; 20 miles south-east of Cooma.

W.S. Leigh, 28th July, 1890, Annual Report of Department of Mines for 1890, p. 311.

W.S. Leigh, 3rd November 1890, M. 90/22,487.

W.S. Leigh and R. Etheridge, Junr., Records Geol. Survey, N.S.W., iii, Pt. 1, p. 21.

NARRANGULLEN CAVE (Murrumbidgee River) [Taemas]

R. Etheridge, Junr., 1892, Records Geol. Survey, N.S.W., 1892, 111, Pt. 2, p. 68.

ROSEBROOK CAVES (near Cooma).

W.S. Leigh, 12th April, 1892, Annual Report, Department of Mines and Agriculture for 1892, p. 176.

W.S. Leigh, 12th April, 1893, Records Geol. Survey of N.S.W. for 1893, iii, Pt. 3, p. 77.

W.S. Leigh, 3rd November, 1894, Annual Report, Department of Mines and Agriculture for 1894, p. 157.

STUART TOWN CAVES.

W.S. Leigh, 30th July, 1896, Annual Report of Department of Mines and Agriculture for 1896, p. 152

TUGLOW CAVES (10 miles south of Jenolan Caves)

O. Trickett, 29th October, 1897, Annual Report of Department of Mines and Agriculture for 1897 [p. 205]

WELLINGTON CAVES.

Sir T. Mitchell, 1831, "Mitchell's Australia," 1838, Ch. XV, Vol. 2, p. 347.

E. Krefft and Dr A.M. Thompson, 1870, Parliamentary Papers, Wellington Caves, 1870; Exploration of Caves and Rivers of N.S.W., 1882.

C.S. Wilkinson, 1876, Annual Report of Department of Mines for 1876, p. 162.

O. Trickett, 23rd December, 1896, M. 96/33,436*

WOMBEYAN CAVES.

L.H.G. Young, 31st December, 1879, Annual Report of Department of Mines for 1879, p. 226.

W.S. Leigh, 7th September, 1888, Annual Report of Department of Mines for 1888, p. 203.

W.S. Leigh, 17th October 1888; unpublished.

W.S. Leigh, 28th January, 1890, Annual Report of Department of Mines for 1889, p. 253.

W.S. Leigh, 12th December, 1892, Annual Report of Department of Mines and Agriculture, 1892, p. 177.

W.S. Leigh, 26th November, 1894, Annual Report of Department of Mines and Agriculture, 1894, p. 158

W.S. Leigh, 2nd March, 1896, Annual Report of Department of Mines and Agriculture, 1896, p. 151.

T.W.E. David, 22nd June, 1885, Annual Report of Department of Mines and Agriculture, 1896, p. 149.

O. Trickett, 25th November, 1896, M. 96/30,640.*

R. Etheridge, Junr., Annual Report Trustees Australian Museum for 1896, p. 5.

WYANBENE CAVES (25 miles southerly from Braidwood).

W.S. Leigh, 21st January, 1889, M. 89/1,404, M. 97/925.

YARRANGOBILLY CAVES.

W. Anderson, 3rd January, 1897, Annual Report, Department of Mines, for 1886, p. 163.

Illustrated Sydney News, 28th March, 11th and 25th April, 1891 (Discovery of Jersey Cave).

W. Anderson and W.S. Leigh, 14th March, 1891, Annual Report, Dept. of Mines and Agriculture for 1891, p. 249.

W.S. Leigh, 14th September, 1891, Annual Report, Department of Mines and Agriculture for 1891, p. 282.

O. Trickett, 18th November, 1896, M. 96/30,645.*

O. Trickett, 20th December, 1897, Annual Report, Department of Mines and Agriculture for 1897 [p. 207].

YESSABAH CAVES (near Kempsey).

C.S. Wilkinson, 19th October, 1897, M. 89/19,068.

Caves are also said to exist at Alum Creek, near Bredbo.

At 4 miles south-south-east of Cudgegong.

And at 6 or 7 miles from O'Connell, Bathurst District.

It may be added that the picturesque scenery of the Kanangra (Kowmung) Walls, near Jenolan, is the subject of a report by W.S. Leigh, 24th October, 1889, Annual Report, Department of Mines for 1889, p. 252.

[* The Archives Office of N.S.W. has advised that these documents are "missing" from its holdings. It is possible that they still exist but have been misfiled or attached to later correspondence—GJM]

APPENDIX 2
Bibliography of Published Works of Oliver Trickett

1889   [with R.W. Harvey] *Handy Register of Mining Companies ... in the Australian Colonies* Messrs Harvey and Trickett: Sydney

1893   *Geological Map of New South Wales* NSW Department of Mines [map, multicoloured, scale 1 in : 16 miles, dimensions 128 x 110 cm] Under legend appears: GEOLOGICALLY PLOTTED AND COMPILED BY O. TRICKETT

1896   Progress report on the caves for the year 1896. *Ann. Rep. Dept. Mines* 1896, pp. 148-149

1897   Appendix 29 - Caves - Progress and other reports on the limestone caves for the year 1897. *Ann. Rep. Dept. Mines* 1897, pp. 202-203 + 11 plans

—   The limestone caves of New South Wales. *Ann. Rep. Dept. Mines* 1897, pp. 203-205 [Reprinted herein as Appendix 1]

—   Appendix 30 - The Grove Cave (Abercrombie Caves). *Ann. Rep. Dept. Mines* 1897, p. 205 + plan

—   Appendix 31 - Tuglow Caves, Tuglow River. *Ann. Rep. Dept. Mines* 1897, pp. 205-206 + plan

—   Appendix 32 - New Cave, Jenolan Caves. *Ann. Rep. Dept. Mines* 1897, p. 206 + plan

—   Appendix 33 - Mutilation of the Copper Mine Cave, Yarrangobilly. *Ann. Rep. Dept. Mines* 1897, p. 207

1898   Appendix 31 - Caves - Progress and other reports on the limestone caves for the year 1898. *Ann. Rep. Dept. Mines* 1898, pp. 192-193

—   Appendix 29 - The Junction Cave—Wombeyan Caves. *Ann. Rep. Dept. Mines* 1898, pp. 193-194 + plan

—   Appendix 30 - Limestone cave at Limekilns. *Ann. Rep. Dept. Mines* 1898, p. 194 + plan

—   *Notes on the limestone caves of New South Wales with plans.* Dept. of Mines & Agriculture: Sydney 17 pp (incl. 13 plans) Reprinted from *ARDM* 1897 plus 2 plans from *ARDM* 1900.

1899   Caves - Progress and other reports on the limestone caves for the year 1899 *Ann. Rep. Dept. Mines NSW* 1899 pp. 210-211 + plan

—   Report on Colong Caves. *Ann. Rep. Dept. Mines NSW* 1899 pp. 211-212 + plan [reprinted as an appendix to Harper 1930]

—   Report on the Wyanbene Cave. *Ann. Rep. Dept. Mines NSW* 1899 p. 213 [plan-1900]

—   *Guide to the Jenolan Caves, New South Wales.* Geological Survey of NSW : Sydney 1st Edition 64 pp, 43 photos, 2 maps

1900   Progress and other reports on the limestone caves for the year 1900 *Ann. Rep. Dept. Mines NSW* 1900 pp. 196-198

—   Report on Bungonia Caves *Ann. Rep. Dept. Mines NSW* 1900 pp. 198-199 + plan

—   New chamber off the Jubilee Cave, Jenolan Caves *Ann. Rep. Dept. Mines NSW* 1900 p. 199 + plan

—   New passage, Lucas Cave, Jenolan Caves *Ann. Rep. Dept. Mines NSW* 1900 p. 199 + plan

—   New branch of the Lucas Cave, Jenolan Caves *Ann. Rep. Dept. Mines NSW* 1900 p. 199 + plan

—   Wellington Caves *Ann. Rep. Dept. Mines NSW* 1900 p. 200

1901   [Report on the limestone caves for 1901] *Ann. Rep. Dept. Mines NSW* 1901 pp. 176-177

1902	[Report on the limestone caves for 1902] *Ann. Rep. Dept. Mines NSW* 1902 p. 129
1903	Report on the limestone caves *Ann. Rep. Dept. Mines NSW* 1903 pp. 135-136
—	Discovery of new branches of the Lucas Cave, Jenolan *Ann. Rep. Dept. Mines NSW* 1903 p. 136 + plan
—	Bouverie Cave, Wombeyan Caves *Ann. Rep. Dept. Mines NSW* 1903 p. 136 + plan
—	[with R. Etheridge, Junr.] Report on the discovery of a human skeleton in a branch of the Lucas Cave, at Jenolan. *Ann. Rep. Dept. Mines NSW* 1903 pp. 137-138
1904	[Report on the limestone caves] *Ann. Rep. Dept. Mines NSW* 1904 p. 148
—	[with R. Etheridge, Junr.] The discovery of a human skeleton at Jenolan Caves. *Rec. Geol. Surv. NSW*, VII(4):325-328 + photo + plan
1905	Caves *Ann. Rep. Dept. Mines NSW* 1905 p. 158
—	*Guide to Yarrangobilly Caves, NSW* Geological Survey of NSW : Sydney 1st Edition 30 pp, 19 photos, 2 maps
—	*Guide to the Jenolan Caves, New South Wales.* Geological Survey of NSW : Sydney 2nd Edition 82 pp, 63 photos, 2 maps
1906	[Report on the limestone caves] *Ann. Rep. Dept. Mines NSW* 1906 p. 173
—	*Guide to the Wombeyan Caves, NSW* Geological Survey of NSW : Sydney 1st Edition 36 pp, 19 photos, 2 maps
—	*The Abercrombie Caves* Government Tourist Bureau : Sydney 12 pp, 3 photos, map
—	*The Bungonia Caves* Government Tourist Bureau : Sydney 8 pp, 3 photos
—	*The Wellington Caves* Government Tourist Bureau : Sydney 12 pp, 3 photos, map
1907	Limestone caves - report by O. Trickett, L.S.M.S. *Ann. Rep. Dept. Mines NSW* 1907 p. 174
1908	Report of the Cliefden Caves, warm spring and fossil hill, Belubula River *Ann. Rep. Dept. Mines NSW* 1908 p. 172
1909	*The Blue Mountains from Lawson to Lithgow - their geological and topographical features.* [map, multicoloured, 1 in to 1 mile, dimensions 40 x 63 cm] Immigration and Tourist Bureau : Sydney
—	*The Blue Mountains from Lawson to Lithgow - their topographical features, pleasure resorts and points of interest.* [map, 3 colours, 2 cm to 1 mile, dimensions 30 x 48 cm] Government Tourist Bureau : Sydney
1910	Report on caves *Ann. Rep. Dept. Mines NSW* 1910 p. 182
—	The Jillabenan Cave *Ann. Rep. Dept. Mines NSW* 1910 p. 182-183 + plan
1911	Limestone caves *Ann. Rep. Dept. Mines NSW* 1911 pp. 193-194
1912	Limestone caves *Ann. Rep. Dept. Mines NSW* 1912 p. 193
—	The construction of mine models *A'asian Inst. of Mining Engineers Proc.*, Supp No. II New Series #6:1-5, 6 plates
1913	Limestone caves *Ann. Rep. Dept. Mines NSW* 1913 pp. 185-186 + 4 plans
1914	Report by O. Trickett *Ann. Rep. Dept. Mines NSW* 1914 pp. 212-213 + plate
1914	Notes on the Jenolan Caves [in] *Notes on Excursion to the Jenolan Caves* British Association for the Advancement of Science 14th Meeting, Sydney pp. 12-13
1915	*Guide to the Jenolan Caves, New South Wales.* Geological Survey of NSW : Sydney 3rd Edition 88 pp, 64 photos, 2 maps
1917	*Guide to Yarrangobilly Caves, NSW* Immigration & Tourist Bureau : Sydney 2nd Edition 44 pp, 38 photos, diagram, 2 maps
1919	Bibliography of the Economic Minerals of New South Wales. *Mineral Resources* No. 28 Dept. of Mines, Geological Survey : Sydney

1922   *Guide to the Jenolan Caves, New South Wales.* Geological Survey of NSW : Sydney 4th Edition 90 pp, 63 photos, 2 maps

1923   Notes on the Jenolan Caves [in] *Guide-book to the excursion to the Blue Mountains, Jenolan Caves and Lithgow.* [for Pan-Pacific Science Congress] Government Tourist Bureau : Sydney pp. 32-34

1925   *The Jenolan Caves, New South Wales* [map, scale 1:1200, coloured, dimensions 64 x 106 cm] Government Tourist Bureau : Sydney

undated   *The Blue Mountains, NSW, from Glenbrook to Lithgow - showing their geological and topographical features.* [map, 3 colours, 1 in to 1.5 mile, dimensions 31.5 x 56 cm] Printed by Alfred James Kent, Government Printer [1923-36]

INDEX

COLOPHON

This book was written, composed and designed entirely on Apple Macintosh™ computers, using Microsoft® Word and PageMaker® programs. The main body of the text is set in Palatino™ typeface 10 point, with Palatino italic used for lengthy quotations. Figure captions, references, appendices and index are in Times™ typeface. The digitally encoded machine-readable outline data for producing the typefaces is copyrighted © 1981 Allied Corporation and Adobe Systems Inc.

The black and white line graphics were scanned on an Apple Scanner™ at a resolution of 300 dpi and were modified using AppleScan® and MacScan® software. The modifications were intended only to remove marks and blemishes which impaired the quality of the images (some of which had been damaged or were imperfect copies). Inevitably, however, because of the capabilities of the technology, there has been a tendency to overdo the 'cleaning up' and even to try to 'improve on the original'; hence it is likely that minor modifications have been introduced, along with scale changes. While Trickett's plans, in particular, are believed to be fair reproductions of the originals, no detailed analysis of the cartography or lettering should be attempted on the basis of the images in this book, except the coloured maps which have been produced entirely photographically and should vary from the originals only in terms of scale, and perhaps slightly in terms of colour.

The text and line graphics have been generated using an AM Varityper 4300 imagesetter with a resolution of 2,400 dpi and printed by offset process. Colour separations by Imagemakers, Launceston, Tasmania.

The book was printed on 115 gsm Primatrend Matt Art paper by Telegraph Printery, Launceston.

The 1925 coloured map of Jenolan Caves in the pocket at the rear of the book was printed on 150 gsm Precision Offset paper by Telegraph Printery. It is also available unfolded from the Sydney Speleological Society.

Publishing consultants: Artemis Publishing, Hobart.

GJM